D1169737

BY DESIGN:
EVIDENCE FOR NATURE'S INTELLIGENT DESIGNER—THE GOD OF THE BIBLE

BY JONATHAN SARFATI, PH.D.

BOSTON BAPTIST COLLEGE
LIBRARY
950 METROPOLITAN AVENUE
BOSTON, MA 02136
TEL (617) 364-3? 0 EXT 216

CREATION
BOOK PUBLISHERS

Published and distributed by
Creation Book Publishers

www.creationbookpublishers.com

Copyright © 2008 *Creation Ministries International (Australia)*
ABN 31 010 120 304. All rights reserved. No part of this book
may be reproduced in any manner whatsoever without written
permission of the publisher, except in the case of brief quotations
in articles and reviews.

ISBN: 978 0 94990672 4

COVER DESIGN: by Amanda Greenslade—a composition of:
    front: Arctic tern photo by Robert LaFollette
    <www.robertlafollette.com>; cosmology illustration by
    European Space Agency and Wolfram Freudling
    (Space Telescope—European Coordinating Facility/
    European Southern Observatory, Germany); chromosome
    illustration from <crestock.com>; moon illustration from
    <stockxpert.com>, and **back**: Gecko photo by
    Grego Pogöschnik <sxc.hu>.

LAYOUT: by Vanessa Fitzgerald.

PRINTED: August 2008

For information on this book or on creation/evolution issues,
contact:

(addresses last page)

CreationOnTheWeb.com.org

CONTENTS

ABOUT THE AUTHOR

Jonathan D. Sarfati, Ph.D, F.M., was born in Ararat, Australia, in 1964. He moved to New Zealand as a child, where he later studied mathematics, geology, physics, and chemistry at Victoria University in Wellington. He obtained honors level in physical and inorganic chemistry, as well as in condensed matter physics and nuclear physics. He received his Ph.D. in physical chemistry from the same institution in 1995 on the topic of spectroscopy, especially vibrational. He has co-authored various technical papers on such things as high temperature superconductors and sulfur and selenium-containing ring and cage molecules.

As well as being very interested in formal logic and philosophy, Dr Sarfati is a keen chess player. He represented New Zealand in three Chess Olympiads and is a former New Zealand national chess champion. In 1988, F.I.D.E., the International Chess Federation, awarded him the title of F.I.D.E. Master (F.M.). He is wellknown at major creation conferences for successfully playing, while blindfolded, up to 12 sighted challengers simultaneously.

A Christian since 1984, he was for some years on the editorial committee of *Apologia*, the journal of the Wellington Christian Apologetics Society, of which he was a co-founder.

Dr Sarfati currently works full-time in Brisbane, Australia for *Creation Ministries International* (CMI), a non-profit ministry grouping, as a research scientist, speaker and editorial consultant for *Creation* magazine and the associated *Journal of Creation*, and has written many articles for both. He has authored the books *Refuting Evolution* (the biggest selling creation book of all time), *Refuting Evolution 2* and *Refuting Compromise*, as well as co-authoring several others, including the popular *Creation Answers Book*. He also contributes specialist information to CMI's multi-country website (CreationOnTheWeb.com)

FOREWORD

Don Batten, Ph.D: scientist, speaker and writer for *Creation Ministries International, Australia.*

My colleague, Dr Jonathan Sarfati, is renowned as a leading thinker, writer, scientist and logician—a champion for the truth of Genesis as history. And virtually all exegetes would agree that Genesis is history, were it not for the sad fact that many have been bluffed and intimated into accepting the 'scientific' revisionist version of history.

Jonathan's books, *Refuting Evolution (1 and 2), and Refuting Compromise*, are some of the world's best-selling and highly regarded creation books. I think that this powerful new book is a definitive one on 'intelligent design'.

Sarfati's passion for describing the incredible designs in the natural world shines through. While never disparaging the ID movement, he forthrightly presents and builds on the design argument. He also sets the record straight about how creationists of the past have pioneered design arguments (including 'irreducible complexity', albeit with different terminology)—but he does this without detracting from the contributions of our natural allies within ID.

Not surprisingly, given his doctorate in physical chemistry, the author devotes a chapter to decisively exposing 'chemicals-to-life' evolution as a product of wishful thinking. This is a treatise in itself.

Sarfati deals head-on with the objections that Genesis-avoiding ID folk tend to sidestep, or handle badly. For example, the issue of so-called 'poor design', and also why there are 'bad things' in nature. And of course, he dispatches with aplomb the old canard, revived in modern form by God-hater Richard Dawkins, namely, 'Who designed the Designer?'

Many, both laypeople and scientists, owe their confidence in God's Word (and humanly speaking, even their faith in Christ) to design arguments for biblical creation, and doubtless many more will as a result of this potent book.

Enjoy the feast!
Dr Don Batten

A BRIEF HISTORY OF DESIGN

The Design Argument has a long and distinguished history. Philosophers have used the design of life and the universe to point to a Designer for millennia. Since life originated in the past, neither its design nor alleged evolution can be observed directly by experimental science. But evolution or creation might conceivably have left some effects that can be observed. This chapter discusses the criteria that are used in everyday life to determine whether something has been designed, and applies them to the living world.

ARGUMENT FROM DESIGN TO DESIGNER

Many philosophers have argued that the living world shows evidence of design, which points to one or more designers. This is often called the *teleological argument*.

Plato and Aristotle[1]

Plato (c. 428–c. 348 BC) said that two things 'lead men to believe in the gods', one based on the soul, and the other 'from the order of the motion of the stars, and of all things under the dominion of the mind which ordered the universe.'[2]

His greatest student, Aristotle (384–322 BC),[3] argued from the order in the stars that there must have been a 'First Unmoved Mover which is God, a living, intelligent, incorporeal, eternal and most good being who is the source of order in the cosmos.'[1]

<wikipedia.org>

Plato

Cicero

The Roman orator and statesman Marcus Tullius Cicero (106–43 BC), in his book *De Natura Deorum* (*On the Nature of the Gods*), vigorously used design arguments against the evolutionist Epicurus (341–270 BC). Epicurus taught that everything formed by chance collisions of particles, which could form even something as beautiful as the world. Cicero replied that this was on a par with believing that if the letters of the alphabet were thrown on the ground often enough they would spell out the *Annals of Ennius*. And he pointed out that if chance collisions of particles could make a

1.   After Craig, William Lane, *Apologetics: An Introduction*, **3**.123, Moody Press, Chicago, 1984.
2.   Plato, *Laws* **12**.966e.
3.   Aristotle, Metaphysics Λ.**1**.982610–15.

world, why then cannot they build much less difficult objects, like a colonnade, a temple, a house, or a city, that nobody doubts were designed?

Paul the Apostle

One of Paul's most famous passages on the designer is Romans 1:20
'For his invisible attributes, namely, his eternal power and divine nature, have been clearly perceived, ever since the creation of the world, in the things that have been made. So they are without excuse.'

Church teachers

The early Latin apologist Felix Marcus Minucius (AD 3rd century) argued for design in his *Octavius*. This was in the form of a Christian v pagan dialogue, and had similarities to Cicero. Gregory the Theologian (of Nazianzus) (AD 329–389) used arguments from design. But one of the most famous is Thomas Aquinas (1225–1274), who proposed 'Five Ways', or what he considered five proofs for the existence of God in his *Summa Theologica*:
'The fifth way is taken from the governance of the world. We see that things which lack knowledge, such as natural bodies, act for an end, and this is evident from their acting always, or nearly always, in the same way, so as to obtain the best result. Hence it is plain that they achieve their end, not fortuitously, but designedly. Now whatever lacks knowledge cannot move towards an end, unless it be directed by some being endowed with knowledge and intelligence; as the arrow is directed by the archer. Therefore, some intelligent being exists by whom all natural things are directed to their end; and this being we call God.'

Sir Isaac Newton

Newton (1642/3–1727), widely regarded as the greatest scientist who ever lived, wrote more about theology than science! For example, he wrote:
'This most beautiful system of the sun, planets, and comets, could only proceed from the counsel and dominion of an intelligent Being. ... This Being governs all things, not as the soul of the world, but as Lord over all; and on account of his dominion he is wont to be called "Lord God" Παντοκράτωρ *[Pantokratōr]*, or "Universal Ruler". ... The Supreme God is a Being eternal, infinite, absolutely perfect.'[4]

'Opposition to godliness is atheism in profession and idolatry in practice. Atheism is so senseless

---

4.   *Principia* **III**; cited in; *Newton's Philosophy of Nature: Selections from his writings*, p. 42, ed. H.S. Thayer, Hafner Library of Classics, NY, 1953.

and odious to mankind that it never had many professors.'[5]

William Paley

<wikipedia.org>

A famous design advocate was the Englishman William Paley (1743–1805), who wrote the best-seller *Natural Theology* (1804). The best known argument was someone finding a watch while walking in a barren countryside. From all the intricate machinery that was organized in the right way, the only logical conclusion was that it had a maker who 'comprehended its construction and designed its use'. Paley also argued that the eye was designed, by comparing it with designed optical instruments such as telescopes and microscopes.

This was once required reading in British Universities for several decades, and was a highly influential work for generations.[6]

The philosopher of science Elliot Sober, an *opponent* of design theory, summarized:

'Before Darwin's time, some of the best and brightest in both philosophy and science argued that the adaptedness of organisms can be explained only by the hypothesis that organisms are the product of intelligent design. This line of reasoning—the *design argument*—is worth considering as an object of real intellectual beauty. It was not the fantasy of crackpots but the fruits of creative genius.'[7]

CRITICS

David Hume

Many claim that Paley's argument was refuted by the Scottish philosopher David Hume (1711–1776) in *Dialogues Concerning Natural Religion* (published 1779). However, Paley's work was written almost 30 years *after* Hume, and according to Frederick Ferré, is not vulnerable to most of Hume's objections.[8] Also, Hume's character Philo, representing Hume's own views against Cleanthes' design argument, in the end agrees that the design argument is cogent!

5.   *A Short Scheme of the True Religion*, manuscript quoted in *Memoirs of the Life, Writings and Discoveries of Sir Isaac Newton* by Sir David Brewster, Edinburgh, 1850; cited in; *Newton's Philosophy of Nature*, p. 65, Ref. 2.

6.   Proctor, R.M., *Value-Free Science? Purity and Power in Modern Science*, Harvard University Press, Cambridge, MA, p. 47, 1991.

7.   Sober, E., *Philosophy of Biology*, Westview, Boulder, CO, p. 29, 1993. Quoted in: Dembski, W., *Intelligent Design*, IVP, Downers Grove, IL, p. 71, 1999.

8.   Ferré, F., Introduction to *Natural Theology: Selections*, by William Paley, pp. xi–xxii, Bobs–Merrill, Indianapolis, 1963.

Charles Darwin and Alfred Russel Wallace

Charles Darwin, 1854

Even the hardened anti-theist Richard Dawkins agreed that Hume's response was inadequate, because he had failed to provide an alternative for the origin of complexity. But Darwin (1809–1882)[9] and Wallace[10,11] took an idea found in Paley and developed by Edward Blyth (1810–1873), *natural selection*.[12] However, Blyth and other design theorists invoked natural selection as a *conservative* force, which weeded out the unfit (thus 'conserving' the quality of an animal population), and had a role in development of new *varieties*. But Darwin and Wallace asserted that it was a *creative* force. Supposedly it could act on small variations and accumulate them, so over eons of time, it could build up increased complexity. Dawkins famously said:

'An atheist before Darwin could have said, following Hume: "I have no explanation for complex biological design. All I know is that God isn't a good explanation, so we must wait and hope that somebody comes up with a better one." I can't help feeling that such a position, though logically sound, would have left one feeling pretty unsatisfied, and that although atheism might have been logically tenable before Darwin, Darwin made it possible to be an intellectually fulfilled atheist.'[13]

CRITICS OF DARWIN

The rise of the modern anti-evolutionist and pro-creation movements in the 20th century led to many works criticizing Darwin. Woodward has summarized the rise of the modern design movement.[14,15] But long before the modern design movement, one

9. Darwin, C.R., *Origin of Species by Means of Natural Selection, or The Preservation of Favoured Races in the Struggle for Life*, John Murray, London, 1859.
10. Wallace, A.R., *On the Tendency of Varieties to Depart Indefinitely From the Original Type*, Ternate (eastern Indonesia), 1858; <www.zoo.uib.no/classics/varieties.html>.
11. Grigg, R., Alfred Russel Wallace—'co-inventor' of Darwinism, *Creation* **27**(4):33–35, 2005; <creationontheweb.com/wallace>.
12. Grigg, R., Darwin's illegitimate brainchild: If you thought Darwin's Origin was original, think again! *Creation* **26**(2):39–41, 2004; <creationontheweb.com/brainchild>.
13. Dawkins, R., *The Blind Watchmaker: Why the evidence of evolution reveals a universe without design*, p. 6, W W Norton & Company, New York, 1986.
14. For a history, see Woodward, T., *Doubts About Darwin: A History of Intelligent Design*, Baker Books, Grand Rapids, MI, 2003; and see review: Blievernicht, E., The rhetoric of design, *J. Creation* **18**(3):46–47, 2004.
15. A sequel, answering the critics, is Woodward, T., *Darwin Strikes Back: Defending the Science of Intelligent Design*, Baker Books, Grand Rapids, MI, 2006; see review: Weinberger, L., Intelligent debate, *J. Creation* **21**(2):48–51, 2007.

of the most notable anti-evolutionists was the former Darwinist ornithologist and barrister Douglas Dewar (1875–1957), of the UK. He was a leader in the Evolution Protest Movement, and wrote a number of books on biological design.[16] In the US, engineer Henry Morris (1918–2006) founded the Institute for Creation Research in 1970. He started the modern creationist movement with his book, co-authored with theologian John Whitcomb, *The Genesis Flood* (1961). His colleague, biochemist Duane Gish (1921–), frequently gave talks that majored on the design in living organisms as well as the fossil record and critiques of evolutionary origin-of-life theories. He was very successful in debates with evolutionists,[17] often on US university campuses.

Information

About the same time, Arthur Wilder-Smith (1915–1995), with three earned doctorates in science, argued against Darwinism on design grounds. He pioneered the use of the *information* concept. This was made more famous and put on a rigorous mathematical footing by mathematician William Dembski (1960–), who has earned doctorates in both mathematics and philosophy of science, in his book *The Design Inference*, published by the prestigious Cambridge University Press (1998).[18] Another mathematical critic of Darwinism is Lee Spetner, who taught information and communication theory at the Applied Physics Laboratory of Johns Hopkins University from 1951 to 1970. He argues that mutation and selection are insufficient to explain the encyclopedic quantities of information in living creatures.[19]

Irreducible complexity

Meanwhile, biochemist Michael Behe (1952–) revisited *practical* examples of design. But he expounded on the discoveries of biochemical processes and sub-microscopic machinery that Darwin never dreamed of.[20] He is most famous for introducing the phrase 'irreducible complexity':

'By irreducible complexity I mean a single system which is composed of several interacting parts that contribute to the basic function, and where the

16. Dewar, D., *The Transformist Illusion*, Sophia Perennis et Universalis, Ghent, NY, 1957.
17. One of the most famous was a televised evolution/creation debate with biochemist Russell Doolitle held before 5,000 people at Liberty University on 13 Oct 1981. The evolutionist Roger Lewin writing in the pro-evolution journal *Science* described the debate as a 'rout' in favour of Gish (*Science*, **214**:638, 1981). The next day, the debate was reported by the pro-evolution *Washington Post* under the headline 'Science Loses One to Creationism'. The sub-headline cited Doolittle's anguished remark: 'How am I going to face my wife?' showing that Doolittle himself knew he was defeated.
18. See Truman, R., Divining design: A review of *The Design Inference: Eliminating chance through small probabilities*, *J. Creation* **13**(2):34–39, 1999.
19. Spetner, L.M., *Not by chance! Shattering the modern theory of evolution*, The Judaica Press, Brooklyn, NY, 1996/7; see review by Wieland, C., *Creation* **20**(1):50–51, 1997; <creationontheweb.com/spetner>.
20. Behe, M. J., *Darwin's Black Box: The Biochemical Challenge to Evolution*, The Free Press, New York, 1996; see interview by Wieland, C., The mousetrap man, *Creation* **20**(3):17, 1998; <creationontheweb.com/behe>.

removal of any one of the parts causes the system to effectively cease functioning. An irreducibly complex system cannot be produced gradually by slight, successive modifications of a precursor system, since any precursor to an irreducibly complex system is by definition non-functional. Since natural selection requires a function to select, an irreducibly complex biological system, if there is such a thing, would have to arise as an integrated unit for natural selection to have anything to act on. It is almost universally conceded that such a sudden event would be irreconcilable with the gradualism Darwin envisioned.'

This describes a biological feature that would meet Darwin's challenge:
'If it could be demonstrated that any complex organ existed which could not possibly have been formed by numerous, successive, slight modifications, my theory would absolutely break down.'

Behe gives the example of a very simple machine: a mousetrap. This would not work without a platform, holding bar, spring, hammer and catch, all in the right place. If you remove just one part, it won't work at all—you cannot reduce its complexity without destroying its function entirely.

The thrust of *Darwin's Black Box* is that many structures in living organisms show irreducible complexity, far in excess of a mousetrap or indeed any man-made machine. He shows that even the simplest form of vision in any living creature requires a dazzling array of chemicals in the right places, as well as a system to transmit and process the information. The blood-clotting mechanism also has many different chemicals working together, so we won't bleed to death from minor cuts, nor yet suffer from clotting of the entire system.

Subsequently Behe wrote *The Edge of Evolution* (2007).[21,22] This book aims to see exactly what the supposed neo-Darwinian processes can achieve. In this, he also refines the concept irreducible complexity that his first book made famous, with additional concepts of *steps* and *coherence*:
'In this chapter, I develop two criteria by which to judge whether random mutation hitched to natural selection is a biologically reasonable explanation for any given molecular phenomenon. The criteria, spelled out in detail over the rest of the chapter, are the following:
• First, *steps*, The more intermediate evolutionary steps that must be climbed to achieve some biological goal without

21.   Behe, M., *The Edge of Evolution: The search for the limits of Darwinism*, Free Press, NY, 2007.
22.   This came in for severe criticism from the evolutionary gatekeepers, e.g. Richard Dawkins, Inferior Design, *New York Times*, 1 July 2007. For refutation, see Sarfati, J., Misotheist's misology: Dawkins attacks Behe but digs himself into logical potholes, <creationontheweb.com/dawkbehe>, 13 July 2007.

reaping a net benefit, the more unlikely a Darwinian explanation.

- Second, *coherence*. A telltale signature of planning is the coherent ordering of steps toward a goal. Random mutation, on the other hand, is incoherent; that is, any given evolutionary step taken by a population of organisms is unlikely to be connected to its predecessor.'[23]

Later, Behe explains:

'The concept of irreducible complexity, with its broad focus on the "parts" of a system, passes over the fact that a part might itself be a special piece that needs explaining in terms of many steps. What's more, it overlooks the steps required to assemble a system—to physically put them together—once the parts are available. Once the spring is forged and the other parts of the future mousetrap manufactured, the smith grabs the various pieces lying at different spots in the shop, transports them to his workbench, and pieces them together in the right orientation.

'The concept of the number of "steps" resembles the idea of irreducible complexity in that both look to see if multiple factors are needed to produce something. But "steps" goes further, asking how many separate *actions*—not just separate *parts*—are needed to make a system. The concept of "steps" is especially useful when fewer actions are needed to coherently arrange parts. It can locate the edge of evolution with greater precision.

'The concept of coherence is implicit in the definition of irreducible complexity in the idea of parts that are "well-matched" to a "system". The standard mechanical mousetrap, with its very well matched parts, is profoundly coherent. Since it is irreducibly complex, it can't be built directly by a gradual process that would mimic a Darwinian scenario.

'But suppose there were some tortuous, indirect route that might lead to the trap. It would be unreasonable to expect the route to be found by a blind process ... there are too many dead ends and opportunities to go wrong. To trap mice, a deep hole in the ground might do just fine. Yet a hole in the ground isn't a route to the standard mechanical mousetrap. If the hole then had to be filled in before starting over to build a better mousetrap (pardon the strained analogy),

---

23.   Behe, Ref. 21, p. 104.

then mice would flourish at least temporarily—ruling out this path. A splotch of glue can catch a mouse, but it can't be turned into a mechanical trap. ...

'The more pieces, and the more intricately they interact, the more opportunities there are to go wrong in building a system.'[24]

HOW DO WE DETECT DESIGN?

Dawkins said:

'Biology is the study of complicated things that give the appearance of having been designed for a purpose.'[25]

Of course, he denies that they are designed in reality, and coined the term 'designoid' (pronounced 'design-oid'). But the onus is on him to prove that the appearance of design is misleading; an illusion. And this book will argue that the design inference is not limited to appearances, but extends to deep analogy with things we *know* have been designed.

Even the idea of 'appearance of design' implies that design has certain features. People detect intelligent design all the time. For example, if we find arrowheads on a desert island, we can assume they were made by someone, *even if we cannot see the designer*.

There is an obvious difference between writing by an intelligent person, e.g. Shakespeare's plays, and a random letter sequence like WDLMNLT DTJBKWIRZREZLMQCO P.[26] There is also an obvious difference between Shakespeare and a repetitive sequence like ABCDABCDABCD. The latter is an example of *order*, which must be distinguished from Shakespeare, which is an example of *specified complexity*.

We can also tell the difference between messages written in sand and the results of wave and wind action. The carved heads of the U.S. presidents on Mt Rushmore are clearly different from erosional features. Again, this is specified complexity. Erosion produces either irregular shapes or highly ordered shapes like sand dunes, but not presidents' heads or writing.

Another example is the SETI program (Search for Extraterrestrial Intelligence). This would be pointless if there was no way of determining whether a certain type of signal from outer space would be proof of an intelligent sender. The criterion is again a signal with a high level of specified complexity—this would prove that there was an intelligent sender, *even if we had no other idea of the sender's nature*. But neither a random nor a repetitive sequence would be

24. Behe, Ref. 21, p. 121–122.
25. Dawkins, Ref. 13.
26. Example of a random sequence from Dawkins, Ref. 13, p. 47.

proof. Natural processes produce radio noise from outer space, while pulsars (ultra-dense collapsed stars that spin very rapidly and emit regular radio signals, hence 'pulsating stars') produce regular signals. Actually, pulsars were first mistaken for signals by people eager to believe in extraterrestrials, but this is because they mistook order for complexity. So evolutionists (as are nearly all SETI proponents) are prepared to use high specified complexity as proof of intelligence, *when it suits their ideology*. This shows once more how one's biases and assumptions affect one's interpretations of any data. See 'God and the Extraterrestrials' for more SETI/UFO fallacies.[27]

EXPLANATORY FILTER FOR DESIGN

Dembski formalized this in *The Design Inference*, proposing a way to reach the design explanation via a process of elimination, using a 'filter'. He proposed three possible explanations of a feature: *law*, *chance* or *design*. Dembski's method entails seeking an explanation on the basis of these three possibilities and in that order:

1. **Natural Law explains regularity.** This applies even if, as the Bible indicates, the natural law is just our *description* of the regular way in which God upholds the universe. Dembski says:
   'For the filter to eliminate regularity, one must establish that a multiplicity of possibilities is compatible with the given antecedent circumstance (recall that regularity admits only one possible consequence for a given antecedent circumstance); hence to eliminate regularity is to establish a multiplicity of possible consequences.'
2. **Chance explains real randomness.** For law to explain an outcome there must be only a limited number of possible outcomes all predictable from the circumstances. These are events of high probability. If there are many possible different outcomes, then law cannot explain it.
3. Only after law and chance have been excluded is **design** assumed to be the cause. These events are characterized by patterns that are both specified and of vanishingly small probabilities, as Dembski points out: 'Specified events of small probability do not occur by chance.'

Naturally, critics have reacted to Dembski's criteria for detecting design for living organisms. But if they are right, then it is impossible to detect design of *any* sort, divine, human or even ET.

Dembski illustrates his filter with a practical example of differentiating genuine randomness and design. In his example there was an accusation of *cheating*, i.e. that certain sequences that should have been random were not, and thus the result of 'design':

---

27.   Gitt, W., God and the Extraterrestrials, *Creation* 19(4):46–48, 1997.

'TRENTON, July 22[28]—The New Jersey Supreme Court today caught up with the "man with the golden arm", Nicholas Caputo, the Essex County Clerk and a Democrat who has conducted drawings for decades that have given Democrats the top ballot line in the county 40 out of 41 times ... the court noted that the chances of picking the same name 40 out of 41 times were less than 1 in 50 billion.'[29]

When creationists point out the infinitesimally small probability of the origin of life, many evolutionists respond, 'So what, *any* sequence is just as improbable. E.g. it was extremely improbable for me to be dealt that hand, but it still happened.' However, the crux of Dembski's filter is not the low probability alone; after all, any particular random sequence of 41 outcomes is also highly improbable. The proof is, try to duplicate the same series a *second* time. Critical are *two* conditions: both a small probability and that an event be *specified*, not just any event (see also ch. 14, Cheating with Chance, p. 226).

In voting, being on the first position on the ballot is a great advantage, since lazy voters are more likely to vote for that person. So the very high proportion of Democrat (D) candidates in the first position put them at a great advantage, and the clerk in charge of drawing the ballots was a Democrat. Thus the 40/41 draws for Ds in the first position is an outcome of recognizable significance, and since Caputo was a D, this counts as a pattern that could be specified in advance. Since the probability of arising at this sequence by chance was minuscule, it's no wonder New Jersey Supreme Court reasonably said:

'Confronted with these odds, few persons of reason will accept the explanation of blind chance' (cited on p. 19).

However, Dembski explains that while cheating:

'certainly is the best explanation of Caputo's golden arm ... the court stopped short of convicting Caputo, ... [because] the court had no clear mandate for dealing with highly improbable ballot line selections'.

APPLICATION TO LIVING THINGS

Dembski's three categories reflect an earlier recognition of these three basic categories. The leading evolutionary origin-of-life researcher, Leslie Orgel (1927–), confirmed this:

---

28.   *New York Times*, 23 July 1985, p. B1.
29.   For more details on this incident, see Dembski's on-line article at: <www.arn.org/docs/dembski/WD_explfilter.htm>.

'Living things are distinguished by their specified complexity. Crystals such as granite fail to qualify as living because they lack complexity; mixtures of random polymers fail to qualify because they lack specificity.'[30]

Unfortunately, a materialist like Orgel here refuses to make the connection between specified complexity and design, even though this is the precise criterion of design.

INFORMATION

The design criterion may also be described in terms of *information*. *Specified complexity* means high *information content*. In formal terms, the information content of any arrangement is the size, in bits, of the shortest algorithm (program) required to generate that arrangement. A random sequence could be formed by a short program:

(1) Print any letter at random.
(2) Return to step 1.

A repetitive sequence could be made by the program:

(1) Print ABCD.
(2) Return to step 1.

But to print the plays of Shakespeare, a program would need to be large enough to print every letter in the right place.[31]

The information content of living things is far greater than that of Shakespeare's writings. Dawkins says:

'[T]here is enough information capacity in a single human cell to store the *Encyclopædia Britannica*, all 30 volumes of it, three or four times over.'[32]

If it's unreasonable to believe that an encyclopedia could have originated without intelligence, then it's just as unreasonable to believe that life could have originated without intelligence.

Even more amazingly, living things have by far the most compact information storage/retrieval system known. This stands to reason if a microscopic cell stores as much information as several sets of *Encyclopædia Britannica*. To illustrate further, the amount of information that could be stored in a pinhead's volume of DNA is staggering. It is the equivalent information content of a pile of paperback books 500 times as tall as the distance from Earth to the moon, each with a different, yet specific content.[33]

30. Orgel, L., *The Origins of Life*, John Wiley, NY, 1973, p. 189.
31. Information can be defined mathematically in a way that distinguishes randomness, order and specified complexity. In terms of signal transmission, a receiver may exist in a large number of possible states (Ω_0); after a message has been received, the number of possible states drops to Ω_1. The information content of the message $I_1 = k \ln (\Omega_0/\Omega_1)$, where k = Boltzmann's constant. From M.W. Zemansky, *Heat and Thermodynamics*, McGraw-Hill, 4th ed. 1975, p. 190.
   Note that the definition is consistent: with a repetitive sequence, there is a restriction of possibilities, so Ω_0 is low, so the information is low. Random sequences also contain little information, because there are many possible random sequences (so Ω_1 is almost as large as Ω_0).
32. Dawkins, Ref. 13, p. 115.
33. Gitt, W., 'Dazzling Design in Miniature', *Creation* **20**(1):6, 1997.

CAN MUTATIONS GENERATE INFORMATION?

Even if we grant evolutionists the first cell, the problem of increasing the total information content remains. To go from the first cell to a human means finding a way to generate enormous amounts of information—billions of base pairs ('letters') worth. This includes the instructions to build eyes, nerves, skin, bones, muscles, blood, etc. Evolution relies on copying errors and natural selection to generate the required new information. However, the usual claimed examples of 'contemporary evolution' presented are all **losses** of information.

This is confirmed by Spetner:

> 'In this chapter I'll bring several examples of evolution, [i.e., instances alleged to be examples of evolution] particularly mutations, and show that information is not increased ... But in all the reading I've done in the life-sciences literature, I've never found a mutation that added information.'[34]

> 'All point mutations that have been studied on the molecular level turn out to reduce the genetic information and not to increase it.'

> 'The NDT [neo-Darwinian theory] is supposed to explain how the information of life has been built up by evolution. The essential biological difference between a human and a bacterium is in the information they contain. All other biological differences follow from that. The human genome has much more information than does the bacterial genome. Information cannot be built up by mutations that lose it. A business can't make money by losing it a little at a time.'[35]

Beneficial mutations or scorched earth?

This is not to say that no mutation is 'beneficial', that is, it helps the organism to survive. Antibiotic and pesticide resistance may sometimes result from a *transfer* of information (via a loop of DNA called a 'plasmid'), but this is not new information in the sense that the evolutionary story requires, as it already existed somewhere in another organism. Where such resistance is caused by mutation, it **never** involves *new* information. Other beneficial mutations include wingless beetles on small, windy desert islands—if beetles lose their wings and so can't fly, the wind is less likely to blow them out to

---

34 There may be one lonely example to date of an information-gaining mutation (in a situation where the theory requires hundreds to be credible), but even that needs to be carefully qualified. See www.CreationOnTheWeb.com/nylon.

35. Spetner, Ref. 19, *pp.* 131–2, 138, 143.

sea.[36] Obviously, this has nothing to do with the origins of flight in the first place, which is what evolution is supposed to explain (see ch. 4). Another beneficial mutation is creatures in dark caves with shrivelled eyes—in the darkness, there is no natural selection against blind creatures, while the shrivelled eyes are less vulnerable to infection and damage.

Malarial resistance

Behe's second book[21] covers the issue of beneficial mutations and the limits of Darwinian processes. As his Ph.D. research involved malaria, he applies his expertise to the malarial parasite (*Plasmodium falciparum*) and the mutations that have enabled humans to combat it, and the parasite's measures to counter human-made drugs.

One of the most effective anti-malarial drugs has been *chloroquine*, because the parasite took a while to develop resistance. Behe shows that chloroquine resistance likely involves *two* specific mutations occurring together in the one gene. This explains why resistance to chloroquine took a long time to develop, whereas resistance to other anti-malarial drugs, which only need *one* mutation each, occurs within weeks. Behe works out the probability of this double mutation occurring in the same gene, using other scientists' figures for the parasite's population, etc.

If it took so much time for a double mutation to occur in an organism that has a huge population and short life cycle (and therefore huge opportunity for all manner of mutations to occur), then how long would it take for a double mutation to occur in an organism like a human, with a long generation time and relatively small population? Behe showed that it would never occur, even with evolutionary time assumed. And this is just one double mutation in a gene. So, any adaptation that requires two or more specific mutations to work will *never* evolve in a human, and yet such must have happened *numerous* times if humans arose through evolutionary processes.

Behe also points out that the chloroquine-resistant parasites do *worse* than the non-resistant ones where there is no chloroquine. This suggests that the double mutation is informationally downhill, as usual. It seems that the reason that the parasite is resistant to chloroquine is that concentration in the parasite's vacuole is reduced, and one mechanism is *impaired uptake*. According to one paper:

> 'Chloroquine-resistant parasite isolates consistently have an import mechanism with a lower transport activity and a reduced affinity for chloroquine.'[37]

36. Wieland, C., Beetle Bloopers: Even a defect can be an advantage sometimes, *Creation* 19(3):30, 1997; <creationontheweb.com/beetle>.
37. Sanchez, C.P., Wünsch, S. and Lanzer, M., Identification of a Chloroquine Importer in *Plasmodium falciparum*: Differences in import kinetics are genetically linked with the chloroquine-resistant phenotype, *J. Biol. Chem.* 272(5):2652–2658, 1997.

This is the same *principle* that explains some antibiotic-resistant bacteria, where resistance is conferred by a mutation impairing a cell pump so the germ pumps in less of its would-be executioner.[38]

This leads to another of Behe's major points: *there is not so much an arms race as trench warfare or a **scorched earth policy**. Many of the changes are destroying machinery that the enemy could otherwise use.* E.g. defenders will destroy their own bridges to prevent an enemy crossing, sabotage their own factories if the enemy is using them to churn out armaments, burn their own crops so the enemy will run out of food ...

Sickle cell anemia

This also explains some of the human defences to malaria, such as *sickle cell anemia*. Here, a mutation causes the hemoglobin to be more prone to clumping together. One of the world's leading authorities on sickle-cell anemia, Felix Konotey-Ahulu, explains:

'These mis-shapen cells can block the smaller blood vessels, depriving tissues and organs of oxygen. However, sufferers have done very well *with proper treatment*, becoming doctors, lawyers etc.'[39]

However, those with only *one* gene for sickle cell anemia only have half their hemoglobin molecules defective, thus they won't clump on their own, so they don't suffer from those ill effects. But the defect actually has an advantage.

The malaria parasite feeds on the hemoglobin, which is very concentrated in our red blood cells. Behe points out that the sickle mutation makes the hemoglobin more prone to clumping together when the parasite enters the cell. This clumping distorts the shape, so the spleen detects the damaged cell and destroys it, along with the parasite. So those who carry only *one* gene will suffer no ill effects from anemia, and also enjoy protection from malaria.

However, Konotey-Ahulu cautions, 'Demonstrating natural selection does not demonstrate that "upward evolution" is a fact, yet many schoolchildren are taught this as a "proof" of evolution.' He says that 'the sickle-cell gene is still a defect, not an increase in complexity or an improvement in function which is being selected for'. And he points out the unhappy downside, that 'having more carriers of the sickle-cell genes results in more people suffering from this terrible disease.'[39]

Clearly the sickle cell hemoglobin is an example of scorched earth: this useful oxygen carrier was sacrificed to destroy the invader.

---

38. See Sarfati, J., Anthrax and antibiotics: Is evolution relevant? 2001–2005, <creationontheweb.com/anthrax>.

39. Exposing Evolution's Icon: World leader on sickle-cell anemia: 'Nothing to do with evolution!' Jonathan Sarfati interviews Felix Konotey-Ahulu, *Creation* **29**(1):16–19, 2006.

Breaking is easier than making

Behe provides a number of other examples of how breaking something will help an organism in a battle with another. Yet this is no marvel of Darwinism. It is far simpler to break something than to make it, and there are many ways to break something while there are few ways to make it. Something as simple as sand can grind gears to a halt, and a wad of chewing gum can foul up other moving parts. Honey in the fuel tank can stop a car in its tracks. Some defensive mechanisms are like this: a sticky molecule that prevents a molecular machine from working.

SCOPE OF THIS BOOK

Most of the chapters will cover *practical* examples of design, and point out *practical* difficulties with proposed evolutionary explanations, if indeed any have been proposed for those systems. Ch. 12 covers the origin of life, and again mainly points out *practical* chemical problems. The *theoretical* mathematical arguments of Dembski *et al.* are mainly outside this book's scope.

EYES AND SIGHT

One of the most important senses is sight: it is our main means of sensing objects at a distance and quickly analyzing a wide area of our surroundings. The organ of sight is of course the eye, and this has long been popular as a design argument. This chapter shows how eyes both parallel our own optical instruments, and surpass them. New discoveries of the information processing in the eye itself, before the brain even receives the image, add to the complexity. Also, there are a number of very different ways that organisms form images of their surroundings. Finally, evolutionary scenarios are addressed.

EYES AND CAMERAS

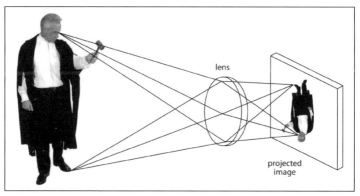

Focusing with a lens: light from any one point of the object corresponds to just one point of the image.

William Paley, in his classic *Natural Theology*,[1] compared the eye to obviously designed instruments such as the telescope and camera.[2] Their function is to produce an image, where *every point has a one-to-one correspondence with a point on the object* (see diagram above). If one point on the object links to more than one point on the image, the image is blurred.

In a camera, there is an *aperture* to admit light, an *iris diaphragm* that can change the size of the hole to control the amount of light entering, a *lens* to focus the light, and the *film* to capture the image. Similarly, our eye has a *pupil* to admit light, an *iris* to enlarge or

---

1. Paley, W., *Natural Theology; or, Evidences of the Existence and Attributes of the Deity*, ch, 3, 1802; <www-personal.umich.edu/~emcurley/paley.htm>.
2. Actually, he discussed the *camera obscura* (Latin for 'dark room'), a forerunner to our camera and the reason for the name. This comprised a darkened chamber or box, into which light is admitted through an aperture and focused by a double convex lens. This forms a *temporary* image of external objects, on a surface of paper, glass, etc., so in this respect is closer in design to our eyes.

contract the pupil to control the amount of light, a *lens* to focus the light on the *retina*, which is full of photoelectric cells that convert the image to electrical signals. The lenses are somewhat different; the camera focuses (varies the focal length) by moving the rigid lens, while our lens has a fixed position and its shape is changed to vary the focal length.

After Bob Mellish, <wikipedia.org>

Focusing with a pinhole camera.

A simpler design is the *pinhole camera.* This achieves the one-to-one correspondence simply because the hole is tiny enough so that light from a point on the object is in a straight line only to one point on the screen. This phenomenon has been known since ancient times— Aristotle (384–322 BC) and Euclid (fl. 300 BC) wrote about the sharper images seen through naturally occurring tiny holes, such as the slits in wicker baskets.

However, because the tiny hole cuts out so much light, the pinhole camera requires bright light. Enlarging the hole to admit more light blurs the image, by allowing light from one point to travel to more than one point on the screen. Hence the camera and eye combine variable opening with a variable lens.

However, as will be seen, the eye has very many complex features that leave the camera far behind. After all, the eye must also be able to repair itself and be connected to an *information processing system.* Also, the living world reveals many ingenious solutions both to the problem of forming a clear image, and processing the information.

The next section will cover some of the design features of the individual components of the eye; followed by some case studies of design in nature; and concludes with analysis of evolutionary scenarios.

THE EYE'S COMPONENTS

Cornea: amazing transparency

Essential for the eye to work is the *transparent window.* Not surprisingly, this is easy to overlook, since we take it so much for granted. However, it is not so easy to make something highly transparent from biological materials. It is especially important, because the cornea also provides about ⅔ of the focusing, while the lens provides only ⅓, but this is variable while the cornea is fixed.

The cornea is of a unique tissue type: it has no blood supply, so nutrients are supplied by the tears. It obtains its oxygen by direct contact with the air—this is why contact lenses should be permeable to oxygen. It has one of the highest nerve densities of any tissue in the body, hence its great sensitivity to touch.

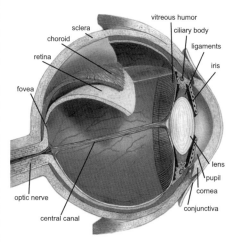

The best explanation for the cornea's transparency is *diffraction theory*, which shows that light is not scattered if the refractive index[3] doesn't vary over distances more than half the wavelength of light. This in turn requires a certain very finely organized structure of the corneal fibres, which in turn requires complicated chemical pumps to make sure there is exactly the right water content.[4] This ceases at death; hence the eyes then become cloudy.

Light detection

Many evolutionary accounts, starting with Darwin, basically commence by saying, 'Assume a light-sensitive cell'. However, Behe has shown that even a 'simple' light-sensitive spot requires a dazzling array of biochemicals in the right place and time to function. He states that each of its 'cells makes the complexity of a motorcycle or television set look paltry in comparison'. His following description, although written for a semi-popular audience, describes a small part of the eye's complexity:

> 'When light first strikes the retina a photon interacts with a molecule called 11-*cis*-retinal, which rearranges within picoseconds to *trans*-retinal. (A picosecond [10^{-12} sec] is about the time it takes light to travel the breadth of a single human hair.) The change in the shape of the retinal molecule forces a change in the shape of the protein, rhodopsin, to which the retinal is tightly bound. The protein's metamorphosis alters its behavior. Now called metarhodopsin II, the protein sticks to another protein, called transducin. Before bumping into metarhodopsin II, transducin had tightly bound a small molecule called GDP. But

3. The refractive index (n) of a substance is given by n = c/v, where c is the speed of light in a vacuum, and v the speed of light in the substance.
4. Gurney, P.W.V., Dawkins's Eye Revisited, *J. Creation* **15**(3):92–99, 2001.

when transducin interacts with metarhodopsin II, the GDP falls off, and a molecule called GTP binds to transducin. (GTP is closely related to, but different from, GDP.)

'GTP-transducin-metarhodopsin II now binds to a protein called phosphodiesterase, located in the inner membrane of the cell. When attached to metarhodopsin II and its entourage, the phosphodiesterase acquires the chemical ability to 'cut' a molecule called cGMP (a chemical relative of both GDP and GTP). Initially there are a lot of cGMP molecules in the cell, but the phosphodiesterase lowers its concentration, just as a pulled plug lowers the water level in a bathtub.'[5]

Retina

The retina is a very thin layer composed of the photosensitive cells described above. It has a number of features that eclipse man-made devices, such as the photoelectric sensors used in digital cameras.

Super sensitivity and dynamic range

The retina can detect a single photon of light, so it's impossible to improve on this sensitivity! More than that, the eye works marvellously in a wide variety of light intensities, i.e. from hardly any light to very bright light. In technical terms, it has a *dynamic range* of 10 billion (10^{10}) to one; that is, it will still work well in an intensity of 10 billion photons. Modern photographic film has a dynamic range of only 1,000 to one.

Even specialist equipment hasn't anywhere near the dynamic range of the eye, and I have considerable experience in state-of-the-art supersensitive photomultipliers. My Ph.D. thesis and published papers in secular journals largely involve a technique called *Raman spectroscopy*, which analyses extremely weak scattering at a slightly different frequency from that of the incident laser radiation. The major equipment hazard for Raman spectroscopists is scanning at the incident frequency—the still weak Rayleigh scattering at the same frequency would destroy the photomultiplier (the newer ones have an automatic shut-off). I managed to safely scan the Rayleigh line (for calibration) only by using filters to reduce the intensity of light entering the photomultiplier by a factor of 10^7 to 10^8. But having to take such extreme precautions made me envious and admiring of the way the eye is so brilliantly designed to cope with a far wider range of intensities.

---

5.   Behe, M.J., *Darwin's Black Box: The Biochemical Challenge to Evolution*, p. 46, The Free Press, New York, 1996.

So how does it work? When you emerge from a darkened room out into bright sunlight, muscles in your iris automatically shrink the pupil, cutting down the amount of light entering the eye. There is also a blink reflex.

But the biochemists Craig Montell and Seung-Jae Lee have discovered that there is also biochemical machinery involved, not just the large-scale motion of the iris and eyelids. They examined fruit fly eyes, which have similar proteins and light detector cells to ours. These cells have the light-detecting proteins in one end of the cell. But another protein, called arrestin, is moved around in the cell in response to light. In dim light, arrestin is in a 'holding area'. But in bright light, it is shuttled so that it can bind and 'calm' the light-detecting protein.

The arrestin doesn't just drift into place. Rather, it is moved quickly by a motor protein, myosin, along 'train tracks' of the cell's internal skeleton. The myosin and arrestin are 'glued' together with sticky fats called phosphoinositides.[6]

Dr Montell explains, 'For the cell to properly adapt to bright light, arrestin needs to move. If it doesn't, the cell remains as sensitive to light as it was when it was dark.'[7]

And this latest research shows the intricate machinery behind the eye's dynamic range—a motor, glue, 'calmer' and internal 'train tracks'. All these features would need to be present and coordinated; otherwise, the eye would be blinded by bright light. Thus mutations and natural selection could not build this system up step-by step, since each step by itself has no advantage over the previous step, until all is complete.[8]

Signal processing

Another amazing design feature of the retina is the signal processing that occurs even before the information is transmitted to the brain. This occurs in the retinal layers between the ganglion cells and the photoreceptors. For example, a process called *edge extraction* enhances the recognition of edges of objects. John Stevens, an associate professor of physiology and biomedical engineering, pointed out that it would take 'a minimum of a hundred years of Cray [supercomputer] time to simulate what takes place in your eye many times each second.'[9] And the retina's analog computing needs far less power than the digital supercomputers and is elegant in its simplicity. Once again, the eye outstrips any human technology, this time in another area.

6. Lee, S.-J. and Montell, C., Light-dependent translocation of visual arrestin regulated by the NINAC Myosin III, *Neuron* 43:95–103, 2004.

7. *Johns Hopkins Medicine*, <www.hopkinsmedicine.org/Press_releases/2004/07_16_04.html>, 2004.

8. This section was based on Catchpoole, D. and Sarfati, J., Excellent Eye: Better than any camera—the eye's response to light, *Creation* 30(3):23, 2008; <creationontheweb.com/eye-ex>, 2006.

9. *Byte*, April 1985.

Indeed, research into the retina shows that the 12 different types of ganglion cells send 12 different 'movies', i.e. distinct representations of a visual scene, to the brain for final interpretation. One movie is mainly a line drawing of the edges of objects, and others deal only in motion in a specific direction, and still others transmit information about shadows and highlights. How the brain integrates these movies into the final picture is still a subject of intense investigation. Understanding this would help researchers trying to design artificial light sensors to help the blind to see.[10]

EFFICIENT IMAGE PROCESSING

The eye would be little use without the brain to make the final interpretation of the image. And here there are more amazing features.

Fovea and saccades

Only a small (<1%) part of the eye in the centre, called the *fovea*, has very high resolution for fine detail. It sees only the central 2° of the visual field, or about twice the width of your thumbnail at arm's length. The fovea has a higher density of receptors, and needs a much larger area of our brain to process its information—over 50% of the visual cortex. [11]

But most of the eye's area is used for the peripheral (non-central) vision, which has much lower resolution, and therefore needs less brain processing power. You can understand this for yourself by trying to read this page without moving your eyes. Rather, normally the low-resolution parts of the eye detect objects of interest, and our eyes have unconscious motions (*saccades*) to aim our foveas at these objects.[12] This way we can see the details of a wide area with minimal brain computing power.

So why not simply have the whole retina in sharp focus? Because there is no point having much detail unless the brain can process it, and our brain would need to be 50 times larger to process such information! This would give only a minute advantage over our current system, where the peripheral area can pick out possible areas of interest, then zoom in the fovea to analyze more closely— with much less brain processing power. But the 'superior' design would have a major disadvantage in our head being unable to fit through doorways.[11]

Also, there would actually be a *disadvantage* to seeing too well in the periphery. For example, it would also make it impossible to

10. Roska, B., Molnar, A., Werblin, F.S., Parallel processing in retinal ganglion cells: How integration of space-time patterns of excitation and inhibition form the spiking output, *J.Neurophys.* **95**:3810–3822, 2006. The lead researchers wrote a semi-popular article: Werblin, F. and Roska, B., The movies in our eyes, *Scientific Amer.* **296**(4):54–61, 2007.
11. Catania, K.C., The nose takes a starring role, *Scientific American* **287**(1):40, 2002.
12. There are other vital motions of the eye—see Wagner, T., Darwin vs the Eye, *Creation* **16**(4):10–13, 1994; <creationontheweb.com/eye>.

read, because if every word was in equal focus, they would all be attracting the reader's attention—'pick me, pick me!'—instead of being able to concentrate on a few words at a time.[13] So the lack of clear focus in the periphery is consistent with an *intentional* design of the eye-brain system, quite aside from the much more efficient information processing.

The fovea-saccade method also has applications in other senses: fovea/saccade combination occurs in the tactile (touch) and auditory (hearing) senses in some creatures (see next chapter).[14]

Why eyes 'jitter'[15]

When a person fixes their gaze on something, their eyes 'jitter', i.e. they make small, involuntary movements. These movements wiggle the image on the retina. In the 1950s, researchers using mirrors to negate the jitter when volunteers looked at an object discovered that the volunteers began to lose sight of the object (disappearing into a featureless grey), so the researchers concluded that jittering kept the image from fading.

Decades later, Boston University neuroscientist Michele Rucci and his colleagues, using computer technology to track the eye's movements, discovered that the jitters are in fact crucial to helping the brain discern the finer details of an image.[16] Negating the jitters resulted in a 16% reduction in volunteers' ability to pick out the details in fine-lined patterns—the same ability needed to locate a single tree in a forest, or a berry on a bush.

'Vision isn't like a camera, where you take a picture and the brain processes it,' explains Rucci. 'The actual process of looking ... affects what you see.'[17]

Thus the jitters are crucial to picking out the details of what we see. The fact that we have such 'an eye for detail' surely points to design, not evolution.

COLOUR VISION

Our eyes have two types of light-detectors, *rods* and *cones*. The cones are mainly in the central part of our retina, and need bright light—they detect colour. The rods are in the peripheral part, and are good in dim light, but can't distinguish colours.

13. Menton, D., *The Hearing Ear and the Seeing Eye* (DVD).
14. See also Gurney, P.W.V., Our eye movements and their control, *J. Creation*: part 1—**16**(3):111–115, 2002; Part 2—**17**(1):103–110, 2003.
15. After Catchpoole D., An eye for detail—why your eyes 'jitter', <creationontheweb.com/jitter>, 2007.
16. Rucci, M., *et al.*, Miniature eye movements enhance fine spatial detail, *Nature* **447**(7146):852–855, 2007.
17. Telis, G., Shifty eyes see finer details, *ScienceNOW Daily News*, <sciencenow.sciencemag.org/cgi/content/full/2007/613/2>, 2007.

There are three types of cone. One is sensitive mainly to red, a second to green, and a third blue. Each of them sends a signal to the brain if it detects light. But the signal by itself says nothing about colour, only about the brightness of the light it can detect. Yet from this simple system, we can distinguish millions of different colours. Here's how.

If a small beam of red light hits three adjoining cones, only the red one will fire, sending a signal to the brain. But this signal doesn't by itself say 'red'—it is only the lack of signal from the adjoining blue and green cones that makes the brain see 'red'.

But what about yellow? Here, a beam of yellow light, wavelength about 580 nm (nanometres), will still land on three cones. But as they have a *range* of detectable wavelengths, *both* the red and green cones will detect the light. When the brain receives signals from adjoining red and green cones, it sees 'yellow'. If the light is somewhat greenish yellow, the green cone will send a slightly stronger signal, so the brain sees a greener shade of yellow.

The brain can distinguish between many different wavelengths of light by how they affect the three types of cone. And if all three are fired equally strongly, the brain sees white.

Primary colours

This design of the eye means that it's simple to make our eyes 'see' all different colours from just three primary colours. If you look at a TV screen or computer monitor under a magnifying glass, you will see tiny dots of the primary colours that match the cones: red, green and blue (hence RGB). Look carefully at a yellow area on your screen—you will find it has red and green dots shining about equally. At a distance, your red cone fires from the red dot, and the neighbouring green cone fires from the green dot. *So the brain sees the exact same signal as would come from a single yellow dot.* But it is a type of illusion—a spectrometer would measure a very different signal.

Additive and subtractive

The above primary colours are called *additive*, because they add to the light we see. But they are not the primary colours most people are familiar with. Paints, photographs and even this book you're reading have a different set of primary colours. These are called *subtractive*, because they take out one primary colour from white light. Cyan removes red, so only the blue and green cones are stimulated. The brain interprets this as cyan; the same signal as a single wavelength of light about 500 nm. Yellow removes blue and magenta removes green.

So when you mix yellow and cyan, red and blue light are both absorbed, and only green is left to be scattered into your eyes.

CMY are thus the *complementary colours* to RGB. Newton showed with his prisms that a colour plus its complement add up to white—because this will make up all three additive primaries. Real pigments tend not to be perfectly CMY, i.e. don't perfectly absorb RGB, hence they don't combine to make a good black. Therefore printers also have a separate black pigment, hence their colour scheme is CMYK (K stands for black).

Eyes inspiring cameras

One problem with cameras is *lens flare* in bright light. E.g., if you photograph someone with the sun behind them, then the resulting picture looks 'washed out' with poor shadow contrast, no matter how carefully you work out the exposure. This lack of contrast is caused by the sharp change in refractive index between the lens and the air, so the light bounces around in the air-filled space between the lens and the film and hits the film several times. Physicist Edward Kelley explains how he solved this problem:

'So I *copied the design of the human eye*, which uses liquid to fill the gap between lens and retina [thus overcoming this problem].'[18]

Of course you cannot fill your camera with liquid because it would ruin the film. However, the new digital cameras do not have film. So Kelley made a digital camera with silicone oil between the lens and the device which senses the image. The modified camera has up to 70 times better clarity and resolution than one filled with air. Hector Lara, chief optical scientist at Photo Research in Chatsford, CA says:

'Trying to extinguish reflected light is an intrinsic problem that affects all optical devices. Kelley has come up with a clever, simple solution' [although as seen, he wasn't the first!][18]

EXCELLENT EYES IN NATURE

Chameleons: telephoto lizards[19]

Chameleons have large eyes that can move independently. They also use a 'telephoto principle' to measure distances, which is most like man-made cameras but is unique in the animal world.[20] Consider an old-style camera where you turn a dial to bring the object into focus—this can be a way of measuring the distance, by reading the distance setting of the dial when the object is focused.[21]

18. Walker, M., Fill up for a punchier picture, *New Scientist* **160**(2163):17, 1998 (emphasis added); An eye-full of design, *Creation* **21**(3):8–9, 1999.
19. After Sarfati, J., A coat of many colours: Captivating chameleons, *Creation* **26**(4):28–33, 2004; < www.creationontheweb.com/chameleon>.
20. Telephoto lizard, *Creation* **19**(1):7, 1996.
21. Land, M., Fast-focus telephoto eye, *Nature* **373**(6516):658–659, 1995; comment on Ref. 22.

To do this accurately, the image size of the retina must be large, and the chameleon's eye produces the largest of any vertebrate compared to its size. This large image is produced by an 'astonishing'[21] negative lens,[22] likely 'unique among animals',[21] i.e. it makes light diverge rather than converge.

And the chameleon can see a sharp image from objects from almost any distance away. That is, its eye can accommodate very well, so it can even clearly see an object just 3 cm away. In contrast, for people, objects become blurry if they are closer than twice that distance. And we really need objects to be 30 cm away before we can see them as clearly as a chameleon.

Lobster eyes—square facets and refractive focus[23]

The eye of a lobster (and some other 10-legged crustaceans[24] including shrimps and prawns) has a totally different method of forming an image from other creatures. The lobster eye shows a remarkable geometry not found elsewhere in nature—it has tiny facets that are perfectly square, so it 'looks like perfect graph paper'.[25] This is needed, because the eye focuses light by *reflection*, unlike the camera-like eyes discussed above which focus by *refraction* (bending of light) by a lens. The graph paper appearance is caused by the ends of many tiny square tubes on a spherical surface. The sides are very flat, shiny mirrors, and their precise geometrical arrangement means that parallel light rays are all reflected to a focus at about half the sphere's radius of curvature (see diagram, below).[26,27] The square geometry is crucial, because only with the reflectors at right angles can it form an image from light rays from any direction.[27]

Also, only if the tubes are about twice as long as they are wide can they reflect most light rays off exactly two mirrors, so the light ends up travelling in a plane parallel to the incident one (in the plane of the page in the diagram below).[27] This is a two-dimensional analogue

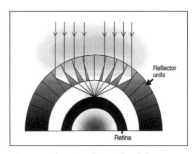

Diagram showing how the lobster eye focuses light.

---

22. Ott, M. and Schaeffel, F., A negatively powered lens in the chameleon, *Nature* **373**(6516):692–694, 23 February 1995.

23. After Sarfati, J., Lobster eyes—brilliant geometric design: Lobster eyes, X-ray telescopes, and microchips, *Creation* **23**(3):12–13, 2001; <creationontheweb.com/lobster>.

24. 10-legged crustaceans are called decapods, and in particular, these ones are of the suborder Macrura—see Ref. 27.

25. Hartline, B.K., Lobster-eye x-ray telescope envisioned, *Science* **207**(4426):47, 4 January 1980.

26. Land, M.F., Superposition images are formed by reflection in the eyes of some oceanic decapod crustacea, *Nature* **263**:764–765, 1976.

27. Land, M.F., Animal eyes with mirror optics, *Scientific Amer.* **239**(6):88–99, December 1978.

of the corner cubes in familiar reflectors that reflect light back in the same direction. Concentrating light from a relatively wide area is useful when it's quite dark, but in bright light, there is cellular machinery to move opaque pigment to block all light rays to the retina except those parallel to the tubes.[28]

Not only does the lobster eye have all the hallmarks of being designed by a master designer, it has also inspired human designers. Astronomers had wanted a telescope that could focus X-rays from certain heavenly bodies (e.g. X-ray binaries and nuclei of active galaxies are best 'seen' by their X-rays, especially if a device could magnify them), but there was no practical lens that would focus X-rays. An ordinary concave mirror wouldn't work, because X-rays would just go through, and reflect only at glancing angles. But Roger Angel of the University of Arizona pointed out that this problem 'might be overcome by copying the design of crustacean eyes.'[29,30] The Lobster Eye, launched by a satellite, should enable astronomers 'to observe a quarter of the sky at any one time'.[29] An elaborate process produces a 5 by 5 cm array of tiny (0.01–0.2 mm across) square hollow tubes made of X-ray reflecting lead glass, about 0.5–10 mm deep, then heated and curved into part of a sphere, just like the lobster eye. A hundred of these would be grouped into modules, and 20 modules fitted to the telescope.

'Reverse' Lobster Eye designs fine microchips

The lobster eye design could also help design computer chips with electronic components hundreds of times smaller than is possible today. Chips are made with photolithography, where a beam of parallel light shines through a stencil-like mask onto a semi-conducting material with a thin film of a photoresistant substance, and changes it so that acid will no longer etch that part. Then acid etches the rest away, leaving the desired pattern. However, there is a limit to how small the pattern can be, because light bends around the stencil edges (diffraction), thus spoiling the pattern. Shorter wavelengths mean less diffraction, and use of ultraviolet light has resulted in components only 0.18 mm across. X-rays would be ideal because of their tiny wavelength, but it had been expensive to produce a parallel beam. This is solved by a device like the Lobster Eye telescope—but running in reverse, as it were. X-rays are produced by a laser zapping a small point of metal and heating it to about 1 million °C (almost 2 million °F)—this spot is strategically located at

---

28. Denton, Michael, *Nature's Destiny: How the laws of biology reveal purpose in the universe*, ch. 15, The Free Press, NY/London, 1998.
29. Chown, M., I spy with my lobster eye, *New Scientist* **150**(2025):20, 1996.
30. See also Angel, J.R.P., Lobster eyes as X-ray telescopes, *Astrophysical Journal* **233**:364–373, 1979; and Hartline, Ref. 1.

the focus of the lobster eye, and a parallel beam emerges out from the eye, making it possible to use X-rays in making chips.[31]

Trilobites: exquisite eyes on 'primitive' water bug

The complex compound eyes of some types of trilobites, extinct and supposedly 'primitive' invertebrates, are among the most complex eyes of any creature that ever lived. They comprised tubes that each pointed in a slightly different direction, and had special lenses that focused light from any distance. The lens had a layer of calcite on top of a layer of chitin—materials with precisely the right refractive indices—and a wavy boundary between them of a precise mathematical shape.[32] This is consistent with their being designed by a master physicist, who applied what we now know as the physical laws of Fermat's principle of least time, Snell's law of refraction, Abbé's sine law and birefringent optics.[33] The eye of this humble creature displays some pretty fancy physics!

Brittlestar: 'one big compound eye'

The brittlestar or serpent star is similar to a starfish, but has five waving arms attached to a disc. Although it doesn't seem to have any eyes, it has a puzzling ability to flee from predators and catch prey. And it even changes colour from dark brown in daytime to grey at night.

Joanna Aizenberg, an expert in material science, especially biological mineral structures, at Lucent Technologies' Bell Laboratories, led a team that solved this mystery.[34] According to one report, its 'entire skeleton forms a big eye ... brittlestars were one big compound eye'.[35] They found that the brittlestar species *Ophiocoma wendtii* secretes tiny crystals of calcite (calcium carbonate, $CaCO_3$) which formed 'spherical microstructures that have a characteristic double-lens design',[34] and 'form nearly perfect microlenses'.[35] The array of microlenses focuses light a small distance into the tissues (4–7 μm) where nerve bundles detect the light.[34] Brittlestar species that were indifferent to light lacked these lenses.

The abstract of their paper states:

'The lens array is designed to minimize spherical aberration and birefringence and to detect light from a particular direction. The optical performance is further optimized by phototropic chromatophores that regulate the dose of illumination reaching the receptors. These structures represent an example of a multifunctional

31. Chown, M., X-ray lens brings finer chips into focus, *New Scientist* **151**(2037):18, 1996.
32. K. Towe, Trilobite eyes: calcified lenses, *Science* **179**:1007–11, 1973.
33. Stammers, C., Trilobite technology: Incredible lens engineering in an 'early' creature, *Creation* **21**(1):23, 1998, <creationontheweb.com/trilobite>
34. Aizenberg, J., *et al.*, Calcitic microlenses as part of the photoreceptor system in brittlestars, *Nature* **412**(6849):819–822, 2001; <www.nature.com/nature/journal/v412/n6849/abs/412819a0.html>.
35. Abraham, J., Eyeless Creature Turns Out to Be All Eyes, <www.arn.org/docs2/news/neweyedesign90401. htm>, *Access Research Network*, 12 September 2001.

biomaterial that fulfills both mechanical and optical functions.'[34]

Aizenberg used much easier-to-understand language when explaining to reporters the nuts-and-bolts significance of what the team's findings actually mean. For example, she said that the visual system of lenses in the brittlestar is far superior to any manufactured lenses:

> 'This study shows how great materials can be formed by nature, far beyond current technology,' said Dr Aizenberg. She went on to point out: 'In general, arrays of microlenses are something that technology tried a couple of years ago. Nobody knew something like that already existed in nature.'[35]

Commenting on the brittlestar discovery in the same issue of *Nature*, Roy Sambles, of the University of Exeter's Dept of Physics, explained that:

- There has to be 'exquisite control' of the calcite growth to form the lens structures
- The calcite must grow as single crystals with the optical axis parallel to the axis of the double lens (to avoid birefringence effects)
- 'each microlens should ideally have minimal optical aberration, and that seems to be the case.'[36]

And how did such intricate and efficiently coordinated microlenses come to exist 'in nature'? Dr Aizenberg's colleague and co-author of the study, Gordon Hendler, made his views clear to *National Geographic*:

> 'Thanks to evolution, they [brittlestars] have beautifully designed crystal lenses that are an integral part of their calcite skeleton. Those lenses appear to be acting in concert with chromatophores and photoreceptor tissues.'[37]

However, he fails to explain *specifically* how these creatures could have evolved 'beautifully designed' microlenses acting 'in concert' with other (incredibly specialized) parts of the body. His evolutionary 'explanation' is totally vacuous—where is even a *proposed* sequence of small changes guided by natural selection at every step, let alone one *demonstrated* in the fossil record? But the brittlestar eye is consistent with a designer, and this explanation makes sense of Sambles' admission:

> 'Once again we find that nature foreshadowed our technical developments.'[36]

36. Sambles, R., Armed for light sensing, *Nature* **412**(6849):783, 2001 (commentary on Ref. 34).
37. Roach, J., Brittle Star found covered with optically advanced 'eyes', *National Geographic News*, <http://news.nationalgeographic.com/news/2001/08/0822_starfisheyes.html>, 2001.

COULD THE CAMERA EYE HAVE EVOLVED?

It's interesting to note that the eye has long presented a challenge to evolutionists, so not surprisingly evolutionists claim to have solved the mystery. Yet they tend to concentrate only on the evolution of the camera-eye shape and *ignore much of the biochemical and electronic complexity*. E.g. *Scientific American* says in a much publicized anti-creationist article:[38]

> 'Generations of creationists have tried to counter Darwin by citing the example of the eye as a structure that could not have evolved. The eye's ability to provide vision depends on the perfect arrangement of its parts, these critics say. Natural selection could thus never favor the transitional forms needed during the eye's evolution—what good is half an eye? Anticipating this criticism, Darwin suggested that even 'incomplete' eyes might confer benefits (such as helping creatures orient toward light) and thereby survive for further evolutionary refinement.'[39]

However, it's fallacious to argue that 51 percent vision would necessarily have a strong enough selective advantage over 50 percent to overcome the effects of genetic drift's tendency to eliminate even *beneficial* mutations.[40] Then *Scientific American* continues:

> 'Biology has vindicated Darwin: researchers have identified primitive eyes and light-sensing organs throughout the animal kingdom and have even tracked the evolutionary history of eyes through comparative genetics. (It now appears that in various families of organisms, eyes have evolved independently.)'[39]

Scientific American contradicts itself here. If the evolutionary history of eyes has been tracked through comparative genetics, how is it that eyes have supposedly evolved independently? Actually, evolutionists suppose that eyes must have arisen independently at least 30 times because there is no evolutionary pattern to explain the origin of eyes from a common ancestor. What this really means is that since eyes cannot be related by common ancestor, and since they are here, and only materialistic explanations are allowed, hey presto, there's proof that they evolved independently many times! Furthermore, since this has happened so many times, it must be relatively easy for eyes to evolve. So goes the circular reasoning.

---

38. Thoroughly refuted in Sarfati, J., 15 ways to refute materialistic bigotry: A point by point response to *Scientific American*, <creationontheweb.com/sciam>, 20 June 2002.

39. Rennie, J., 15 Answers to Creationist Nonsense (article by the editor), *Scientific Amer.* **287**(1):78–85, July 2002; p. 83 (first published on their website 17 June).

40. Spetner, L.M., *Not By Chance: Shattering the modern theory of evolution,* Judaica Press, Brooklyn, NY, 1996, 1997.

Eye evolution by computer?

A number of evolutionary propagandists rely on a computer simulation by Dan Nilsson and Susanne Pelger from a widely publicized paper.[41] Taking their cue from Darwin, who started with a light-sensitive spot when 'explaining' the origin of the eye, their simulation starts with a light-sensitive layer, with a transparent coating in front and a light-absorbing layer behind.

Here is how the simulation proceeds. First, the light-sensitive layer bends gradually into a cup, so it can tell the direction of light rays increasingly well. This continues until the cup is curved into a hemisphere filled with the transparent substance. Second, bringing the ends together, closing the aperture, gradually increases the sharpness of the image, as a pinhole camera does, because a smaller hole cuts out light. But because of the diffraction of light if the hole is too small, there is a limit to this process. So third, the shape and refractive index gradient of the transparent cover change gradually to a finely focusing lens.

But even if we were generous and accepted that such simplistic computer simulations really have something to do with the real world of biochemistry, there are more serious problems. See the earlier sections on what is needed even for a single light-sensitive spot (pp. 25–27) and a transparent window (pp. 24–25). Therefore, *these simulations do not start from simple beginnings but presuppose vast complexity even to begin with.*

Another major problem with the just-so story above is that the hypothetical ancestor starts with the nerve *behind* the light-sensitive spot. The vertebrate eye has the nerves *in front* of the photoreceptors (which is actually a very good design despite many evolutionists complaining about it—see chapter 12). Yet the evolutionary just-so story *provides no transitions from behind to in front,* with all the other complex coordinated changes that would have to occur as well.[42]

Also, in their original paper, the researchers admitted that 'an eye makes little sense on its own,' because the ability to perceive light is meaningless unless the organism has sophisticated computational machinery to make use of this information. For example, it must have the ability to translate 'attenuation of photon intensity' to 'a shadow of a predator is responsible' to 'I must take evasive measures,' and be able to act on this information for it to have any selective value. Similarly, the first curving, with its slight ability to detect the direction of light, would only work if the creature had the appropriate nerves (hardware) and processing power (software) to interpret this. Perceiving actual images is even more complicated. And having the right hardware and software may not be enough—people who have their sight restored after years of blindness take some time to learn

---

41. Nilsson, D.-E. and Pelger, S., A pessimistic estimate of the time required for an eye to evolve. *Proc. R. Soc. Lond.* **B 256**:53–58, 1994.

42. Sodera, V., *One Small Speck to Man: The Evolution Myth*, pp. 292–302, Vija Sodera Publications, Bognor Regis, UK, 2003.

to see properly. It has been noted that much information processing occurs in the retina before the signal reaches the brain.

Gradation of complexity in nature

It is also fallacious to point to a series of more complex eyes in nature, and then argue that this presents an evolutionary sequence. That would be like arranging a number of different types of aircraft in order of complexity, then claiming that the simple aircraft evolved into complex ones, as opposed to being designed. For one thing, eyes can't descend from other eyes *per se*; rather, organisms pass on genes for eyes to their descendants. This is important when considering the nautilus eye, a pinhole camera. This cannot possibly be an ancestor of the vertebrate lens/camera eye, because the nautilus as a whole is not an ancestor of the vertebrates, even according to the evolutionists.

Colour vision evolution?

As explained in the section on colour vision (pp. 29 ff.), our three-colour vision is the result of three different receptors, R, G and B. Many evolutionists claim that they arose by gene duplication from two-colour vision:

> 'The "blue" opsin is encoded on human chromosome 7, while the red and green opsin genes are located next to each other, head to tail, on the X chromosome. The red and green opsin genes are the product of an evolutionary recent gene duplication because they are 98% identical.'

However, similarity doesn't prove descent. And there are a number of problems with this idea:

- There would be little point in changing the red receptors to green receptors unless the brain also changed at the same time to recognize the difference, otherwise there would be no selective advantage.
- If the allegedly duplicated red opsin gradually changed to the green one, where are the intermediate opsins sensitive to intermediate wavelengths (orange, yellow)? How was the brain rearranging to cope?
- What selective force would drive this change in our alleged arboreal ancestors? It is not clear that there is much disadvantage to having only RB vision, also called red-green colour-blindness. Indeed, this condition makes it easier to detect camouflage, and South American monkeys manage just fine with RB vision.
- Mammals are supposed to have evolved from fish, but bony fish have good full RGB colour vision. So this scenario entails that colour vision has been lost then regained.[43]

---

43.   Sodera, Ref. 42, pp. 305–311.

Lobster eyes: more problems with evolution

Evolutionists generally believe that the lobster eye (see pp. 32 ff.) evolved from a refracting compound eye with round or hexagonal (six-sided) tubes, as other crustaceans have. Claimed supporting evidence is that the free-swimming lobster larva has a refractive eye, which is transformed into the reflective eye of the adult. However, this is just a variant of the thoroughly discredited embryonic recapitulation theory, which was supported by forged drawings.[44] Lobsters clearly have the genetic 'programming' for the transformation already in place—this does not explain how this information arose in the first instance! Neo-Darwinist theory requires:

* A pathway of many tiny steps, with each new change caused by genetic copying mistakes (mutations).
* Each step must be more advantageous than the previous one, so its possessor will leave more offspring (natural selection).

The lobster eye seems to illustrate 'irreducible complexity', that is, unless all the right parts were in the right arrangement, light rays would not focus. Also, the mirror arrangement produces an upright image, while a lens produces an inverted one, so the brain would also need to be reprogrammed to interpret this major change. Hypothetical intermediate steps between a refractive and reflective eye, e.g. a halfway stage between a hexagonal and square tube, or between a mirror and a lens, would produce a much worse image.[28] An organism with such an eye for life would have a serious disadvantage, so natural selection would work against such intermediates.

And even a fully formed reflective eye (mathematically impossible to produce in a single step) seems to have little or no selective advantage over the refractive eye, since crabs—which have roughly the same lifestyle in roughly the same type of environment— manage fine with refractive eyes. (Note, too, that despite these two crustaceans having *radically different eyes*, crabs and lobsters are supposedly *evolutionary 'cousins'*!) So if even a fully formed reflective eye has little advantage, how much less could natural selection work on hypothetical intermediates, which must have been even less advantageous?[45]

SUMMARY

Eyes shout 'design'. There is just no way that a blind 'eyemaker' (evolution) made eyes. Even the simplest of eyes needs so many complex components functioning together for any vision to occur. And there is no evidence for the origin of any of the more than thirty quite different eye designs by common ancestry (evolution).

44. Grigg, R., Ernst Haeckel: Evangelist for evolution and apostle of deceit, *Creation* 18(2):33–36, 1996; <creationontheweb.com/haeckel>.

45. Biophysicist Dr Lee Spetner shows mathematically that such weak natural selection could not be responsible for generation of new information, because it would be swamped by chance—see *Not By Chance,* The Judaica Press, Brooklyn, NY, 1997.

CHAPTER 2

OTHER SENSES

Sight is not the only important sense. New discoveries in hearing, smell and touch also demonstrate intricate design that is teaching human engineers new techniques. Hearing has its own ingenious features, and one particular type of hearing, echolocation, is vital for navigation in dolphins and bats. Man-made sonar uses the same principles. And our sense of smell seems to work on the principles of vibrational spectroscopy.

FOVEAS AND SACCADES[1]

The previous chapter explained the fovea/saccade system of our visual system (pp. 28–29), with its great efficiency in information processing. This section elaborates on fovea/saccade systems in touch and hearing.

Touch

There is a type of mole called the 'star-nosed mole', North America's only semi-aquatic variety. Its name comes from its nose ('star') that has 22 'tentacles', which are not used for smell but for touch. The star is more mobile, complex and touch-sensitive than even the elephant's trunk.[2] It comprises over 25,000 incredibly specialized papillae (projections) called *Eimer's organs*, supported by more than 100,000 nerve fibres that carry information to the central nervous system.[3]

After Carl Ernst Poeschel, <wikipedia.org>

The bottom pair of tentacles above the mouth, although among the smallest, has a higher density of nerve endings, and by far the largest brain area involved in processing their information. This is like our eyes' fovea. The other tentacles are like our peripheral vision—they don't provide as much detail, but they allow the sensory apparatus to explore a wide area. The mole scans its environment with nose movements too fast for our eyes to see, and these movements are like our saccades. When the other tentacles locate an interesting object, the nose moves to bring the 'fovea' or super-sensitive bottom tentacles to feel its texture in detail. This enables it to find food very quickly. This is so efficient that one mole found five separate pieces of earthworm in a single second during a laboratory test.[3]

1. After Weston, P. and Wieland, C., The Mole, and Sarfati, J. Superb sense organ sheds light on alleged eye imperfection, *Creation* **25**(2):46–50, 2003; <creationontheweb.com/mole>.
2. The mole tunnel, star-nosed mole, <home.cc.umanitoba.ca/~rmacarth/starnose.html>, 2002.
3. Catania, K.C., The nose takes a starring role, *Scientific American* **287**(1):40, 2002.

Some scientists believe the star-nosed mole evolved its specialized appendages over time. This is based on the way in which the star develops in the embryo (the star is initially embedded in the mole's face, then slowly breaks free from the skin; two weeks after birth the appendages bend forward to form the adult star). This, they say, suggests that 'ancestral star-nosed moles might have had strips of sensory organs lying flat against the sides of the snout. These might have been slowly raised up over many generations until the star was formed'.[4]

First, this presupposes the discredited idea of Embryonic Recapitulation.[5] Second, why would a 'primitive' mammal suddenly start to develop such a specialized appendage? If it was already successfully hunting food without the star, what was the evolutionary 'trigger' for the star's development?

Acoustic fovea in echolocating bats

Echolocating bats have many receptors and much brain area devoted to a narrow sound frequency ('pitch') range roughly matching the ultrasound pulses the bat emits. But echoes of moving objects have a different frequency, therefore the bat's 'fovea' might miss them. So the bat also uses 'sound saccades'—it's always changing the pitch of the sound it emits, so that the echoes become tuned to the 'fovea'.[3,6] For more on echolation in bats, see pp. 48 ff.

Convergent evolution?

These ingenious systems of fovea and saccades in three totally different senses are a remarkably efficient design. *Scientific American*'s article on the Star-nosed Mole explains them as 'convergent evolution'.[3] But there wasn't the slightest effort to explain how this system could have evolved separately three times by tiny steps, each with an advantage over its predecessor. Rather, the 'explanation' has nothing to do with science, and everything to do with materialistic bias (materialism is true so convergent evolution must have happened).

FLY EAR INGENUITY
IS INSPIRING ENGINEERS[7]

The main mechanism for discerning the direction of a sound involves measuring the slight difference in the time of arrival of the sound at each ear (inter-aural time difference, ITD), as well as the slightly greater intensity at the nearer ear.

---

4.   Catania, ref. 3, p. 43.
5.   Grigg, R., 'Ernst Haeckel: Evangelist for evolution and apostle of deceit', *Creation* 18(2):33–36, 1996; <creationontheweb.com/embryonic>.
6.   The frequency change is due to the Doppler Effect, and the saccades are called Doppler–shift compensation.
7.   After Sarfati, J., Ear Now … An incredible design in a tiny fly is inspiring engineers, *Creation* 23(4):55, 2001.

A tiny female fly, *Ormia ochracea*, can track a male cricket's chirping so she can lay her eggs on him. However, the fly's ears are only 0.5 mm apart, meaning that the ITD is only 1½ μs (microseconds = millionths of a second), and the intensity difference is almost nil.

How does she do it? A bridge like a flexible lever couples the fly's eardrums together. The resulting resonance effectively increases the time difference about 40 times, and the eardrum nearest the sound vibrates about 10 decibels more strongly (which is a big difference!).

Also, the fly's nerves respond in a type of code so that the time difference increases a further five times. Finally, the fly's flight programming links to its ears' signals. This all adds up so that the fly can tell directions to within 2°—as well as humans can.

This fly's mechanical and signal-processing technology is being used to improve hearing aids, which normally can't tell direction, and it could also be used to design miniature directional microphones.

Once more, the design in nature has taught top human designers some lessons. While this strongly supports a Designer, the research paper[8] called the fly's ear an 'evolutionary innovation', without the slightest explanation of how the mechanical structure and nervous coding system could arise by small mutations and natural selection.

OWLS: SHARP HEARING DUE TO MICROPROCESSORS[9]

The *Ormia* fly is not the only creature with an amazingly high-tech mechanism in its nerves of hearing to help it determine the direction of sound. An owl's fine directional hearing is also largely due to the way the nerves process the sound time and intensity differences. Most neurons (nerve cells) 'fire' when the incoming signals *add* up to a threshold, and act 'like a transistor in an electronic circuit'. But 'neurons in the owl's auditory map *multiply*', so each 'is more like a little processor; computationally it's much more powerful'.[10]

Olfactory Design: Smell and Spectroscopy[11]

Our sense of smell is actually a complex system designed to detect thousands of chemicals. It helps warn us of danger, e.g. rotting food—we can sense one component of rotten meat, ethyl mercaptan, at a concentration of 1/400,000,000[th] of a milligram per litre of air.[12]

8.   Mason, A.C., *et al.*, Hyperacute directional hearing in a microscale auditory system, *Nature* **410**(6829): 686–690, 2001; Narins, P.M., In a fly's ear, same issue, pp. 644–645; Cricket pitch, p. ix .

9.   After Sarfati, J., Wising up to design, *Creation* **23**(4):55, 2001.

10. Peña, J.L. and Konishi, M., Auditory spatial receptive fields created by multiplication, *Science* **292**(5515):249–252, 2001; Helmuth, L., Location neurons do advanced math, same issue, p. 185.

11. After Sarfati, J., Olfactory design: smell and spectroscopy, *J. Creation* **12**(2):137–138, 1998; <creationontheweb.com/smell>.

12. Sensory Reception: Smell (Olfactory) Sense, *Britannica CD*, Version 97, Encyclopædia Britannica, Inc. 1997.

Smell also helps us distinguish types of foods and flowers. The sense of smell is actually responsible for most of the different 'tastes' of foods. In many animals, this sense is even more important than in humans—it helps bees find nectar, for example.

Recently, biophysicist Luca Turin proposed that the smell sensors actually detect the energy at which the different chemical molecules vibrate.[13] Thus these receptors seem to work on the same quantum mechanical principles as vibrational spectroscopy (the field in which I wrote my doctoral thesis).

This energy depends on the chemical make-up—certain groups of atoms have similar energies. Chemicals with sulfur bonded to hydrogen tend to vibrate similarly and so often have 'rotten egg' smells—rotten eggs themselves produce such chemicals.

Turin's theory was supported by the rotten-egg smell of certain rocket fuels (boranes)—they have nothing in common with sulfur compounds except for similar vibrations.

The receptors generate signals in a complex way, and these signals are first processed and sorted by the olfactory bulb before being sent on to the brain.

Whether or not Turin's idea is correct, the olfactory system exhibits *irreducible complexity*, and is therefore evidence of design. The chemical sensing machinery needs proteins with just the right shape to accommodate the odour molecules. And under Turin's model, the right energy levels as well. And even if the sensors were fully operational, the chemical information gathered by the nose would be useless without nerve connections to transmit it and the brain to process it.

Nose design

The nose contains millions of receptors, of 500–1000 different types. They are in the yellow *olfactory epithelium*, that covers about 2.5 cm^2 on each side of the inner nose. The different types of receptors are proteins folded so a particularly shaped odour molecule can dock. Each receptor is coupled to a *g-protein*. When the odour molecule docks with the receptor, the g-protein releases. This sets off a second messenger to stimulate a neuron to send a signal. This is transmitted by olfactory nerve fibres which enter either of two specialized structures (*olfactory bulbs*), stem-like projections under the front part of the brain. They sort the signals, and transmit them to the brain for processing.[12,14]

---

13.   Turin, L., A spectroscopic mechanism for primary olfactory reception. *Chemical Senses* **21**:773, 1996. Dr Turin himself wrote (email 9 February 2000) in response to my article (Ref. 11): 'Dear Dr Sarfati, I write to congratulate you on your lucid and accurate description of my spectroscopic theory of smell ....' He said he didn't necessarily agree with my conclusion that a Designer was responsible. But he continued, 'I entirely agree, however, that if true, my theory is one more example of the wonderful design of living things', but he left the question of the cause of this design open.

14.   Hill, S., Sniff'n'shake, *New Scientist* **157**(2115):34–37, 1998.

Quantum tunnelling

Turin proposed a mechanism where an electron tunnels from a donor site to an acceptor site on the receptor molecule, causing it to release the g-protein. Tunnelling requires both the starting and finishing points to have the same energy, but Turin believes that the donor site has a higher energy than the receptor. The energy difference is precisely that needed to excite the odour molecule into a higher vibrational quantum state. Therefore when the odour molecule lands, it can absorb the right amount of the electron's energy, enabling tunnelling through its orbitals.

Vibrational spectroscopy

This means the smell receptors actually detect the energy of vibrational quantum transitions in the odour molecules, as first proposed by G.M. Dyson in 1937.[15] This energy decreases with increasing mass of the atoms, and increases with increasing bond strength. It also depends on the symmetry of the molecule. For a diatomic molecule,[16] the fundamental transition energy is:

$$E = \hbar(k/\mu)^{\frac{1}{2}}$$

where $\hbar$ is $h/2\pi$ where h is Planck's constant; k is the force constant of the bond; and μ is the reduced mass, which is related to the masses of the two atoms by:

$$\mu = m_1 m_2/(m_1 + m_2)$$

Incident electromagnetic radiation of the right frequency (ν) can sometimes cause a transition. This is related to the energy by:

$$E = h\nu$$

Vibrational energy and the corresponding radiation are normally measured in *wavenumbers*, the reciprocal of the wavelength, related to energy by:

$$\nu\sim = E/hc$$

As this energy is in the infrared region, *infrared absorption spectroscopy* is a common tool for measuring vibrational energies and bond strengths (together with the complementary technique of *Raman spectroscopy*).

This means certain groups of atoms have similar energies, so have similar vibrational spectra. For example, chemicals with sulfur-hydrogen bonds tend to vibrate at about 2500 cm^{-1} and this is often perceived as a 'rotten' smell—rotten eggs produce chemicals like hydrogen sulfide (H_2S), and ethyl mercaptan produced by rotting meat is C_2H_5SH.

Turin supports his theory by noting that decaborane ($B_{10}H_{14}$) smells very similar to S-H compounds, and it has nothing in common with them apart from similar vibrational energies. Although boron

15. Sell, C., On the Right Scent, *Chemistry in Britain* **33**(3):39–42, 1997.
16. For more complicated molecules, see Wilson, E.B., Decius, J.C. and Cross, P.C., *Molecular Vibrations: the theory of infrared and Raman vibrational spectra*, McGraw-Hill, New York, 1955.

has a much lower atomic mass than sulfur, B-H bonds are much weaker than S-H bonds, and these effects happen to cancel out.

Further support came from the analogous compounds ferrocene and nickelocene. These have a divalent metal ion (iron and nickel respectively) sandwiched between two cyclopentadienyl anions ($C_5H_5^-$). The main vibrational difference between them is that the metal ring bond in ferrocene vibrates at 478 cm^{-1}, while in nickelocene it is 355 cm^{-1}. Ferrocene smells rather spicy, while nickelocene smells like the aromatic hydrocarbon rings. Turin proposes that below a threshold of 400 cm^{-1}, 'background noise' swamps the vibrational signal, so the nose cannot detect it.

As different isotopes have different masses but similar chemical properties, they affect the vibrational energy. It can be seen from the formula for reduced mass that the biggest difference results from replacing hydrogen ($A_r = 1$) with deuterium ($A_r = 2$); the numerator is doubled. Indeed, deuterated acetophenone smells fruitier than ordinary acetophenone ($C_6H_5COCH_3$). It also smells slightly of bitter almonds, just like many compounds containing the cyanide or nitrile group (C≡N); both C-D and C≡N bonds vibrate at about 2200 cm^{-1}. The different smells of different isotopes is explained logically by Turin's theory, but very hard to explain with other theories.

One challenge to Turin's theory is the different smells of some enantiomers (optical isomers), as they have identical vibrational spectra. For example, R-carvone smells like spearmint, and S-carvone like caraway. The answer is: the spectra are identical only in an *achiral* medium, as in solution or gas phase. But the smell receptors are *chiral* and orient the two enantiomers differently. This means that different vibrating groups lie in the tunnelling direction in each enantiomer. Turin thinks that the caraway S-carvone is oriented so a carbonyl (C=O) group lies in that direction, so is detected; in the minty R-carvone, it lies at right angles, so is ignored. Turin supported this by manufacturing a caraway scent by mixing the minty carvone with the carbonyl-containing butanone ($C_2H_5COCH_3$).

If Turin's theory is true, then infrared and Raman spectroscopy should be essential tools for the perfume industry! Turin is also using *inelastic tunnelling spectroscopy*—'inelastic' refers to the energy loss before tunnelling, as with the proposed sensory mechanism.

The precise chemistry of olfaction is still little understood. But Turin believes he has found a peptide (short protein) that could function as the electron donor together with NADPH. He has also found five amino acid residues coordinated to a zinc atom that could be the acceptor site. One warning sign of zinc deficiency is loss of the sense of smell, and zinc is often involved in biological electron-transfer reactions.

ECHOLOCATION

A number of creatures navigate and find prey by echolocation (e.g. echolocating bats, previously mentioned on p. 42). This relies on sending out sound pulses, and listening for the echoes. The greater the time for the return of the echo from an object, the further away it is.

The pitch of the echo provides information on the object's speed via the Doppler Effect, named after the Austrian physicist Christian Doppler (1803–1853), who analyzed sound from moving sources in 1842. The effect is well known—as a train moves toward you, more sound wave crests can reach the ear in a given time, so you hear a greater frequency, or higher pitch. The reverse happens when the train moves away from you—then fewer wave crests per unit time reach you, so you hear a lower frequency. So you hear a sudden drop in pitch as the train passes, which remains low as it moves away. So if the object is moving towards the creature, the echo's pitch will increase, while it decreases if it is moving away.

Echolocation works best at high frequency, i.e. ultrasound, because the wavelengths are smaller and thus the echolocator is able to detect smaller objects.

Dolphins

Many cetaceans find objects by echolocation. They have a sonar system which is so precise that it's the envy of the U.S. Navy. It can detect a fish the size of a golf ball 70 m (230 feet) away. It took an expert in chaos theory to show that the dolphin's 'click' pattern is mathematically designed to give the best information.[17]

NASA, <wikipedia.org>

There is no evidence that this system evolved from simpler steps. According to an evolutionist, 'the ancestors of today's dolphins had an ear structure that suggests that they could echolocate as well as their modern relatives can.'[18]

Volume control

Since sound intensity decreases over distance, an echolocating device needs to adjust for this. Commercial sonar adjusts the sensitivity of the *receiver*, and it turns out that bats do the same (see p. 48), but dolphins adjust the intensity of the *transmitter*.[19]

17. Howlett, R., Flipper's secret, *New Scientist* **154**(2088):34–39, 1997.
18. Perkins, S., Learning to listen: How some vertebrates evolved biological sonar, *Science News* **167**(20):314, 2005.
19. Au, W.W.L and Benoit-Bird, K.J., Automatic gain control in the echolocation system of dolphins, *Nature* **423**:861–863, 2003; Tromans, A., Echolocation: Volume Control, perspective, same issue, p. 815.

Researchers found that as the dolphins homed in on their target, the amplitude of clicks decreased by 6 decibels (75%) every time the distance halved.

They do this automatically. The dolphin produces clicks by pressurizing the nasal system, then manipulating air through its phonic lips. The dolphin also allows an echo to return before emitting the next click. So as the dolphin approaches, the echoes return more quickly, so the click rate increases. Therefore, if the dolphin keeps the total acoustic energy constant over a whole pressurization cycle, then when the click rate increases, the energy *per click* must decrease. Thus the click loudness automatically adjusts for distance.

Sound lens

Echolocating cetaceans have special oil-filled sinuses in the lower jaw which pass the echoes to the inner ear. They also have an amazing adaptation called the 'melon', a fatty protrusion on the forehead. This 'melon' is actually a sound lens—a sophisticated structure designed to focus the emitted sound waves into a beam that the dolphin can direct where it likes. This sound lens depends on different lipids (fatty compounds) bending the ultrasonic sound waves travelling through them in different ways. The different lipids have to be arranged in the right shape and sequence in order to focus the returning sound echoes. Each separate lipid is unique and different from normal blubber lipids, and is made by a complicated chemical process that requires a number of different enzymes.[20]

For such an organ to have evolved, random mutations must have formed the right enzymes to make the right lipids, and other mutations must have caused the lipids to be deposited in the right place and shape. A gradual step-by-step evolution of a functional organ is not feasible, because until the lipids were fully formed and at least partly in the right place and shape, they would have been no use. Natural selection could not have even created a partly-functional system to get started.

Bats

Bats are a very successful animal—one in every five mammals is a bat, and the only type of mammal with more species is the rodent. Bats are unique among mammals because they are capable of fully powered flight (see also pp. 74 ff.), and many bats also have an exquisitely designed sonar system. By coincidence, scientists discovered this at about the time engineers were developing top secret sonar during WW2. At a conference of zoologists, when researchers announced their discovery that bats had sonar, one of the 'distinguished scientists' present in the audience was 'so indignantly incredulous' at the notion that bats could possibly do anything

---

20. Varanasi, U., Feldman, H.R., and Malins, D.C., Molecular basis for formation of lipid sound lens in echolocating cetaceans, *Nature* 255(5506):340–343, 1975.

remotely analogous to the latest triumph in electronic engineering that he grabbed one of the researchers by the shoulders and shook him![21]

Echolocating fishing bats can detect a minnow's fin, as fine as a human hair, extending only 2 mm above the water surface. This fine detection is possible because bats can distinguish ultra-sound echoes very close together. Man-made sonar can distinguish echoes 12 millionths of a second apart, although with 'a lot of work this can be cut to 6 millionths to 8 millionths of a second'.[22] But bats 'relatively easily' distinguish ultra-sound echoes only 2 to 3 millionths of a second apart, according to researcher James Simmons of Brown University.[22] This means they can distinguish objects 'just $^3/_{10}$ths of a millimetre apart—about the width of a pen line on paper.'[22]

There is no fossil evidence that such a system evolved. One evolutionist admitted:

'The oldest bat fossils, belonging to an extinct lineage, were unearthed from rocks about 54 million years old, but the creatures that they represent aren't dramatically different from living bats, says Mark S. Springer, an evolutionary biologist at the University of California, Riverside.

'Hallmark features of these creatures include the elongated fingers that support the wing membranes and the extensive coiling of bony structures in the inner ears, a sign that they were capable of detecting the high-frequency chirps used in echolocation.'[18]

Another problem for Darwinists is that most echolocating bats use vocal cords to create their echoes, but some megabats use tongue clicks. Did they evolve separately, or did one type diverge?[23]

Hearing gain control

Like man-made sonars, the closer they are to their target, the less sensitive their hearing must be, otherwise they risk deafness. Indeed, why are bats not deafened by their own clicks?

Man-made sonars use *time-varying gain* (TVG), where the gain of the receiver increases (logarithmically) with elapsed time since the pulse.[24] We have known for decades that bats have a similar automatic gain control.

Their middle ear muscles, which are very well developed and have fine nerve control, play a key role. The stapedius muscle that controls the tiny bone called the stirrup (stapes) is coordinated with the larynx muscles (which create the emitted sound). Just before a click, the stapedius contracts, reducing the sensitivity, then relaxes

21. Dawkins, R., *The Blind Watchmaker*, p. 43, Norton & Company, Inc., New York, USA, 1986.
22. Simmons was cited in the appropriately titled article, Bats put technology to shame, *Cincinnati Enquirer*, 13 October 1998. His research paper: Simmons, J.A. *et al.*, Echo-delay resolution in sonar images of the big brown bat, *Eptesicus fuscus*, *Proc. Nat. Acad. Sci. USA* **95**(21): 12647–12652, 1998.
23. Bergman, J., Evidence for the evolution of bats [a critique], *Origins* (BCS) **47**:10–15, February 2008.
24. Medwin, H. and Clay, C.S., *Fundamentals of Acoustical Oceanography*, Academic, San Diego, 1998.

in about 10 milliseconds. When the bat is very close, so that the clicks are frequent and echoes loud, the stapedius stays contracted throughout a series of pulses.[25]

Avoiding clutter

So how does a bat tell the echo of its flying insect meal from all the other echoes around, such as from leaves? A team led by Cynthia Moss of the University of Maryland used high-speed infrared cameras and strategically placed microphones in their 'Batlab' to see how.[26] They found that when a bat approaches a promising target, it emits a series of quick repetitive pulses, called *sonar strobe groups*. And just before it's ready to capture, the bat sends a rapid fire series of sounds, the *final buzz*. When an insect was tethered close to a plant, 'In each case we found that the bats spent more time strobing when the insect was positioned near a plant, a strong indication that they used sonar strobe groups to try to distinguish the insect from the background clutter,' said Moss. 'They also varied the intervals between pulses in the strobe group, depending on the distance between the prey and clutter.'[27]

This study also refuted the idea that bat echoes are strictly coordinated with wing beat. This was not an unreasonable suggestion, because the wingbeat was shown in 1971 to be co-ordinated with breathing—inhaling on the downstroke and exhaling on the upstroke. (This surprised the discoverers since one would think that the power stroke downwards would compress the thorax and expel air from the lungs.)[28]

But as Moss pointed out, 'Breaks in the sonar strobe groups would be expected to occur during a particular phase of the downstroke if wingbeat and respiration were strictly driving the production of sound groups.' Instead, she says, 'we found that the sound groups occur across all phases of the wingbeat cycle, and definitely through the entire final buzz. This suggests that the bat's vocal control can override the wingbeat-respiration cycle. Most importantly, the results of this study clearly show that bats control the timing of their calls to directly influence the patterns of echoes used for perception.'[27]

25. Henson, The activity and function of the middle-ear muscles in echo-locating bats, *J. Physiol.* **180**(4): 871–887, October 1965.
26. Moss, C.F., Bohn, K., Gilkenson, H. and Surlykke, A., Active Listening for Spatial Orientation in a Complex Auditory Scene, *PLoS Biology* **4**(4):e79, 7 March 2006, doi:10.1371/journal.pbio.0040079.
27. Bats Have Complex Skills to Deal with 'Clutter', *PhysOrg.com*, <www.physorg.com/news11494.html>, 2006.
28. Suthers, R.A. *et al.*, Respiration, wing-beat and ultrasonic pulse emission in an echo-locating bat, *Exp. Biol.* **56**:37–48, 1972.

Oilbirds[29]

While bats and dolphins are well known for their echolocating, not so well known is that a few birds also use this sense. One is the *oilbird* (or Guacharo, *Steatornis caripensis*) of Central and northern South America. It is the only nocturnal, fruit-eating bird in the world, but is officially a bird of prey. This single species is placed in a family all of its own, Steatornithidae,[30] because it is so distinct from other birds.

These birds live in pitch-black caves, and use echolocation to navigate. Unlike bats, which use ultrasound, oilbirds emit squeaks that humans can hear.[31] This is precise enough for the mother oilbird to avoid knocking its chicks out of the nest, which is pretty good considering its one-metre wingspan. The chicks themselves are born with echolocating ability—they don't need to learn it.

Super sight

Unlike the proverbial 'blind' bats, oilbirds have the most light-sensitive eyes of any vertebrate. In 2004, researchers found that the rods, the photoreceptors responsible for detecting dim light, were unusually tiny, only 1.3 μm in diameter by 18.6 μm long.[32] Also, the rods are stacked up in three banks/tiers, an arrangement

The Lilac Breasted Roller, <flickr.org>

that has only previously been seen in deep-sea fish.[33] The resulting density is 1 million rods per sq. mm, higher than any other vertebrate eye known. In contrast, only a small number of cone photoreceptor cells (for discerning colour) are present, because they require bright light (which is why you can't see colours well in the dark).

Also, despite its small size, an oilbird's eye nevertheless has 'a light-gathering capacity that is the highest recorded in a bird', because its pupil can enlarge to 9 mm in diameter.[32] These unique eye features make oilbirds extremely sensitive to low light levels and, in tandem with their other senses (smell and echolocation) demonstrate the oilbird's supreme design for a nocturnal lifestyle.

Convergent evolution?

Another type of bird uses echolocation: the cave swiftlets of southern Asia.[30] But they eat insects instead of fruit. These birds are very different to oilbirds, so this echolocation could not have

29. *After* Bell, P., The super-senses of oilbirds: Bizarre birds elude an evolutionary explanation, *Creation* **28**(*1*):38–41, 2005; <*creationontheweb.com/oilbird*>.
30. Scott, P. (Ed.), *The world atlas of birds*, Colour Library Books Ltd, Godalming, Surrey, p. 243, 1989.
31. Konishi, M. and Knudsen, E.I., The oilbird: hearing and echolocation, *Science* **204**(4391):425–427, 1979.
32. Martin,G., *et al.*, The eyes of oilbirds (*Steatornis caripensis*): pushing the limits of sensitivity, *Naturwissenschaften* **91**(1):26–29, 2004.
33. Pilcher, H.R., Bird's—eye view, *Nature* **427**(6977):800, 2004.

evolved from a common ancestor. Instead, evolutionists attribute it to 'convergence'—a term they coined to describe the situation where the same feature appears in different organisms but it cannot be due to having a common ancestor (i.e., evolution). It's a word masquerading as an explanation. But this entails that such complex machinery evolved not just once but *twice*. Believing that it evolved once is difficult enough, but twice?

CHAPTER 3

COLOURS AND PATTERNS

Some of nature's colours are particularly dazzling, and have provided human designers with ideas on improving man-made colours. Some of the brightest colours are not due to pigment but are *structural colours* where the colours arise from the material's structure. Some of these colours are produced by a *photonic solid*, where light is manipulated by the fine structure of the material. These effects can also produce very bright whiteness and very dark blackness. Nature's patterns are also consistent with intricate mathematical design.

IRIDESCENT BLUE

Overview: The iridescent blues in butterflies and birds are not due to a special pigment, but a natural diffraction grating, a type of structural colour. This has led to humans copying this design to make brighter and deeper colours without messy chemicals.

Morpho and blue don butterflies

Some butterflies have the most striking iridescent blue wings, such as the blue morpho (*Morpho menelaus*) of South America and the male mountain blue don (*Papilio ulysses*) of northern Australia.[1] How is this striking blue produced? It was long known that the blue was not produced by a pigment, but by some optical effect.

In 2001, Pete Vukusic of the University of Exeter (U.K.) found that *optical interference* produces the blueness in butterflies.[2] The scales that cover the wings have multi-layering that reflects light waves so that they travel different distances (see fig. 1, right). With some wavelengths, the light reflected from top and bottom surface will have a travel distance of a whole number of wavelengths, so the crests align with other crests (see fig. 2). This is

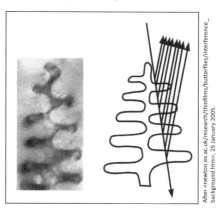

After <newton.ex.ac.uk/research/thinfilms/butterflies/interference_background.htm>, 25 January 2005.

Figure 1. *Left*: Morpho butterfly multilayer structure under a microscope. *Right*: How light reflects from different surfaces.[1]

1. Cardno, S. and Wieland, C., Mr Butterflies, *Creation* **19**(2):44–46, 1997.
2. Vukusic, P., *et al.*, Sculpted-multilayer optical effects in two species of *Papilio* butterfly, *Applied Optics* **40**(7):1116–1125, 2001.

called *constructive interference*, and makes this colour (blue in this butterfly) much brighter and purer (see fig. 3, p. 55). To produce a particular colour, the layer thickness must be accurate to within about 0.05 µm. The opposite is *destructive interference*, where the wave crests align with troughs, cancelling each other out (fig. 4 p. 55).

Scientists learn from 'nature'

'We started examining butterfly wings using electron microscopy and we learned how complex the structures are and difficult to fabricate. So we came up with a new approach of using micro-gratings with random orientation as a means to achieve colour with a wider viewing angle.'[3]

So they made a honey-comb-like array of tiny hexagons, each of which had diffraction gratings with the grooves in different directions (see fig. 5, below). They used a technique called electron beam lithography (EBL). This resulted in a structure that looked blue from a viewing range of 16–90°.[4]

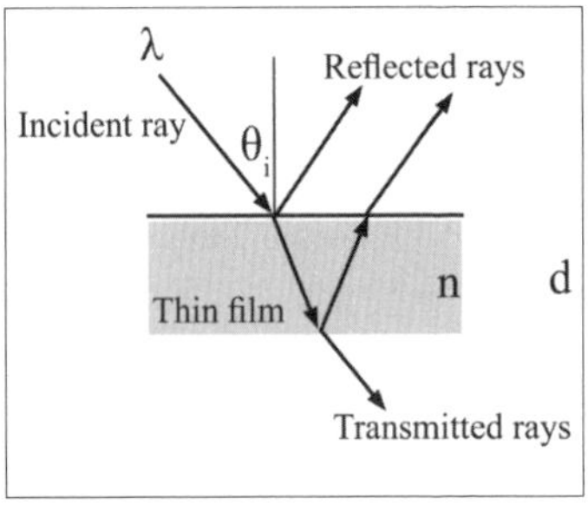

After <newton.ex.ac.uk/research/thinfilms/butterflies/interference_background.htm>, 25 January 2005.

Figure 2. If the difference in path length of the reflected ray is a whole number of a particular wavelength, then constructive interference (see fig. 3) will occur for that wavelength—that is, if the thickness d satisfies the formula $m\lambda = 2nd\cos\theta_i$, where m is the order of diffraction, n the refractive index, λ the wavelength in air, and θ_i the angle of incidence.[1]

In future, these new techniques could be used in display devices, and to replace paints for coating surfaces, thereby producing better colours. They would avoid the problems of chemical waste in the production of pigments and dyes.[5]

Blue budgies

Interference also produces the bright blue colour of some budgie feathers. But in this case it's caused by the spongy structure of the keratin, the protein that feathers (and skin and nails) are made of.[6] Interference also creates the dazzling colours of the peacock tail (see pp. 57 ff).

3.   Graydon, O., Blue microstructures mimic nature, *Optics.org*, 2003.
4.   Wong, T.-H., *et al.*, Color generation in butterfly wings and fabrication of such structures, *Optics Letters* **28**(23):2342–2344, 2003.
5.   Lerner, E.J., Butterfly blues, *The Industrial Physicist*, Briefs, April 2004.
6.   Prum R.O., *et al.*, Coherent Light Scattering by Blue Feather Barbs, *Nature* **396**(6706):28–29, 1998; Two-dimensional Fourier Analyses of the Spongy Medullary Keratin of Structurally Coloured Feather Barbs, *Proc. R. Soc. London* **B 266**:13–22, 1999.

DEEP BLACK

Overview: Blackness is produced by absorption of all visible light. Our pigments are imperfect in that they still reflect a fair amount of light. However, some butterflies can produce deeper blacks by their geometric structures that trap the light so it can't return. Once more, this has inspired human designers.

Black pigments appear black because they absorb all frequencies of visible light. However, this is not perfect, and some light scatters back. A notable example is the moon—it looks bright silvery-white from Earth, but its surface largely comprises the black rock basalt.

A well-known experiment can demonstrate the imperfection of black paints. Take an enclosed cardboard shoebox and paint it the blackest black possible. Then cut a small hole in it, 1–2 mm. This hole should appear far blacker than even the blackest paint. While the paint scatters some light back, light entering the hole hardly ever escapes. Indeed, that's why the pupil of the eye is so black—it's a hole to let light in, and it doesn't get out again.

Vukusic (see previous section) has shown that an optical light-trapping design creates the black outline of the blue don.[7] This special blackness is almost twice that which could be achieved by pigment alone, and causes the bright blue to stand out even more. Tiny pits, about

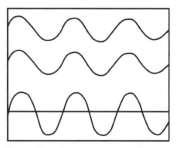

Figure 3. Constructive interference. When two waves are in phase, i.e. the crests line up with crests and the troughs line up with troughs, their intensities reinforce each other. The bottom wave with the greater amplitude is the result of such a sum of the top two waves.

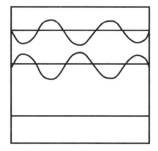

Figure 4. Destructive interference. When two waves are totally out of phase, i.e. the crests line up with troughs, they cancel each other out. The bottom line, with no wave at all, is the result.

a micron across, cover the scales forming a honeycomb-like array.[8] These scales have a high refractive index, so they take advantage of total internal reflection. That is, the light enters the material, but whenever the light meets another part of the surface, instead of crossing, it is reflected back into the material (optical fibres work that

---

7. Butterflies plumb the depths of blackness with a trick of the light, *New Scientist* **181**(2433):18, 2004.
8. Hopkin, M., Butterflies boast ultrablack wings: Insects use optical trick to get the blackest black out of dark pigments, *Nature science update*, 2004, <www.nature.com/nsu/040126/040126-4.html>.

way, including the natural ones of the Venus flower basket sponge—see ch. 8, pp. 121–122). Since hardly any light can escape from the wings, they appear very black.

Removing the refractive effect

Vukusic's success in working out the blue don's light-trapping design came about because he wanted to see what would happen if he could somehow remove the refractive effect. But how can one remove that effect?

Light refraction (i.e. change of direction) and reflection can occur at surfaces between substances where the speed of light inside each substance is different, e.g. light travels more slowly through water than through air, so water's refractive index is higher.[9] This is why, when one immerses a straight stick into a swimming pool, it looks 'bent' at the surface of the water. If the different substances have the same index, then the light does not bend and so there is little reflection or refraction.

We can demonstrate this with a pane of frosted glass. This is deliberately made with a rough surface so that light scatters in all directions at the glass–air interface, making a clear image impossible. However, an image IS possible if this scattering can be eliminated. We can do this by smearing a viscous liquid, e.g. golden syrup, with about the same refractive index as glass onto the frosted glass, then covering it with smooth glass. With hardly any reflection or refraction from the frosted glass surface into the liquid, it is now possible to see a clear image through it. Vukusic applied the same principle to the butterfly. He immersed the wings in bromoform ($CHBr_3$), which has about the same refractive index as the wing tissue. As a result, the wings could only absorb just over 50% of the light, while in air they absorbed over 90%.

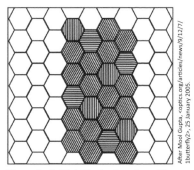

Figure 5. Artificial butterfly colour. The grooves in each hexagon are 125 nm deep and 220 nm wide.[2]

After Mool Gupta, <coptics.org/articles/news/9/12/7/1butterfly2>, 25 January 2005.

More biomimetics

Chemical engineer Richard Brown of Britain's National Physical Laboratory in Teddington, near London, has used this principle to make 'Super Black'. This is a nickel-phosphorus alloy coating with pits that also exploit light refraction. This absorbs 99.7% of the light. This is yet another example of how the design in nature has

---

9. The refractive index (n) of a substance is given by $n = c/v$, where c is the speed of light in a vacuum, and v the speed of light in the substance.

inspired human engineers. Vukusic says, 'Biomimetics is growing in popularity. Wherever we can we should take cues from nature.'

IRIDESCENT BEETLES

Some scarabs have bright iridescent colours. One type, *Gymnopleurus virens* from southern Africa, can be iridescent red with green on the edges, or green with blue edges. Their surfaces have the unusual property of reflecting only 'left-handed' light (i.e. left-handed circularly polarized light).

This is the result of their surface structure. This comprises many layers of parallel microscopic fibres, and this selects for light polarized in their direction. But each layer has the fibres rotated slightly compared to the layer above, and this makes a spiral stack. This reflects light with the polarization rotating in one direction.

A research team from South Africa and New Zealand discovered that the bright colours were due to *specific structural 'defects'* (variations) in the layers.[10] The electron microscope showed that there was a boundary where layer spacing suddenly changes by about 10%. This increases the reflectance band four times.

Team leader Johan Brink said:

'Possible applications of this kind of 'defect engineering' could be broadband laser reflectors for semiconductor lasers, and narrow-band spike filters that are sometimes used in spectroscopy to identify and classify materials and minerals.'[11]

PEACOCK TAIL[12]

The tail of the male peacock is one of the most spectacular sights of all birds. But the fan combines many different features.

Fan

The fan comprises bright colours, evenly spaced eye spots, and 'T-feathers' on the border. It spreads out over 180°, which requires the feather axes to project back a common geometrical centre. The fan is displayed with muscles in the tail, which can also cause the fan to vibrate with a characteristic hum.

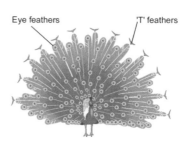

Peacock with tail feathers displayed.[12]

10. Brink, D.J., *et al*., Unusual coloration in scarabaeid beetles, *J. Phys D: Appl. Phys.* **40**: 2189–2196, 2007.
11. Zyga, L., Beetles' bright colors may influence new light technology, Physorg.com, <www.physorg.com/news95513144.html>, 2007.
12. After Burgess, S., The beauty of the peacock tail and the problems with the theory of sexual selection, *J. Creation* **15**(2):94–102, 2001; <creationontheweb.com/peacock>. Stuart Burgess is Professor of Design and Nature, Head of Department, Mechanical Engineering, University of Bristol (UK), and a world expert on biomimetics. NB: 'Professor' in the UK, and some British Commonwealth countries, is a title given only to the highest academic rank.

Colours

The bright colours of the peacock tail are again structural, as has been known for decades[13]—thin film interference caused by the structure of the feather barbules. Each is 60 μm wide and 5 μm

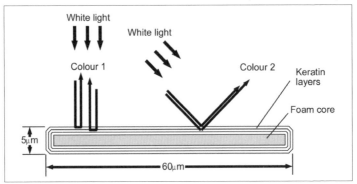

Cross-section of a peacock barbule.[12]

thick, comprising a foam core 2 μm thick, covered with three very thin layers of keratin on each side. These layers are about 0.4–0.5 μm thick, just right to cause interference when light reflects off them. The different colours are caused by different angles of incidence (see diagram, above), which is helped by the slight curve of the feathers. The feathers also contain melanin, so their non-structural colour is dark brown, which prevents light shining in from the back.

Eye feathers

They have a number of unique features:[12,14]

- Bright colours
- Intricate eye pattern
- Loose barbs below the eye pattern
- Absence of stem in the top half of eye pattern
- Narrow stem in the bottom half of eye pattern
- Brown coating of the stem near the eye pattern

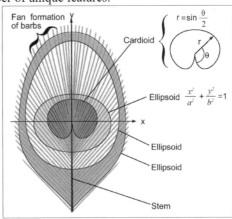

Mathematical curves in the eye pattern.[12]

13. Mason, C.W., Structural colours in feathers II, *J. Physical Chem.* **27**:440, 1923.
14 Bergman, J., Problems in sexual selection theory and neo-Darwinism, *J. Creation* **18**(1): 112–119, 2004.

Combinations of mathematical curves cause the patterns, as shown. And the pattern is not the result of a simple mathematical growth pattern like the spirals of sunflower seeds and the nautilus shell. Rather it is a *digital* pattern that combines the effects of thousands of individual barbules, perfectly coordinated with each other. Since the different colours are caused by different thicknesses of keratin, and the boundaries are sharp, the feather barbules must be programmed to *abruptly* increase and decrease their thickness at precisely the right time in their growth.

'T' border feathers

These beautifully complete the fan, because of their unique 'ogee' curve on each side of the feather. This is both concave and convex, and complements the eye feathers perfectly (left). Architects use ogee curves in structures such as arches. To form the ogee curve, there must be genetic programming to coordinate the length and curvature.

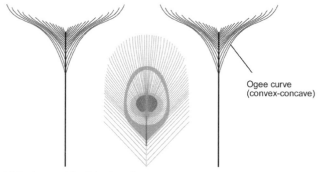

Ogee curve
(convex-concave)

The 'T' feathers and 'eye' feathers.[12]

Beauty

The peacock tail is so complicated that a leading evolutionary expert was baffled as to how it could even be maintained, let alone how it could have evolved in the first place:

> 'The theory of thin films as the cause of iridescence, although it fits all the observed facts, cannot but inspire one to marvel at the perfection of nature's method of producing these colours with such uniformity through successive generations, especially when a slight general variation in thickness of the films of the feathers of a bird, such as a peacock, would be enough to alter its coloration completely.'[15]

---

15   Roughgarden, J., Oishi, M. and Akcay, E., Reproductive social behavior: cooperative games to replace sexual selection, *Science* 311(5763):965–969, 2006.

Sexual selection?

Indeed, the whole tail structure seems so cumbersome that it would be a hindrance more than a help in survival, so natural selection would tend to eliminate it. So how have evolutionists tried to overcome that difficulty? The usual explanation is 'sexual selection',[16] where genes for a structure are passed on preferentially because the other sex happens to like that structure when choosing a mate. However, this doesn't explain the origin of the precisely coordinated mutations required to form the tail, quite aside from why females would select for beauty and even how they could do so. So it is quite understandable that even some evolutionists now speak of the accumulated 'fatal problems' of sexual selection theory, referring to case studies showing it 'is always mistaken' and therefore 'needs to be replaced'.[15,16]

Indeed, new research has empirically damaged this theory, by showing that peahens aren't impressed with the peacock display, and care more for the mating calls. The researchers summarize their seven-year study:

> 'We found no evidence that peahens expressed any preference for peacocks with more elaborate trains (i.e. trains having more ocelli, a more symmetrical arrangement or a greater length), similar to other studies of galliforms showing that females disregard male plumage. Combined with previous results, our findings indicate that the peacock's train (1) is not the universal target of female choice, (2) shows small variance among males across populations and (3) based on current physiological knowledge, does not appear to reliably reflect the male condition.'[17]

A report on this research noted:

> 'The feather train on male peacocks is among the most striking and beautiful physical attributes in nature, but it fails to excite, much less interest, females, according to new research. The determination throws a wrench in the long-held belief that male peacock feathers evolved in response to female mate choice. It could also indicate that certain other elaborate features in galliformes, a group that includes turkeys, chickens, grouse, quails and pheasants, as well as peacocks, are not necessarily linked to fitness and mating success.'[18]

16. Catchpoole, D., Peacock poppycock? *Creation* **29**(2):56, 2007; <creationontheweb.com/ poppycock>.
17. Takahashi, M. *et al.*, Peahens do not prefer peacocks with more elaborate trains, *Anim. Behav.* 2007, doi:10.1016/j.anbehav.2007.10.004.
18   Viegas, J., Female Peacocks Not Impressed by Male Feathers, *Discovery News*, March 26, 2008; <dsc. discovery.com/news/2008/03/26/peacock-feathers-females.html>.

It's not as if the researchers set out to contradict the theory—just the opposite in fact—they had planned to *confirm* it. So Charles Darwin's 'theory of sexual selection' *fails to explain the very thing Darwin concocted it for!* [19]

Architects and beauty

It's worth noting that many human architects design features that have no structural function, but merely look beautiful. E.g. a plain cylindrical column would be good enough to support the roof, but Corinthian columns are fluted (grooved) and topped by an ornate capital decorated with acanthus leaves and scrolls. So the beauty of the peacock tail is consistent with an intelligent designer, for whom aesthetic as well as structural issues were important. [12]

---

19   Catchpoole, D., Peacock tail tale failure, <creationontheweb.com/tale>, 2008.

FLIGHT

Flight is very sophisticated, and we have mastered it only in the last century. But many types of animal have been flying for much longer. Indeed, four groups of animals have distinct types of flight: birds, pterosaurs, bats and insects. The Wright Brothers gained many insights by watching birds fly. And in labs around the world, biologists and aviation experts are studying the different types of flying animals for new ideas to improve aircraft of the future.

One of the first flights, 120 feet in 12 seconds, 10:35 a.m.; Kitty Hawk, North Carolina. Orville Wright at the controls of the machine and Wilbur Wright running alongside to balance the machine.

James DeLaurier, a professor emeritus at the University of Toronto who spent decades studying flapping wings, said, 'It's respectable to look at nature for inspiration. We don't come close to doing all the things that nature does.' 'It's absolutely good design if you copy nature', concurred Terry Weisshaar, an aeronautics professor at Purdue University. John McMasters, an aerodynamics expert at jet manufacturer Boeing, has taught aircraft design for 40 years, and agreed, 'One of the rules is never invent anything you don't have to. If you can find a precedent that solves a problem, use that.' He added that lessons learned from nature will play an increasing role in new aircraft.[1]

However, many of them attribute the design to natural selection. Oxford University research fellow Graham Taylor asserted, 'Natural selection has already done much of the brute computation for us by solving problems evolutionary.'

So how does flight work, and how have new discoveries helped aircraft designers? Could natural selection really explain it?

BIRD FLIGHT

A number of evolutionists propose that birds evolved from running dinosaurs, but they overlook what birds need to fly. In a bird's flap for powered flight, the primary flight feathers are angled in such a way that they force air *backwards* so the bird is propelled *forwards*, according to Newton's 3rd Law (every action produces an equal and opposite reaction). And the wings have an aerofoil shape like an airplane's wings, angled to deflect air downwards as the bird moves forward. This produces lift, again by the reaction.

---

1.   Levin, A., Flying creatures may help create aviation of future, <www.usatoday.com/tech/science/discoveries/2007-02-13-aviation-birds_x.htm>, *USA Today*, 13 February 2007.

Bernoulli effect or Newton's Third Law?

The Bernoulli effect states that as a fluid (liquid or gas) flows faster, its pressure drops. This is named after the Dutch/Swiss mathematician/scientist Daniel Bernoulli (1700–1782), and is a simplification of the principle that the sum of all forms of energy in a fluid flowing in an enclosed path is equal at all points.

Many explanations of bird and aircraft flight involve faster airflow on top causing a pressure drop. This would produce lift by the greater pressure on the bottom surface.

But more recent studies emphasise the 3rd Law. There are two reasons that the wings deflect air downwards with forward motion: first, the wings are slanted slightly upwards into the air stream (a positive 'angle of attack'); second, the Coanda Effect where a fluid follows the curve of the surface, which from the upper surface points downwards. The 3rd Law explanation, unlike the Bernoulli Principle, explains for example why there is such a downdraft under helicopter blades, and why aircraft can fly upside down with a high enough angle of attack.[2,3]

PULLEY SYSTEM

For flapping flight, the wing has to be lifted ready for the next downstroke. Birds accomplish this with an intricate *pulley* system— the supracoracoideus muscle pulls on its tendon, which winds around a pulley comprising the coracoid and clavicle bones, then inserts into the humerus or upper arm/wing bone.

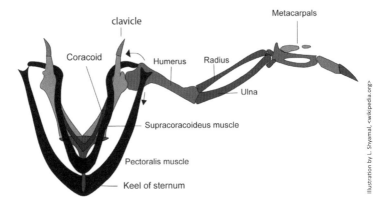

Illustration by L. Shyamal, <wikipedia.org>

---

2.   See Anderson, D.F. and Eberhardt, S., *Understanding Flight*, McGraw–Hill, 2001; <www.aa.washington.edu/faculty/eberhardt/lift.htm>.

3.   Aerodynamics expert Prof. Andy McIntosh of Leeds university, UK, teaches his students that fundamentally lift is due to *circulation* (technical term for the turning of the flow), which will generate lift by reaction. The flow leaves the trailing edge of a real wing smoothly (the *Kutta condition*) which invokes circulation. Lift is given by $l = \rho v \gamma$, where l = lift per unit of wingspan, ρ = density, v = velocity, γ = circulation strength (the *Kutta–Zhukovsky theorem*).

Birds can still fly with the tendon cut, but takeoff is badly hindered.[4] So it's questionable that natural selection would drive the many co-ordinated changes needed to form this pulley system. Indeed, there is no evidence of transitional half-pulley systems in the fossil record, and would such a half-pulley be any use at all?[5]

FEATHERS

Alan Feduccia, a world authority on birds at the University of North Carolina at Chapel Hill and an evolutionist himself, says, 'Feathers are a near-perfect adaptation for flight' because they are lightweight, strong, aerodynamically shaped, and have an intricate structure of barbs and hooks. This structure makes them waterproof, and a quick preen with the bill will cause flattened feathers to snap into fully aerodynamic shape again.[6]

Examine the amazing close-up picture (right, below) of the barbules of a feather showing the tiny hooklets and grooves (magnified 200 times).

Did feathers evolve from scales?

The antitheistic evolutionist and neo-eugenicist, Richard Dawkins, glibly states: 'Feathers are modified reptilian scales,'[7] a widely-held view among evolutionists. But scales are folds in skin; feathers are complex structures with a barb, barbules, and hooks. They also originate in a totally different way—from follicles inside the skin in a manner akin to hair.

Chris Broomell, <flickr.com>

Clearly, the information required to code for the construction of a feather is of a substantially different order from that required for a scale. For scales to have evolved into feathers means that a significant amount of new genetic information had to arise in the DNA of the bird's alleged reptile ancestor.

As usual, natural selection would not favour the hypothetical intermediate forms. Many evolutionists claim that dinosaurs developed feathers for insulation and later evolved and refined them for flight purposes. But like all such 'just-so' stories, this fails to

4. Fastovsky, D. amd Weishampel, D., *The Evolution and Extinction of Dinosaurs*, p. 298, Cambridge University Press, 1996.
5. Sodera, V., *One Small Speck to Man: The Evolution Myth*, pp. 292–302, Vija Sodera Publications, Bognor Regis, UK, 2003.
6. Feduccia, A., *The Origin and Evolution of Birds*, p. 130, Yale University Press, 1996.
7. Dawkins, R., *Climbing Mount Improbable*, p. 113, Penguin Books, Harmondsworth, Middlesex, England, 1996.

explain *how* the new genetic information arose so it could be selected for.

Another problem is that selection for heat insulation is *quite different* from selection for flight. On birds that have lost the ability to fly, the feathers have also lost much of their structure and become hair-like. On flightless birds, mutations degenerating the aerodynamic feather structure would not be as much a handicap as

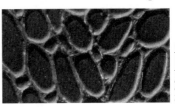

The detailed structures of a feather (left) and scales (right)

they would be on a flying bird. Therefore, natural selection would not eliminate them, and might even select *for* such degeneration. As usual, loss of flight and feather structure are *losses of information*, so are irrelevant to evolution, which requires an *increase* of information. All that matters is that the feathers provide insulation, and hair-like structures are fine—they work for mammals.[6] That is, natural selection would work *against* the development of a *flight* feather if the creature needed the feathers for insulation. And hairy feathers are adequate.

Downy feathers are also good insulators and are common on flightless birds. Their fluffiness depends on their *lack of the hooks* of flight feathers. Again, natural selection would work to *prevent* evolution of aerodynamic feathers from heat insulators.

Finally, feather proteins (φ-keratins) are biochemically different from skin and scale proteins (α-keratins), as well. One researcher, Alan Brush, concluded:

> 'At the morphological level feathers are traditionally considered homologous with reptilian scales. However, in development, morphogenesis [shape/form generation], gene structure, protein shape and sequence, and filament formation and structure, feathers are different.'[8]

Concession to creationists: scales-to-feathers fails

It's thus no wonder that Brush has discarded the feathers-from-scales idea, arguing that evolutionists made a false 'assumption that the primitive feather evolved by elongation and division of the reptilian scale.' He and his colleague even admitted:

---

8. Brush, A.H., On the Origin of Feathers, *J. Evolutionary Biol.* **9:**131–142, 1996.

'Creationists and other evolutionary skeptics have long pointed to feathers as a favorite example of the insufficiency of evolutionary theory. There were no transitional forms between scales and feathers, they argued.'[9]

However, they have instead proposed a replacement model, *evolutionary developmental biology,* or 'evo-devo.' This argues that 'the complex mechanisms by which an individual organism grows to its full size and form can provide a window into the evolution of a species' anatomy.' But this is reminiscent of the discredited 'ontogeny recapitulates phylogeny' idea.[10]

AVIAN LUNG

To turn a reptile lung into a bird lung needs drastic changes. Reptile lungs draw the air into a chamber subdivided into *faveoli* by ingrowths called *septae* where blood extracts the oxygen and releases carbon dioxide. The stale air is then breathed out the same way it came in. But birds have a complicated system of air sacs, even involving their hollow bones. This system keeps air flowing in one direction through special tubes (*parabronchi,* singular *parabronchus*) in the lung, and blood moves through the lung's blood vessels in the opposite direction for efficient oxygen uptake,[11] an excellent engineering design.[12]

How would the 'bellows'-style lungs of reptiles evolve gradually into avian lungs? The hypothetical intermediate stages could not conceivably function properly, meaning the unfortunate animal would be unable to breathe. One of the first stages would be a poor creature with a diaphragmatic hernia (hole in the diaphragm), and natural selection would work *against* this.

Also, even assuming that we could construct a theoretical series of functional intermediate stages, would natural selection 'drive' the changes? Probably not—bats manage perfectly well with bellows-style lungs—some can even hunt at an altitude of over two miles (three km). The avian lung, with its super-efficiency, becomes especially advantageous only at very high altitudes with low oxygen levels. There would thus have been no clear selective advantage in replacing the reptilian lung.[13] We should probably not be surprised that Alan Feduccia's major work on bird evolution doesn't even touch this problem.[6]

---

9. Prum, R.O. and Brush, A.H., Which came first, the feather or the bird? *Scientific Amer.* **288**(3): 84–93, 2003.

10. Grigg, R., 'Ernst Haeckel: Evangelist for evolution and apostle of deceit', *Creation* **18**(2):33–36, 1996; <creationontheweb.com/haeckel>.

11. Denton, M., *Evolution, a Theory in Crisis,* pp. 199–213, Adler & Adler, Bethesda, MD, 1986; K. Schmidt-Nielsen, How Birds Breathe, *Scientific American,* December 1971, pp. 72–79.

12. Engineers make much use of this *principle of counter-current exchange* which is common in living organisms as well—see P.F. Scholander, The Wonderful Net, *Scientific Amer.* **196**:96–107, April 1957.

13. Denton, M., Blown away by design, *Creation* **21**(4):14–15; <creationontheweb.com/birdlung>.

Some recent researchers of *Sinosauropteryx's* (a supposed feathered dinosaur) lung structure showed that 'its bellows-like lungs could not have evolved into the high performance lungs of modern birds.'[14]

Interestingly, some defenders of dinosaur-to-bird evolution discount this evidence against their theory by saying, 'The proponents of this argument offer no animal whose lungs could have given rise to those in birds, which are extremely complex and are unlike the lungs of any living animal.'[15] Of course, only evolutionary faith requires that bird lungs arose from the lungs of another animal.

SWIFTS AND THE LEADING-EDGE VORTEX[16]

A study of swifts[17,18] shows that there is even more to flight than downward deflection of air. They also make use of a *leading-edge vortex* (LEV; a vortex is a spiralling tube-like pattern of airflow like a mini-tornado) to generate even more lift by lowering the pressure.[19] Thus 'the current understanding of how birds fly must be revised.'[18]

The bird wing actually has two parts: the inner 'arm-wing' and an outer 'hand wing'. The arm wing deflects air downwards just like an airplane wing, according to the lead researcher, John Videler of the Leiden and Groningen universities in The Netherlands.[20] But analysis of the fluid[21] flow[22] showed that the sharp leading edge of the hand wing easily formed the mini-tornados that helped suck the bird upwards.[23] These form at a wide range of wing angles, so the bird wing is far less likely to stall (suddenly lose lift) than an aircraft wing.[24]

Swifts have scythe-shaped wings, comprising a relatively small arm wing and a very long hand wing that generates a powerful LEV.

14. Gibbons, A., New Feathered Fossil Brings Dinosaurs and Birds Closer, *Science* **274**:720–721, 1996. See also: Doyle, S., Feathery flight of fancy: Alleged 'protofeathers' fail under close scrutiny; <creationontheweb.com/protofeathers>.

15. Padian, K. and Chiappe, L.M., The Origin of Birds and Their Flight, *Scientific Amer.* **278**(2):38–47, 1998, p. 43.

16. After Sarfati, J., Fancy flying from advanced aeronautics: the design of swifts and jet fighters, *Creation* **29**(1):37–39, 2006.

17. Videler, J.J., Stamhuis, E.J. and Povel, G.D.E., Leading-edge vortex lifts swifts, *Nature* **306**(5703):1960–1962, 2004.

18. Müller, U.K. and Lentink, D., Turning on a dime, *Science* **306**(5703):1899–1900, 2004 (comment on Ref. 18).

19. Here the Bernoulli Effect really does matter, cf. note 2.

20. Cited in Britt, R.R., Secret of Bird Flight Revealed (Hint: Think Fighter Jets), *Live Science*, <www.livescience.com/animalworld/041209_birds_fly.html>, 2004.

21. A fluid is a liquid or a gas.

22. It doesn't matter what fluid is used for a simulation, as long the *Reynold's Number* is constant (providing *dynamic similitude*). This number is a ratio of inertial to viscous forces named after the British engineer Osborne Reynolds (1842–1912), given by Re = ρvl/μ, where ρ is density, v is mean velocity, l is a characteristic length and μ is viscosity.

23. These researchers used a 1.5-times-enlarged scale model in a water tunnel, which was easier to analyze than a wind tunnel.

24. As a pilot reduces an aircraft's speed, the angle of the wing to the air has to increase to maintain lift (the pilot pulls back on the stick or control column). But there comes a point where the smooth flow of air over the wing's top surface suddenly fails and so the wing loses all its lift. The nose of the aircraft suddenly pitches down, causing an accident if it happens near the ground.

So swifts can sweep their wings back for fast flight, but can 'turn on a dime'[19] by reducing the wing sweep (straightening the wings). It enables them to catch insects in flight. And perching birds need LEVs to produce high lift at low speeds, otherwise they could not land on a branch.

The importance of LEVs was previously discovered in insect flight (see p. 78). And aerospace engineers have also exploited swifts' superb lift when it comes to landing supersonic jets safely. Their small, swept-back wings make fast flight possible, but without the LEVs, their small wings would not produce enough lift when they slow down to land.

As happens often, the commentators paid fact-free homage to evolution:

'To maximize flight speed as well as maneuverability, evolution and aeronautic engineering converged on the same solution—variable wing sweep. Swifts and the Tomcat jet fighter keep their wings swept back to reach high speeds. To execute tight turns, both flyers reduce their wing sweep.'[19]

However, since we know that the jet fighter has been intelligently designed, then why not the swift as well, since good science works by analogy? Furthermore, the authors point out:

'The gliding flight of storks inspired the first airplane designs of Otto Lilienthal in the late 19th century. The benevolent flight characteristics of these slow and stately gliders invested airplane pioneers with the confidence to take to the skies.'

The article concluded:

'In the future, the swift's flight control might inspire a new generation of engineers to develop morphing microrobotic vehicles that can fly with the agility, efficiency, and short take-off and landing capabilities of insects and birds.'[19]

Morphing [shape-changing] wings

As it happens, more recent wind tunnel research has further explored 'the astonishing benefits' to swifts through 'morphing wings'.[25,26] For example, swifts are able to *double* their gliding time and *triple* their turn rate by morphing their wings. Little wonder that aeronautics engineers are eager to implement such a capacity in robotic (and other) aircraft.

25. Laursen, L., A swift understanding of flight, *ScienceNOW Daily News*, 2007, <sciencenow.sciencemag.org/cgi/content/full/2007/425/4>.
26. Lentink, D., *et al.*, *Nature* **446**(7139):1082–1085, 2007.

LEADING EDGE FLAPS[27]

When large aircraft such as jumbo jet aircraft take off or land, their speed is relatively low. So to gain lift and thus avoid catastrophic stalling, pilots deploy flaps on the leading edges of the wings, increasing the angle of attack. Without this technology, the modern aviation industry would be impossible. The Nairobi air disaster of 1974 shows this, where a jumbo's flaps were inadvertently retracted during take-off. The plane shuddered violently, a prelude to stalling, and crashed killing 58 people, although 98 survived.[28]

Recently, Oxford University researchers studying flight manoeuvres of the steppe eagle (*Aquila nipalensis*) recorded video evidence of 'leading edge feather deflections' during landing sequences.[29] The video shows that the birds 'deploy a wing flap on the front edge of the wing' just as jumbo jets do.[30] And it has the same effect as in jumbos, increasing the lift, and enabling increased control during landing and other manoeuvres.[31] Now other large birds are also thought to use leading edge wing flaps.

The birds' 'leading edge' technology had not been noticed before because the birds deploy the flap only at precisely the critical moment needed when landing. Thus the researchers required a *high-speed* video camera—500 frames per second. This could catch the wing-flap movement as a feathery 'travelling wave' that spread from the wrist of the wing to the shoulder.

Strong evidence has been discovered that pterosaurs, too, had a forward-moving leading edge flap on the wing, which solved the mystery of the purpose of a tiny bone (see p. 78).

COULD BIRD FLIGHT HAVE EVOLVED?

There are two main theories for the origin of flying birds: that birds evolved 'ground up' from running dinosaurs (the *cursorial* theory), and that they evolved 'trees-down' from small reptiles (the *arboreal* theory). Both sides produce devastating arguments against the other side. The evidence indicates that the critics are *both* right—birds did not evolve either from running dinos or from tree-living mini-crocodiles. Yet whenever one or the other theory is proposed, the popular press fosters the impression that this new 'evidence' mounts a cumulative case for bird evolution, when in reality this new evidence *cancels out* at least one of the theories.

27. After Catchpoole, D., Amazing discovery: Bird wing has 'leading edge' technology, <creationontheweb. com/flaps>, 2007.
28. International Aviation Safety Association, The Nairobi 747 Crash, <www.iasa.com.au/folders/Safety_ Issues/others/Nairobi747Crash.html>, accessed 1 June 2007.
29. Carruthers, A., *et al.*, Use and Function of a Leading Edge Flap on the Wings of Eagles, 45th *AIAA (American Institute of Aeronautics and Astronautics) Aerospace Sciences Meeting and Exhibit*, 8–11 January 2007, Reno, Nevada; <http://pdf.aiaa.org/preview/CDReadyMASM07_1064/PV2007_43.pdf>.
30. The steppe eagle has landed, *New Scientist* **194**(2599):19, 2007.
31. Bakhtian, N., Spot the Difference?—An aerodynamic investigation of leading edge flaps in low Reynolds Number flight, <www.eng.cam.ac.uk/photocomp/2006/noelly42_1.shtml>, 2007.

Cursorial theory

One recent theory is that a bird's flight apparatus first evolved to aid traction as their ancestors ran up slopes. Dr Kenneth Dial of the Flight Laboratory, University of Montana, Missoula, observed the behaviour of chukar partridge chicks as they ran, and worked out why they flapped their wings. [32] He found that the birds employed 'wing-assisted incline running' (WAIR).

Here, the flapping did not lift the birds, but rather, the opposite—they pressed them into the ground for better traction, working like spoilers on race cars. Dial performed experiments on a number of chicks. He trimmed the flight feathers (remiges) to various lengths, and made them run up slopes of different angles and textures.

He found that even hatchlings can get up inclines of up to 45°, without flapping. But if they flapped, they could scale greater slopes: hatchlings could climb a 50° incline, four-day old chicks could climb a 60° slope, 20-day-old chicks could climb a 95° almost vertical surface, and adults could run up a 105° overhang.

Dial also compared birds at the same day of development, seven days after hatching, but with different lengths of flight feather removed. The hatchlings with remiges removed could not scale an incline above 60°, even on a surface covered in sandpaper to aid traction. Those with half-trimmed remiges could climb greater slopes, but still 10° to 20° below that of the control birds with full remiges.

He tested all three groups on smooth surfaces. None could climb slopes greater than 50°, because of slippage, and the presence or absence of remiges made no difference. This is consistent with traction being an important factor.

For more rigorous demonstration of the forces involved, Dial also used two accelerometers to measure the acceleration in the forward and vertical directions. He found that during a large part of the flapping cycle, the bird was forced against the surface regardless of its angle, which would increase traction.

So far, this is careful scientific work, testing a hypothesis and ruling out alternatives, and it provides new insight into running chicks. But that's where the science ends. Then evolutionary speculation takes over, and leads to conclusions that are not warranted by the evidence.

Problems

Here, Dial uses undoubted birds (not mooted 'transitional' forms) to postulate a theory about their origin. It makes sense that birds, which *already* have the musculature and great control over flying wings, should also have programmed instincts to use them to aid traction. But it makes no sense that natural selection for traction

---

32. Dial, K.P., Wing-Assisted incline running and the evolution of flight, *Science* 299(5605):402–404, 2003.

should lead to flight. Rather, on the face of it, traction would require the *opposite* force to lift, so the selective direction would be *away* from flight. So Dial proposes that somehow the motions that lead to traction were redirected to produce the movement required for flight.

However, if running up slopes were a major selective factor, then one would expect increased musculature in the hindquarters to drive the legs. Then greater slopes could be scaled simply by momentum. Also, the extra weight of the muscles would increase traction automatically. These effects are probably the main reason the older birds are better slope climbers. However, increasing the weight on the hindquarters of a dinosaur is precisely the *wrong* way to turn it into a bird. In fact, the heaviness of dinosaur hindquarters is a major argument, even by evolutionists, against the theropod ancestry of birds. E.g. Feduccia stated:

> "'It's biophysically impossible to evolve flight from such large bipeds with foreshortened forelimbs and heavy, balancing tails" exactly the wrong anatomy for flight.'[33]

All this analysis shows how much evolutionary theorizing is 'just-so' story-telling. Dial's story would entail small running dinosaurs in a wonderful environment, with a handy gradation of inclined planes. Here, natural selection would supposedly gradually craft an improvement in wing-assisted traction—while mysteriously ignoring the *greater* effects of weight-assisted traction and muscle-assisted speed!

Kevin Padian is President of the pretentiously named and humanist-founded-and-operated anti-creationist/design organization, the National Center for Science Education. He was very enthusiastic about Dial's research. Padian said that the alleged dinosaur ancestors of birds 'could have used a forward predatory grab similar to a flight stroke.'[34] This is similar to a claim by the Skeptic-dominated Australian Museum that asserted that certain dinosaurs evolved a certain bone that 'also allowed them to move their hands in a broad fan-shaped motion and to snap their long arms and grasping fingers forward to grab fleeing prey. This powerful, flapping motion has today become an important part of the flight stroke in modern birds.'[35]

However, this, like motions to produce downward traction, would be just the wrong sort of motion for flight. A flap in the forward direction would have the effect of pushing the bird *backwards*. Also feathers are not the sorts of structures that would be useful on limbs

---

33.   Feduccia, A., cited in Gibbons, ref. 15.
34.   Gorman, J., Chicks offer insight into origin of flight, *New York Times*, 2003.
35.   Sarfati, J., Skeptics/Australian Museum 'Feathered Dinosaur' display: Knockdown argument against creation? <creationontheweb.com/dinodisplay>, 2002.

that flap at a prey animal to catch it, since they would be damaged by the pounding.

Finally, the purpose of the wings is to force air backwards and downwards so the bird is propelled forwards and kept aloft. So wings should form a wide surface that has *high air resistance*, so it can move large volumes of air. But for a limb designed to grab forward at prey, it's an advantage to have a surface that has *low* air resistance, i.e. let air through easily. Think of the holes in a fly swatter, or streamlined shapes designed to move *through* the air as opposed to moving the air *itself*. Also, the rush of air from the proto-wing would warn the prey of its impending doom!

Arboreal theory

Feduccia, and other researchers aligned with his views, reject the idea that birds evolved from dinosaurs, with good reason. But they are unwilling to abandon evolution, so instead they believe that birds evolved from reptiles called *crocodilomorphs*. They propose these small, crocodile-like reptiles lived in trees, and 'initially leapt, then glided from perch to perch.'[36]

The imagined transition from para-chuting (where the 'wings' merely offer resistance to downwards movement through the air) to true gliding

Artist drawing of a *Hesperosuchus gracilis*, a sphenosuchian from Late Triassic rocks of North America.

ArthurWeasley, <wikipedia.com>

represents a major evolutionary hurdle in itself. But an even greater obstacle is the supposed development of the musculature and skeletal frame required for powered flight. The main point of the wings in flapping flight is **not** to act as a moving parachute by directing air downwards and forcing the bird upwards by reaction. Rather, as shown, the flapping wings mainly direct air *backwards* to force the bird *forward* by reaction, so the airflow over the airfoil-shaped wings generates *lift*.

Therefore flapping flight also requires highly controlled muscle movements to achieve flight, which in turn requires that the brain has the program for these movements. Ultimately, this requires new genetic information that a non-flying creature lacks.

Another problem with the arboreal theory is the lack of fossil intermediates:

> 'Neither their hypothetical ancestor nor transitional forms linking it to known fossil birds have been found. And although they rightly argue that cladistic

---

36.   Shipman, P., Birds Do It … Did Dinosaurs? *New Scientist* **153**(2067):26–31, 1997, p. 28.

analyses [comparisons of shared characteristics] are only as good as the data upon which they are based, no cladistic study has yet suggested a non-theropod ancestor.'[37]

BATS

Bats are the mammalian flyers, and have many unique features which make them very agile fliers.

Unique wing design[37]

Researchers from Brown University, Providence, Rhode Island, revealed some unexpected aerodynamics of bat flight.[38] Using high-speed video cameras to record the 3D wing and body movements of flying lesser short-nosed fruit bats, *Cynopterus brachyotis*, the researchers observed some flight characteristics unique to bats. The stretchy skin on a bat's wings interacts with air in a different manner to the firmer wings of birds and insects. This elasticity, combined with dozens of joints (even more than in a human hand),[39] allows bats to generate unusual wing shapes and motions, e.g. ones that give more lift at higher angles of attack—the angle at which the wing meets the air on the downstroke. This may allow bats to fly at low speeds with less risk of stalling.

And the bats' multiple-jointed wings not only allow for subtle adjustments to the wing shape during flight—thus improving efficiency—but can also be folded very close to the body to reduce drag. This means that the upstroke of a bat's wing is very different to that of birds. 'The bat almost completely collapses its wings,' said one of the researchers, Kenneth Breuer of Brown University (USA).

The bats' versatile flying ability is thus due to their ability to generate different wing shapes and motions to other flying creatures. And this knowledge could help in the design of small aircraft, such as those being developed for unmanned military reconnaissance.[40]

Bat evolution?

This team also wanted to understand 'the evolutionary path that created it'.[41] But not only does the fossil record provide no support at all for their idea, but this new research poses more problems. As *LiveScience* put it:

37. After Catchpoole, D., Going batty over evolution: Flexible, highly articulated wings leave bats without evolutionary ancestors, <creationontheweb.com/batty>, 1 May 2007.
38. Tian, X., *et al.*, Direct measurements of the kinematics and dynamics of bat flight, *Bioinspiration and Biomimetics* 1(4):S10–S18, 2006.
39. Than, K., Why bats are more efficient flyers than birds, *LiveScience*, <www.livescience.com/animalworld/070122_bat_flight.html>, 2007.
40. Pearson, A., Bats in flight may provide military inspiration, *NewScientist.com news service*, <www.newscientist.com/article/dn11105-bats-in-flight-may-provide-military-inspira>, 2007.
41. Bats in flight reveal unexpected aerodynamics, *Brown University news release*, <www.brown.edu/Administration/News_Bureau/2006-07/06-082.html>, 2007.

'The complexity of bat's wings also challenges some current theories that say bats evolved from some kind of flying squirrel-type creature.'[40]

As one of the Brown University researchers, Sharon Swartz, an associate professor in ecology and evolutionary biology, explained, 'The assumption has always been that bats evolved from some sort of flying squirrel-type animals.' However, such is the newly-realized complexity of the bat's 'long, skinny flapping wing' compared to the 'square gliding wing' of the various 'flying squirrel-type animals' that Swartz concludes that 'now it doesn't look like bats have any relationship to these gliding things.'[42]

Not that Swartz herself thinks that evolution might not be true, opining that 'gliding appears to have evolved seven times in mammals', but 'not a single one of those groups is closely related to bats.'[40]

The fossil record sheds no light on their alleged evolution from non-flying creatures either. The oldest known (by evolutionary 'dating' methods) fossil bats are practically indistinguishable from modern ones (see picture, right). Evolutionist Paul Sereno admitted:

Palaeochiropteryx tupaiodon—one of the 'oldest' (by evolutionary reckoning) fossil bats. It was found in the Messel oil shale pit near Darmstadt, Germany, and is 'dated' between 48 and 54 million years old. It clearly had fully developed wings, and its inner ear had the same construction as those of modern bats, showing that it had full sonar equipment.

Photo courtesy of Dr Joachim Scheven, LEBENDIGE VORWELT

'For use in understanding the evolution of vertebrate flight, the early record of pterosaurs and bats is disappointing: Their most primitive representatives are fully transformed as capable fliers.'[42]

Evolutionary paleontologist Robert Carroll said:
'The fossil record does not provide evidence for the transition towards either pterosaurs of bats: The earliest known members of these [bat] groups had already evolved an advanced flight apparatus.'[43]

Another evolutionary paper argued:
'The earliest fossil bats resemble their modern counterparts in possessing greatly elongated digits to

42. Sereno, Paul C., The evolution of dinosaurs, *Science* **284**(5423):2137–2147 (quote on p. 2143), 1999.
43. Carroll, R.L., *Patterns and Processes of Vertebrate Evolution*, p. 277, Cambridge University Press, NY, 1998.

support the wing membrane, which is an anatomical hallmark of powered flight.'[44]

PTEROSAURS

Scientists have long wondered how the extinct flying reptiles, the pterosaurs, could fly. They seemed too ungainly to lift into the air from the ground, or to land safely without breaking their delicate wings. Quite reasonably, some scientists proposed that there must have been greater air pressure in the past.

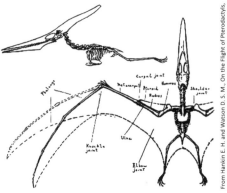

From Hankin E. H. and Watson D. S. M. On the Flight of Pterodactyls, The Aeronautical Journal, Oct 1914, pages 324–225, <wikipedia.com>

As with bats, the fossil record sheds no light on their alleged evolution from non-flying creatures (see note 43, p. 75). However, recent discoveries are showing much more about how their designer elegantly solved the problems of flight.

Brainy flyers

New evidence shows that pterosaurs were not primitive, cumbersome flyers but had a highly developed sense of balance. In fact, they might even have outperformed today's birds in complex aerobatic manoeuvres.

Lawrence Witmer, at Ohio University in Athens, Ohio, and his colleagues used X-ray CT scans to measure two pterosaur skulls. They analyzed *Rhamphorhynchus muensteri*, which according to evolutionists is a 'basal' (primitive) pterosaur, and *Anhanguera santanae*, a 'derived' (advanced) one. Both revealed a massive *flocculus*—the region of the brain that integrates signals from joints, muscles, skin and the balance organs. In birds, this region is unusually large compared to other animals, occupying between 1 and 2% of total brain mass. But in pterosaurs, the flocculus occupied 7.5%,[45] 'ridiculously large', according to Witmer cited in an article about his research.[46] They probably needed it because the wings had such a large surface area generating much sensory data—*Anhanguera* had a wingspan of four metres.

44. Sears, K.E. *et al.*, Development of bat flight: Morphologic and molecular evolution of bat wing digits, *PNAS* **103**(17):6581–6586, 2006 | 10.1073/pnas.0509716103

45. Witmer, L.M., *et al.*, Neuroanatomy of flying reptiles and implications for flight, posture and behaviour *Nature* **425**(6961): 950–953, 2003; perspective by Unwin, D., Smart-winged pterosaurs, same issue, pp. 910–911.

46. Randerson, J., X-rays reveal pterosaurs' aerial expertise, <NewScientist.com>, 2003.

Researchers think that by gathering information from the sensitive wing membranes, the flocculus could build up detailed in-flight maps of the forces being experienced by their 'smart wings', giving the pterosaurs excellent flight control. So they might have been able to outperform today's birds in complex aerobatic manoeuvres.[47]

Flexible wings inspire aircraft designers

Pterosaurs had a unique wing design, which comprised a membrane of leathery skin supported by the forelimb and one very long fourth finger. According to Sankar Chatterjee, of Texas Tech University, 'The fourth finger could be moved backward considerably, morphing the wing shape to change speed.'[48] The wings also included fibres to strengthen and stiffen the membrane, and a fine network of muscles, blood vessels and sensory nerves to send back information to the flocculus.

Chatterjee and Joseph Templin, retired head of the Canadian National Research Council's Aerodynamics Laboratory, performed a computer analysis on pterosaur flight.[49] This indicated that pterosaurs were capable of steady powered flight at speeds up to about 15 m/s (54 km/h). The only possible exception was the largest, *Quetzalcoatlus*, which had a mass of 100 kg and a wingspan of 15m. This was more likely an excellent glider but probably could not sustain powered flight, unless perhaps it flew in a V-formation like large modern migrating birds, which saves a lot of energy (see the golden plover, p. 88).

Templin commented:

> 'Pterosaurs could respond to constantly varying conditions using their sensors to monitor pressure variations over the entire surface of the wing. They could morph their wing shape to exploit flight conditions and control speed.'[49]

He suggested, 'Perhaps one day our aircraft may fly more like pterosaurs, cruising over oceans on convertible wings to save energy and achieve better performance.' This would be an improvement on modern fixed-wing aircraft, because they change the shape of their wings, using flaps and extensions, only during take-off and landing. Aerodynamics expert Richard Kelso of the University of Adelaide, Australia said that the 'convertible' wings of pterosaurs and birds give a much smoother ride in turbulence, as well as saving energy and achieving better performance.[49,50]

47. Terrific pterosaur flyers, *Creation* 26(2):9, 2004.
48. Salleh, A., Winged dragons could inspire new aircraft, ABC Science Online, <www.abc.net.au/science/news/tech/InnovationRepublish_1069737.htm>, 2004.
49. Chatterjee, S. and Templin, R.J., Posture, Locomotion, and Paleoecology of Pterosaurs, *Geol. Soc. Amer.*, Special Paper **376**, 2004.
50. Pterrific pterosaurs, *Creation* 27(2):7, 2005

Soft landing

A fossil trackway left by a pterosaur shows they were not only good flyers, but masters at landing as well. The fossil footprints show the pterosaur slowed its flight to touch down lightly on its hind feet, dragged its toes, and then made a short hop. It then put down its front legs to walk on all fours.[51]

Flight mystery solved by tiny bone[51]

But what about the initial take-off? Great flying ability won't help much if the flier can't get into the air in the first place. So how could pterosaurs gain the initial lift required?

Earlier calculations had overlooked a tiny bone called the *pteroid*. This is unique to pterosaurs, and was previously thought to bend inwards. But Matthew Wilkinson and his team in the animal flight group at Cambridge University, UK, studied pterosaur fossils and showed that the pteroid pointed forward.[52] This evidently supported a front flap of skin that acted as a movable leading edge on the wing. Darren Naish, a paleontologist at the University of Portsmouth, UK, says that fossilized pterosaur soft tissue found in China is strong evidence for this.[53]

The pteroid and flap enabled the pterosaur to use 'aerodynamic tricks like those found in modern aircraft'.[54] Angling this flap would increase lift by a huge 30%, so even the largest pterosaurs could take off by simply spreading their wings into a moderate breeze. And this extra lift would reduce their minimum flying speed (i.e. below which they would stall) by 15%, allowing a smooth landing. Also, by flexing the pteroid on one wing and extending it on the other, they would have different lifts on both wings, enabling them to bank.

INSECTS—HOW CAN THEY FLY AT ALL?

It has often been said that, according to the laws of aerodynamics, insects shouldn't be able to fly. This is because at smaller scales, viscosity dominates, so insects flying through the air are like us swimming through treacle.[55]

But of course they do—brilliantly. Actually, that only highlighted our ignorance of aerodynamics. Research over the past decade or so is revealing how insects do manage to fly, and in ways that put the achievements and manoeuvrability of our most advanced aircraft to shame.

51. After Sarfati, J., Pterosaurs flew like modern aeroplanes, *Creation* 28(3):53, 2006; <creationontheweb.com/pterosaur>.
52. Wilkinson, M.T., Unwin, D.M., Ellington, C.P., High lift function of the pteroid bone and forewing of pterosaurs, *Proc. R. Soc.* 273(1582):119–126, 2006 | DOI: 10.1098/rspb.2005.3278.
53. Cited in Marks, P., Where flying lizards got their lift, *New Scientist* 188(2521):12, 15 October 2005.
54. Lorenzi, R., Pterosaurs flew like jumbo jets, *News in Science*, <abc.net.au/science/news/stories/s1483770.htm>, 2005.
55. The viscosity term of the Reynold's Number dominates—see note 22.

Leading-edge vortex[56]

Conventional analysis showed that insects were generating only about one-half to one-third of the lift needed to carry their weight. However, ingenious experiments have now shown unexpected patterns of vortex flow along the edges of insect wings. Like the swift, the LEVs generate extra lift by lowering the pressure.

We can see LEVs in ordinary folded paper planes—they explain why there can be a final 'boost' before the plane lands. But the LEVs can't keep the paper dart upright for long because it becomes unstable and falls away from the wing's surface. But in insects, LEVs generate the extra lift needed because the vortex stays 'stuck' to the leading edge of the wing for long enough.[57]

One reason why previous models failed to detect how insects could fly is that they used *fixed* wings. However, insect wings have a very complex motion, rotating and changing the camber. It required sophisticated programming from intelligent design to make an experimental 'robot insect' flap properly. Thus it is reasonable to presume that the real insects likewise were programmed by an intelligent designer.

Butterflies[58]

The vortices are not the only feature of insect flight. Two researchers from Oxford University trained red admiral butterflies (*Vanessa atalanta*) to fly freely between artificial flowers in a wind tunnel. Thus they could analyze the flow with smoke trails and a high-speed digital camera. They found:

Joaquim Alves Gaspar, <wikipedia.com>, under licence: <creativecommons.org/licenses/by/3.0/>

> 'The images show that free-flying butterflies use a variety of unconventional aerodynamic mechanisms to generate force: wake capture, two different types of leading-edge vortex, active and inactive upstrokes, in addition to the use of rotational mechanisms and the Weis-Fogh 'clap-and-fling' mechanism. Free-flying butterflies often used different aerodynamic mechanisms in successive strokes. There seems to be no one 'key' to insect flight, instead insects rely on a wide array of aerodynamic mechanisms to take off, manoeuvre, maintain steady flight, and for landing.'[59]

56. After: Insects—defying the laws of aerodynamics? *Creation* **20**(2):31, 1998; <creationontheweb.com/insects>.
57. On a wing and a vortex, *New Scientist* **156**(2103):24–27, 1997.
58. After Catchpoole, D., Why a butterfly flutters by, *Creation* **26**(2):56, 2004; <creationontheweb.com/butterfly>.
59. Srygley, R.B. and Thomas, A.L., Unconventional lift-generating mechanisms in free-flying butterflies, *Nature* **420**(6916):660–664, 2002. Torkel Weis-Fogh (1922–1975) was a Danish entomologist.

Halteres: built-in gyroscope[60]

Flies (Diptera) have only one pair of wings, unlike most insects that have two. But instead of the other pair, they have little sticks with knobs called halteres. These have long been known to act as a gyroscope, because they beat in antiphase to the wings, i.e. in reverse direction. The base of the haltere has mechanical sensors called *campaniform* (bell shaped) *sensilla* that quickly pass on flight information to the wing-steering muscles, so they can respond and stabilize the fly. Thus halteres are the equivalent of an aircraft's *attitude indicator*.

However, a gyroscope confers stability, while a fly is very agile. So somehow it must neutralize this stabilizing effect while it makes sharp turns (e.g. dodging a fly-swat!). But it turns out that it does not need to turn the 'gyroscope' off at all, but merely tweak it from visual cues. A team led by Michael Dickinson, of the University of California at Berkeley, found that nerves from the visual system connect to the halteres. Thus they immediately respond, and their sensilla in turn pass that information to the flight muscles.[61] The position of the head relative to the body also sends signals to the halteres. Dickinson said:

> 'From an engineering point of view, this is much cleverer and more efficient. This way you never turn off your stabilizer—you tune it so the nervous system controls its mechanics on a moment-by-moment basis.'

Did halteres evolve from vestigial wings?

However, Dickinson is a staunch evolutionist, and claims that the halteres evolved from vestigial remnants of proper wings:

> 'The forewing follows what the hindwing is doing, and this is still going on in flies, the same basic circuitry is there in the fly, the hindwing entrains the forewing, they've just reused the muscles and sensors on the hindwing in a very clever way.'

As 'evidence', a single mutation in the *ultrabithorax* gene in Diptera causes the halteres to continue to develop into a second pair of full wings, and this is an 'Icon of Evolution'.[62] However, this evidence is flawed on several grounds:

- *Ultrabithorax* is a huge and very complex gene which is composed of several subunits, 'most of which are involved

---

60. After Wieland, C., Why a fly can fly like a fly, *J. Creation* **12**(3):260–261, 1998; <creationontheweb.com/fly>.

61. Chan, W.P., Prete, F., Dickinson, M.H., Visual input to the efferent control system of a fly's 'gyroscope', *Science*, **280**(5361):289–292, 1998; Pennisi, E., Flying by the seat of their halteres, perspective, same issue, pp. 201–202.

62. Wells, J., *Icons of Evolution: Science or Myth? Why much of what we teach about evolution is wrong*, *Regnery Publishing, Inc., Washington, 2000. See review, Truman, R.*, What biology textbooks never told you about evolution, *J. Creation* **15**(2):17–24, 2001; <creationontheweb.com/icons>.

in regulating when and where the gene is turned on in the embryo'.[63] It regulates an entire gene complex responsible for halteres: 'It is this entire hierarchy, and not just one gene, that had to evolve in order to convert wings into halteres'.[63t]

- In a fruit fly *(Drosophila)*, *Ultrabithorax* is normally turned on in the third thoracic segment, which promotes development of halteres rather than wings. By destroying the normal function, new non-functional wings are generated.

- The duplicate wings had no muscles attached so were a serious *hindrance*—indeed, the poor mutant fly can't even fly! What is happening is that when *Ultrabithorax* is disabled, *existing* information is expressed instead, producing an additional pair of wings. But this expression was not properly coordinated, so the wings were not produced with all the necessary coordinated machinery for them to function. Such a hypothetical intermediate stage between four-winged flies and Diptera would have been *eliminated* by natural selection.

HUMPBACK FLIPPER BUMPS: INSPIRATION FOR AIRCRAFT DESIGNERS[64]

The humpback whale is not one of the flying animals. But it turns out that certain features that help it travel through its fluid are relevant to helping airplanes travel through their fluid (air).

Flipper bumps

Why is the flipper so bumpy? Superficially, this looks like poor design compared with smooth, sleek flippers. However, engineers and US Naval Academy scientists have shown that it's an ingenious design that aircraft designers can learn from![65]

They used a scale model of a flipper 56 cm tall. One was smooth, and the other had the little bumps, called tubercles. In a wind tunnel, the smooth one behaved like a typical airplane wing. But the one with the tubercles had 8% better lift and an astounding 32% less drag. It also resisted stalling (drastically losing lift) at a 40% steeper wing angle.

If that could be applied to airplanes, the better lift would make takeoff and landing easier; the lower drag would mean less fuel would be wasted; and the better stall resistance would be a huge safety advantage. The researchers propose that the tubercle design would also greatly benefit propellers, helicopter rotors and ship rudders.[66]

63. Wells, Ref. 63, 1. 188. Dr Wells is a specialist in developmental biology.
64. After Sarfati, J., Flighty flippers, *Creation* 27(2):56, 2005; <creationontheweb.com/flippers>.
65. Miklosovic, D.S., *et al.*, Leading-edge tubercles delay stall on humpback whale (*Megaptera novaeangliae*) flippers, *Physics of Fluids* 16(5): L39-L42, 2004.
66. Anon., That's a whale of an idea: Mimicking Humpback Whale Flippers May Improve Airplane Wing

So why does this bumpy structure work so much better? The tubercles at the front of the flipper break up the flow of fluid (liquid or gas), and force it into the fluted valleys in between. This generates vortices (eddies) that keep the flow attached to the top surface of the flipper. This increases lift and resists stalling.

Humpback whales are huge—27–36 tonnes and about 9–18 m long. But they are very agile, and the flipper design explains how. In today's fallen world, they catch a school of fish with a unique 'bubble net'. They swim in a circle under their prey, exhaling through their blowhole, making a cylindrical trap with air 'walls'. Then the whale swims through the centre with its mouth wide open, scooping up the fish.

SUMMARY

The animal kingdom has used four main ways to solve the problem of heavier-than-air flight, as exemplified by birds, bats, pterosaurs and insects. All exploit the principles of aerodynamics in ingenious ways that aircraft designers are still learning. The new discoveries of the ingenuity of designs of flying creatures, as well as the continued lack of discoveries of transitional forms, remain huge obstacles to belief in evolution.

Design, *Aero News Network*, <www.aero-news.net/news/featurestories.cfm?ContentBlockID=7b1f3d47-352f-4277-9eda-baaa208b2516&Dynamic=1>, 12 May 2004.

CHAPTER 5

NAVIGATION AND ORIENTATION

How do animals find their way, both in migration and merely finding one's way locally? They must have machinery for both orientation (knowing direction) and navigation (knowing when to change direction). It turns out that there is often amazing computational machinery that is far superior to that of any supercomputer, but often performed in a tiny brain. Some creatures make use of the earth's magnetic field and the sun's polarization.

BEES INSPIRE FLYING ROBOT DESIGN[1]

Honeybees fly with remarkable agility that would be the envy of stunt pilots, yet their navigation 'software' is packed into a brain the size of a sesame seed. Now their techniques are being studied carefully at the All-Weather Beeflight Facility at the Australian National University (Canberra), with plans to implement them in miniature flying robotic spies and unmanned planetary exploration probes.[2]

How bees navigate

Bees have airspeed gauges, gyroscopes, a 'compass' that detects the polarization of sunlight; UV sensors to track the horizon to measure tilt; and two compound eyes, each with 7,000 hexagonal (six-sided) facets. These facets are windows to sub-eyes called *ommatidia*, which

John Nyberg, <sxc.hu>

are tiny tubes containing their own lens and light-detecting cells. Each tube points in a different direction, enabling vision over a wide area. Their shape is ideal. They use as little edge-cell material as possible (which is why the honeycomb is also hexagonal), have the least-sharp corners needing less reinforcement, and it is the most symmetrical structure. And they are superb for detecting motion, since a small shift means different facets detect the image.

Optic flow

Now the researchers have shown that bees use motion detection for navigation. Imagine travelling fast in a car or train. The posts on

---

1.   After Sarfati, J., Can it bee? *Creation* 25(2):44–45, 2003; <creationontheweb.com/bee>.
2.   Fox, D., Electric Eye, *New Scientist* 171(2305):38–42, 2001.

a nearby fence seem to be whizzing backwards, while objects further away seem to move backwards more slowly, and clouds seem almost to travel with you. The movement of images is called *optic flow*, and the faster anything seems to move, the closer it is to the observer.

The researchers proved that the bees use optic flow by making the bees fly in tunnels where patterns on walls could be artificially moved. When the pattern was stationary, the bees flew dead centre in the tunnel, because only then would the image flow rate on both sides be identical. If the pattern on one side moved in the same direction as the bees flew, i.e. slowing down relative to the bees, they detected the slower apparent motion and calculated that the wall was now further away, and veered towards it.

The researchers found that bees are programmed to fly such that the image speed stays constant. E.g. when patterns on both sides of the walls moved with the bees, so that the bees thought they were flying slower, they flew faster. This is vital so that bees will fly fast in open spaces but slow down in more cluttered spaces, or veer away if images suddenly start to move very fast on one side, signalling that an obstacle is very close. It also helps bees land, because they can slow down automatically to keep the optic flow constant as they descend closer to the ground at constant angle. This way they don't need to know their airspeed or height.

Honeybees also use optic flow to measure distances to food sources,[3] which they communicate to the other bees in special waggling dances.[4] Researchers proved this by making foraging bees fly through narrow tunnels which generated higher optic flow, which they calculated as flying further. Then they communicated this misinformation to the other bees, which then started searching for the food at greater distances.

Optic flow does require contrast in the surroundings, so that images change enough to be detectable. This works very well in nature, and fails only in artificial environments such as glass windows and painted walls—explaining why bees sometimes become disoriented and keep bouncing off these surfaces.

Flying robots

Optic flow may solve problems that are unavoidable with conventional guidance systems. The Global Positioning System (GPS) relies on satellite mapping, but an enemy can jam satellite signals, and it only works on pre-mapped objects and won't stop a spy craft from crashing into a rubbish bin, which has a variable position. For a space probe like the Mars Pathfinder mission, it was even worse. Signals between Earth and Mars took 11 minutes to travel the distance of 190 million km, so the robot had to crawl at a

3. Esch, H., *et al.*, Honeybee dances communicate distances measured by optic flow, *Nature* **411**(6837):581–583, 2001.

4. Doolan, R., Dancing bees, *Creation* **17**(4):46–48, 1995.

snail's pace—52 metres in 30 days. Any faster, and the rover might have fallen into a crevasse before mission control even knew that the rover was in danger, let alone send the signal to change course.

In contrast, optic flow would allow a robot to be self-steering. A prototype 1.5-m-long 7-kg helicopter can use optic flow to hover in one spot, a major achievement that outclasses remote-controlled machines. However, there is some way to go before it could navigate winding canyons, and the computer program (algorithm) is not yet perfected. It also currently needs power-hungry Pentium chips to operate. However, a 'specially designed chip that better mimics the bee's energy-efficient design' may enable a '100-fold reduction in power consumption, and a 10-fold reduction in weight.'[2]

Also, engineers have a long way to go to make a bee-sized flying robot, about 1/100th the length and 1/10,000[th] the weight of their prototype. For one thing, ordinary gears and pulleys don't work properly when miniaturized. They plan to mimic the aerodynamics, of insects, which flap their wings by vibrating their outer covering (exoskeleton). Also, insects' wings flap with a very complex motion, rotating and changing the tilt to achieve the required lift—the algorithm for this motion has previously been programmed into robot simulations of insect wing flapping.[5,6]

DRAGONFLY TRACKING SYSTEM[7]

Dragonflies have long been known to be exquisite fliers. And recent research shows that they can track other insects with incredibly intricate manoeuvring that makes them appear stationary to their target.[8] Insects' compound eyes are good at detecting the slightest motion by optic flow, as per the previous section, so the flight patterns must have amazing control systems. Appearing stationary would be very useful for sneaking up on other insects or for eluding a predator.

A brief report in *New Scientist* said, 'Dragonflies overshadow their enemies in complex manoeuvres that military fighter pilots can only dream of. … It demands exquisite position sensing and control.'[9] The researcher, Akiko Mizutani, of the Centre for Visual Science at the Australian National University in Canberra, said, 'This sort of performance is extremely hard to achieve without very expensive and bulky measurement systems.'[9]

What the most ingenious human designers can't achieve with bulky systems, the dragonfly's Maker programmed into the tiny dragonfly brain. Yet evolutionists believe that this evolved by time and chance—and in what they call the 'oldest airborne predator'!

5.   On a wing and a vortex, *New Scientist* **156**(2103):24–27, 1997.
6.   Insects: Defying the laws of aerodynamics? *Creation* **20**(2):31, 1998; <creationontheweb.com/insects>.
7.   After Sarfati, J., Astonishing acrobatics—dragonflies, *Creation* **25**(4):56, 2003; <creationontheweb.com/dragonfly>.
8.   Mizutani, A. *et al.*, Motion camouflage in dragonflies, *Nature* **423**:604, 2003.
9.   Anon., How stealthy insects outsmart their foe, *New Scientist* **178**(2398):26, 2003.

MAGNETIC NAVIGATION

Magnetic compasses have been vital to navigation, as they enable people to use the earth's magnetic field to tell direction. Now, recent experiments have demonstrated that some organisms also navigate with their own 'compasses'.

At different places on the earth, the strength of the earth's magnetic field and its inclination (the angle at which it intersects the earth's surface) are different. So if organisms could sense these changes, they would have something like longitude and latitude readings on a map.

The famous British evolutionist (and communist) J.B.S. Haldane (1892–1964) admitted in 1949 that evolution could never produce 'various mechanisms, such as the wheel and magnet, which would be useless till fairly perfect.'[10] Therefore such machines in organisms should, based on his stated opinion, prove evolution false. Turtles that use magnetic sensors have indeed fulfilled one of Haldane's criteria. Also, 'simple' bacteria propel themselves by a filament called a flagellum, which is propelled by a rotary motor—a very complex type of wheel, thus fulfilling Haldane's other criterion (see chapter 10). I wonder whether Haldane would have had a change of heart if he had been alive to see these discoveries …

Turtles can read magnetic maps[11]

Magnetic navigation is important to young loggerhead turtles (*Caretta caretta*) which live within the North Atlantic Gyre, the circular ocean current system that surrounds the Sargasso Sea. Researchers Kenneth and Catherine Lohmann of the University of North Carolina have shown that the turtles use magnetic measurements to stay in the gyre.

Tan Wah Chew, <sxc.hu>

They placed turtles in water tanks surrounded by computerized electric coils generating an artificial magnetic field. When the field's inclination was the same as that of the northern boundary of the gyre, the turtles would swim south, as if back into the gyre. Conversely, when the inclination was the same as the southern boundary's, the turtles swam north-northeast, again as if away from the 'danger' boundary.

10.   *Is Evolution a Myth? A Debate between D. Dewar and L.M. Davies vs. J.B.S. Haldane*, p. 90, Watts & Co. Ltd / Paternoster Press, London, 1949.
11.   After Sarfati, J., Turtles—reading magnetic maps, *Creation* **21**(2):30, 1999; <creationontheweb.com/turtlemap>.

In other experiments, they also kept the inclination constant but varied the magnetic field strength in the tank. When the strength was the same as that of the western boundary of the gyre, the turtles swam east, again as if into the gyre and away from the boundary. And they swam west when the strength was the same as the eastern boundary's.[12]

Bacterial compasses[13]

Certain bacteria live happily in mud, but unhappily in oxygen. So it's in their interest to know which way is 'down' so they swim away from the surface exposed to the air. But while large creatures have gravity to help them, microscopic creatures do not.

Once again, it is the earth's magnetic field that is used in orientation, and again it is the inclination that's important. In the 1970s, Richard Blakemore, a graduate student at the University of Massachusetts, demonstrated with artificial magnets that the bacteria head towards magnetic north.[14] The further north, the more the inclination dips down. In the southern hemisphere, presumably bacteria would head towards magnetic south.

The magnet in these tiny cells comprises about 20 particles of magnetite or lodestone (Fe_3O_4), arranged in a line along the long axis of the cell. Each particle is roughly cubic, and only about 50 nm on each side. How the bacteria make such well organized magnetite particles is a mystery, because it is difficult for the best human designers in the laboratory.

Interestingly, the famous evolutionist Stephen Jay Gould (1941–2002) proclaimed the new magnetic bacterium to be a 'striking example of good design: an organism that builds an exquisite machine within its own body. The machine is a magnet; the organism a "lowly" bacterium.'[15] Of course, as an agnostic and Marxist,[16] Gould would not have believed that the design requires a Designer, but the explanation fits.

MIGRATING BIRDS[17]

Many types of birds migrate for thousands of miles. Every year the short-tailed shearwater ('muttonbird') travels 13,000 km from Australia to Alaska. The Bristle-thighed curlew flies for 'only' 8,000 km across the Pacific, but this is *non-stop*. But even this non-stop flight is exceeded by the bar-tailed godwit—this flies south from Alaska at about 72 km/h, and doesn't rest until it arrives in New Zealand, 11,000 km away.

---

12. Torr, G., Magnetic map readers, *Nature Australia* 25(9):7–8, Winter 1997.
13. Helder, M., The world's smallest compasses: An amazing discovery of how humble bacteria can sense direction, *Creation* 20(2):52–53, 1998; <creationontheweb.com/compass>.
14. Blakemore, R.P. and Frankel, R.B., Magnetic navigation in bacteria, *Scientific Amer.* 245(6):42–49, 1981.
15. Gould, S.J., Perceptive bees, birds and bacteria, *Natural History*, 88:25–30, November 1979.
16. Martin, Z., What is the evidence that Gould was a Marxist? <creationontheweb.com/gould_marx>, 2006.
17. After Catchpoole, D., Wings on the wind: *How do migrating birds know exactly when, and where, to go? Creation* 23(4):16–23, 2001; <creationontheweb.com/migration>.

The primary purpose of the migrations appears to be the search for food, rather than to escape bad weather or find fine climes. Birds that can continue to find enough to eat during the winter rarely migrate, whereas almost all the bird species that do migrate depend upon weather-sensitive food supplies.

Migration poses two main problems: how they can sustain flight for so long, and how they find their way.

Energy for the flight

The energy problem is solved by eating intensively and storing lots of fat. The birds secrete the fat into special cavities *between* tissues and organs, so it doesn't interfere with the muscles. This fat also contains much less water than ordinary fat, so is more concentrated and lighter. The birds don't need a supply of water, because they obtain it from the 'burning' of the fat, just as camels with their humps (the hydrogen atoms within the fat combine with oxygen to form water).

This fat is an outstanding energy source. The Blackpoll Warbler, on its 5,600 km migration, flaps its wings about three million times. Its fuel consumption can be calculated at 0.33 ml per 100 km (720,000 mpg).[18]

The godwits gorge themselves on shellfish, until the fat builds up into thick rolls under their skin—up to 55% of their total weight. Then they stop eating and their intestines, kidneys and liver shrivel up to a fraction of their usual size, eliminating unnecessary weight.

The golden plover accumulates an extra 70 g of fat; half its normal bodyweight. This is almost the right amount required for its journey from Alaska to Hawaii—4,500 km, taking around 88 hours at about 51 km/h. This is very efficient—converting 0.6% of its bodyweight into motion and heat per flight-hour, compared with a helicopter and a jet plane that use, in relation to their weight, seven times and 20 times more fuel respectively.

However, this would still mean that it would run out of fuel 800 km short of its destination. However, it manages fine, because it flies in flocks in the classical 'V-formation'—this saves each bird, on average, 23% of the energy that would be used in a solo flight.[19] The bird at the apex saves no energy, but they take turns in the lead.

3D magnetic compass

Gerta Fleissner and her team at the University of Frankfurt (Germany) X-rayed the upper beaks of homing pigeons.[20] They found tiny iron-containing particles in nerve branches within the skin

---

18   .That is, if burning a standard motorcar fuel equivalent (mpg = miles per US gal.).
19   Gitt, W. and Vanheiden, K.-H., *If animals could talk*, Christliche Literatur-Verbreitung e.V., Bielefeld, Germany, pp. 107–115, 1994.
20   Fleissner *et al.*, A novel concept of Fe-mineral-based magnetoreception: histological and physicochemical data from the upper beak of homing pigeons, *Naturwissenschaften*, 2007 | DOI 10.1007/s00114-007-0236-0; <http://neurophilosophy.files.wordpress.com/2007/03/03-07pigeonsfulltext.pdf>.

lining. The particles are 90% maghemite[21] and 10% magnetite, and are arranged in a complex three-dimensional pattern. This allows the birds to analyze the three components of the magnetic field, i.e. act as a three-axis magnetometer.

Fleissner and her colleagues write:

> '[I]ron-based magnetoreception needs the presence of both these iron minerals, their specific dimensions, shapes and arrangements, three different subcellular compartments.'[20]

This is because:

> 'The appropriate alignment between the Earth's magnetic field and the maghemite bands would induce a multiple attraction of the magnetite bullets perpendicular to the membrane, thus triggering strain-sensitive membrane channels and a primary receptor potential.'[20]

One report noted how this system has interested human designers, who would have difficulty making the particles involved, but included the all-too-common homage to evolution's millions of years:

> 'Research into how they work has caught the interest of nanotechnologists concerning their potential application for accurate drug targeting and even as a data storage device. The main problem, however, lies in their synthetic production. According to Gerta Fleissner and her colleagues, "Even though birds have been producing these particles for millions of years, the main problem for scientists who want to find benefits from their use will be the technical production of these particles".'[22]

Finding their destination

How do migrating birds find their destination, which they may never have seen before? They must be able to *both* orient themselves, which requires a sort of compass, *and* navigate, which requires a map. Either of these alone would not enable long migrations. It seems that birds use a number of different methods, including the sun, stars and geographical landmarks, and atmospheric clues, as well as the magnetic field as shown above.

But how did they first find their destination, especially as the continents have moved?[23] It seems that birds are programmed to

21. Maghemite (γ-Fe$_2$O$_3$) is a ferrimagnetic mineral like magnetite (Fe$_3$O$_4$), and has the same spinel structure, but is more oxidized.
22. Homing pigeons get their bearings from their beaks, *Photon Science*, <http://hasylab.desy.de/news__events/announcements/beak_sensors_give_birds_bearings/index_eng.html>, 2007.
23. Many biblical creationists accept *catastrophic* plate tectonics—see Plate Tectonics Questions and Answers, <creationontheweb.com/tectonics>.

migrate in a certain direction, and this programming is inherited. But there also seems to be some natural heritable variation in this programming. So with a given continental distribution, most of the birds would follow a certain course. However, there would be some who deviate, but land in an unsuitable place and perish— natural selection would weed them out. With a changed continental distribution, natural selection would favour some of the formerly deviant ones. Such a design feature would not only allow migration but the capacity to adapt to changing conditions.[17]

Experiments with blackcaps support the theory of heritable variation in orientation. These birds normally migrate from Norway and western Europe to the Mediterranean and Africa. However, since the 1950s, more have been landing in Britain. Researchers in Germany bred blackcaps caught in both Britain and on their traditional route. Offspring of English birds oriented on a compass heading of 273° (i.e. towards London), while those German-caught blackcaps tried to fly on a traditional heading of 227°, i.e. towards Spain.[17]

Efficient route

However, arctic shorebirds do not simply follow the lines of a constant magnetic compass direction (*loxodromes*). Rather, they travel in great circle routes (*orthodromes*)—a 'great circle' is a surface formed by intersection of a sphere with a plane going through its centre. They do this because it is the shortest travelling distance between two points on a sphere.

This is hard to do, because the compass bearing constantly changes. Intercontinental airline flights use great circles, which is why they look curved on a flat map. The arctic shorebirds' great circle routes have a sound mathematical basis—this curve is generated by a time-compensated sun compass without resetting the bird's internal clock while travelling across successive longitudes (i.e. moving into different time zones).[24]

SWIFTS NAVIGATE IN THEIR SLEEP![25]

Swifts often fly at great heights at night—3000 m (10,000 feet); as high as small private planes. Yet swifts have even more sophisticated navigational skills, and they do it while sleeping (a swift shuts down half its brain at a time).

Johan Bäckman, an expert in bird migration at Lund University in Sweden, studied over 200 swifts by radar. He found that they kept on course by an unexpected method. Rather than using landmarks

---

24. Alerstam, T., *et al.*, Migration along orthodromic sun compass routes by Arctic birds, *Science* **291**(5502):300–303, 2001; Wehner, R., Bird navigation—computing *orthodromes, Perspective, same issue, pp. 264–265.*

25. After Sarfati, J., Fancy flying from advanced aeronautics: the design of swifts and jet fighters, *Creation* **29**(1): 37–39, 2006.

on the ground, they judged their direction by the wind,[26] so they would not be blown off course. Bäckman said:

> 'We found that swifts have an extraordinary ability to perform orientations in relation to wind. Even the most advanced planes, with good navigational instruments, would probably be unable to judge the wind drift like this. The remarkable thing is that they do all this while flying through the night and sleeping on the wing at these very high altitudes.'[27]

STARLINGS FLOCK USING ADVANCED COMPUTATIONS[28]

Lovattpics, <istockphoto.com>

Huge numbers of starlings fly in flocks that perform impressive aerial acrobatics. How do they fly in such an impressively cohesive group? A number of European researchers (including biologists, physicists and statisticians) took part in the Starling Project to work out how so many birds can fly in unison. They analyzed the three-dimensional positions of several thousand individual birds in a flock.[29]

This research overturned the previous explanation that each bird simply keeps a set distance from its near neighbours. This is wrong. Instead, each starling seems to be continuously monitoring the positions of an average of six or seven of its neighbours, regardless of how far away they are. In other words, starlings have a pre-programmed, numeric, object-tracking ability, by 'computing' the *topological* distance (interactions) with other birds.

The researchers explain how this tracking method enables the flock to resist the attempts of predators to pick off stragglers because:

26. Bäckman, J. and Alerstam, T., Harmonic oscillatory orientation relative to the wind in nocturnal roosting flights of the swift *Apus apus*, *J. Exp. Biol.* **205:**905–910, 2002.

27. Cited in Day, E., Revealed: how the swift keeps to its course at 10,000 feet—even as it sleeps: New research reveals navigational skills of the bird that outperforms the most advanced aircraft, *Sunday Telegraph*, p. 11, 14 March 2004.

28. After Bell, P., Bird behaviour beliefs overturned: A tale of the hummingbird and the starling, <creationontheweb.com/2bird>, 2008; *Creation* **30**(3):9, 2008.

29. Ballerini, M. *et al.*, Interaction ruling animal collective behavior depends on topological rather than metric distance: Evidence from a field study, *Proc. Natl Acad. Sci. USA* **105**(4):1232–1237, 2008.

'By interacting within a fixed number of individuals the aggregation can be either dense or sparse, change shape, fluctuate and even split, yet maintain the same degree of cohesion.'

No wonder that the team members have admitted that these starlings are much cleverer than they had given them credit for.

MIGRATING MONARCHS[30]

After it hatches, this spectacular butterfly flies thousands of kilometres, navigating unerringly to reach a place it has never seen. One famous migration is from Nova Scotia, Canada, to the mountains west of Mexico City, some 5,000 kilometres away. Even more remarkably, they often land on the exact tree their parents came from. And they can do this even if they are taken hundreds of kilometres off course.

What is their secret? A large role is played by the sun's position.

The monarch seems to use something similar to the following method that humans have used:[31]

Determine the sun's position relative to the horizon at different times of the day. If you know the Greenwich Mean Time and have a Navigator's Almanac that states the sun's position at a certain date and time, each sighting can enable a line to be drawn on a map. The intersection of these lines provides the location.

For the monarch to use this, there must be some sort of internal clock, as well as an in-built 'almanac' of the sun's position relative to a date and time. Monarchs can use this method even on a cloudy day, because they can also detect the polarization angle of any light—scattered light is polarized, so the direction of polarization enables the butterfly to determine the direction of the sun even if obscured by clouds.

These butterflies also have a built-in magnetic compass, so they can sense directions from the earth's magnetic field.[32]

ANTS: NAVIGATION BY ADVANCED CALCULUS[33]

The Saharan desert ant, *Cataglyphis fortis*, often travels hundreds of metres in zigzag paths to food. It can also find its way to its nest over a route never previously travelled, despite the near lack of landmarks.

30. Poirier, J.H., The magnificent migrating monarch: An electronic design expert ponders the stunning navigational exploits of the monarch butterfly, *Creation* **20**(1):28–31, December 1997–February 1998, <creationontheweb.com/monarch>; Monarch butterfly navigation, *J. Creation* **13**(1): 105–114, 1999.
31. Sun compass in monarch butterflies, *Nature* **387**:29, 1997.
32. *Science News*, 27 November 1999, p. 343; *Creation* **2**(4):5–7, 2000.
33. After Sarfati, J., Ants find their way by advanced mathematics, *J. Creation* **15**(2):11–12, 2001; <creationontheweb.com/ant>.

Researchers from Germany and Switzerland[34] have performed careful experiments that ruled out the use of visual clues, time or energy. For instance, the ants were tested on uniformly grey and smooth surroundings, but the ants unerringly found their way.

The evidence is consistent with ants having a built-in odometer that performs a complicated mathematical operation called *path integration*. That is, the journey is divided into small vectors, each with a certain length and direction, and they are added to give a 'homing' vector that gives the direction and total distance to the nest.

But what about bumps in the terrain, which would be like 'hills' and 'valleys' to the ant, and cause the ants to walk further than on totally flat ground? To find out, the researchers trained groups of 21 ants on trails with many symmetrical tall hills and deep valleys (to an ant's scale) to locate a food source that would take them 8.7 m to walk, but which was only 5.2 m of ground (horizontal) distance away. Then they transformed the intervening terrain to a flat surface. The ants then walked a far shorter distance which was very close to the ground distance; they were not tricked.

And vice versa, when 17 ants were trained on flat terrain to find a food source 5.2 m away, and the terrain then transformed into hills and valleys, the ants walked a distance very close to the distance (8.7 m) that equates to the ground distance; again they were not fooled.

The experimenters ruled out the possibility that the ants were using only the uphill (or only the downhill) paths by performing similar tests on asymmetric hills.

This means that the ants apparently calculate the *horizontal projection* of the distance travelled. That is, the image of the ant's travel vectors is projected onto an imaginary flat screen underneath the ant's terrain, and the path integration is performed in this x-y plane. To do this, the ants must have a way of estimating the slopes, and multiplying the travelled distance by the cosine of the angle of inclination to work out the corresponding ground distance.

The ants probably use the internal sense called *proprioception*, which animals and humans use to determine the location of their body parts. Ants probably measure slopes by the same means as they sense gravity, i.e. by proprioceptors on various joints between moving parts. These are a number of hairplates, and there may be some backup design so one might take over another's function if it is surgically removed. This makes it hard to determine the exact mechanisms involved in precisely determining ground distance.

The alternative mechanism to horizontal projection is the even more elaborate three-dimensional path integration, which the researchers plan to investigate. One way suggested would be by

---

34.   Wohlgemuth, S., Ronacher, B. and Wehner, R., Ant odometry in the third dimension, *Nature* **411**(6839):795–798, 2001.

training ants to find food at the end of a ramp, then testing them on terrain with a totally vertical channel, where the horizontal projection is zero, at the end of a completely horizontal channel. If the calculated horizontal projection is correct, then they would ignore the vertical channel and search at the end of the horizontal channel corresponding to the ground distance. Only if they are performing 3D integration should they climb up the vertical channel to search for their food.[35]

Implications

Whether the ants are using horizontal path integration or a fully 3D integration, this still involves advanced programming. It's common sense to believe that a program requires a programmer. However, the religious belief in the sufficiency of naturalistic causes means that evolutionists will reject this commonsense view.

They might claim that a homing sense could evolve by random mutations causing better and better improvements, which natural selection would accumulate. But the fallacy in this is assuming that a small change in a program has small changes in effect. Human programmers know that a single step in an algorithm often has far-reaching consequences, and one wrong step can often cause the program to crash. Rather, a path integration program must surely be fully functional or else it would be totally useless.

---

35.   Srinivasan, M.V., Homing in on ant navigation [comment on Ref. 34], *Nature* **411**(6839): 752–753, 2001.

CHAPTER 6

CATAPULTS

A catapult is a machine with a stiff frame, allowing a large force to store energy in an elastic material, and then release it suddenly to accelerate a small mass to great speed. All the components must be in place for it to work at all, so this fulfils the 'irreducible complexity' criterion.

CHAMELEON'S TERRIFIC TONGUE[1]

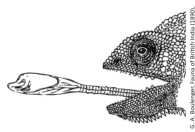

G. A. Boulenger, Fauna of British India (1890),
<wikipedia.org>

The chameleon captures its prey with its tongue. This is another remarkable feature—the tongue can reach up to 1½ times the lizard's body length. The acceleration of this 'ballistic tongue' is amazing—50 g (i.e. 50 times the acceleration due to gravity), while astronauts and jet fighter pilots will pass out at only 10 g—and that with special suits. The chameleon uses special super-contracting muscle, 'unique among vertebrates' and otherwise found only in invertebrates.[2] This is necessary to maintain tension over the great changes in muscle length.

Such is the amazing acceleration, researchers needed a special high-speed X-ray camera to film the tongue through its entire movement (including inside the mouth).[3]

Suction cap

Most lizards catch insects on their tongue just by the stickiness of the moist surface. But the chameleon's fast tongue manages to capture large, smooth prey. It does this with yet another mechanism. Just before the tongue hits the prey, two muscles pull the central part of the tip backwards, forming a suction cap.[4]

Catapult

How does the tongue accelerate so much? Even super-contractile muscle can't explain that totally—it would need to generate 10 times as much power as it does. Some animals generate high accelerations

---

1. After Sarfati, J., A coat of many colours: *Captivating chameleons, Creation* **26**(4):28–33, 2004; <creationontheweb.com/*chameleon*>.
2. Herrel, A., *et al.*, Supercontracting muscle: producing tension over extreme muscle lengths, *J. Exp. Biol.* **205**:2167–2173, 2002.
3. Snelderwaard, P. Ch., De Groot, J.H. and Deban, S.M., Digital video combined with conventional radiography creates an excellent high-speed X-ray video system, *J. Biomechanics* **35**:1007–1009, 2002.
4. Herrel, A., *et al.*, The mechanics of prey prehension in chameleons, *J. Exp. Biol.* **203**:3255–3263, 2000.

by using their legs as levers, but even a kangaroo rat[5] can reach only 19 g while jumping.

Close analysis reveals that the chameleon tongue has an ingenious catapult system. It has a bone, which provides the stiff frame. Surrounding the bone are at least 10 slippery sheaths. These contain coiled collagen fibres, which are the elastic material. The sheaths in turn are surrounded by the powerful accelerator muscles, providing the stretching energy.

When the chameleon wants to flick out its tongue, it activates these muscles. Now muscle is incompressible, i.e. its volume remains the same, e.g. when you flex your biceps, the muscle contracts, and to keep the volume constant, it bulges outward. In the chameleon tongue, the muscles squeeze inward, and to keep the volume constant they lengthen along the tongue. This stretches the sheaths like rubber bands. When the sheaths come to the rounded tip of the tongue bone, they slide off. With the bone out of the way, it can relax inward and contract in length quickly. This forces the tongue off the bone, and the 'sliding spring' mechanism releases the stored energy to shoot the tongue forward at dazzling speed. Then the concentric sheaths extend like tubes of a telescope.[6]

An article in the journal *Science* said, 'The chameleon's "sliding spring" is remarkably compact, efficient and easy to control.'[7] It pointed out that the tongue projector was more efficient than a man-made catapult—the latter loads and releases the energy along the same path, while the chameleon tongue releases the energy in a different path. This means that the tongue needs no extra moving parts to release the tension suddenly, because the energy is released as the tongue slips off the bone. Also, while the acceleration is certainly sudden, the energy is still released steadily as the sheaths slide off in turn, rather than all at once. Otherwise a lot of the energy would be wasted in deforming the tongue and dissipated in vibrations.

Evolutionary vacuity

One of the papers[4] on the tongue's design had a curious section, 'Evolutionary considerations'. The author admitted that the suction cap and the ballistic tongue are both essential to capture prey, i.e. one is useless without the other. Yet he interpreted this as evidence that they must have 'evolved simultaneously … early in their evolutionary history.' The author did not offer an explanation as to *how* this could happen. A far better interpretation is that chameleons have always been chameleons, and were designed with both these mechanisms fully functional.

5. Weston, P., Kangaroo rats, *Creation* **26**(3): 18–20, 2004; <creationontheweb.com/roorat>.
6. Schilthuizen, M., Slip of the chameleon's tongue, *Science Now*, <http://sciencenow.sciencemag.org/cgi/content/full/2004/308/1>, 2004.
7. Müller, U.K. and Kranenbarg, S., Power at the tip of the tongue, *Science* **304**(5668):217–219, 9 April 2004.

There is a good lesson here. *Practical* biological research assumes that features of living things have a point, so it makes sense to find out how they work. This makes perfect sense if these features have been designed for a function. So, all the *useful* research was carried out as if the researchers were creationists for all practical purposes. But then evolutionists try to make up just-so stories to explain how these features evolved. Yet this extra 'Evolutionary considerations' section added nothing whatsoever of practical value, only empty speculation.[8]

HORSE LEGS HAVE CATAPULT MECHANISM

A horse's legs have special features that enable it to gallop beautifully. For example, they work like pogo sticks, storing energy between gallops. And a team led by Alan Wilson of the Royal Veterinary College, Hatfield, UK, showed that a feature previously thought to be useless has an important function. That is, certain small muscles thought to be vestigial, or useless remnants of evolution, are now known to have a vital dampening function.[9,10]

Wilson's further research with different colleagues[11] shows that horses have a catapult mechanism as well. This is 'where energy is stored slowly with a large force but is released quickly to accelerate a small mass, in this case, the foot shooting forward to land on the ground ready for the next jump. This mechanism, however, requires a more sophisticated lever, or cam system, to exert sufficient force on the spring and then release it.' Fleas and grasshoppers also have a catapult system, but this is the first time it has been found in a large animal.

When the horse lands, the carpus (commonly called the 'knee') locks straight, while the shoulder bends forwards. This stretches the biceps muscles, which are very elastic. Eventually the carpus buckles forward, releasing the biceps 'spring'. This flicks the leg forward (protraction) and off the ground, so it's ready to land on the ground for the next gallop. '[T]his muscle's catapult action has an output [of power] that is comparable to over 100 times its mass of non-elastic muscle.'[11]

This highly efficient mechanism would not work at all without a locking and release system and the springy muscle fully in place. This is a problem for evolution, because the hypothetical small intermediate steps would have no advantage by themselves, therefore natural selection would not favour them.

8. See Wieland, C., Evolution and practical science, *Creation* **20**(4):4, 1998; <creationontheweb.com/prac_sci>.
9. Wilson, A.M., *et al.*, Horses damp the spring in their step, *Nature* **414**(6866):895–899, 20/27 December 2001; comment by Alexander, R. McN., Damper for bad vibrations, same issue, pp. 855–857.
10. Sarfati, J., Useless horse body parts? No way! *Creation* **24**(3):24–25, 2002; <creationontheweb.com/useless>, after Ref. 9.
11. Wilson, A.M., Watson, J.C. and Lichtwark, G.A., A catapult action for rapid limb protraction, *Nature* **421**(6918):35–36, 2003.

POWERFUL PUNCH FOR A SHRIMP[12]

For pound-for-pound boxing records, look not to 'Sugar' Ray Robinson or Rocky Marciano. Rather, the 6–10 cm long mantis shrimp or stomatopod has the fastest punch of all. Crustacean[13] expert Shiela Patek and her team at the University of California, Berkeley, needed high-resolution video at 5,000 frames per second to analyze this.[14] They showed that the peacock mantis shrimp (*Odontodactylus scyllarus*) can punch with a force 'well over a hundred times the mantis shrimp's body weight.'[14]

The club-like limb reaches a top speed of 14–23 metres per second, and a peak acceleration of 65–104 km/s^2 (6,600–10,600 g, or times the acceleration due to gravity).[15] They use this to crush the shells of snails they prey on, and in captivity, have shattered the glass walls of their tanks.[14]

Catapult

To reach such speeds, ordinary muscles won't do. Rather, a catapult mechanism is required. Thus the shrimp has a specialized saddle-shaped spring in the hinge of the shrimp's striking appendage.

Its shape has the technical name hyperbolic-paraboloid, but resembles a *Pringles* potato crisp. It is a very strong and efficient structure. Indeed, it is used in engineering and architecture because it distributes stresses and resists buckling, while the nautilus uses this structure to strengthen its shell.[13] However, no other animal uses it as a spring.[15]

But a spring isn't enough for a catapult. There must also be muscles to load it, and a click or latch mechanism to release it. If all these parts were not in place, the mechanism would not work at all. This could not have formed by random small changes and natural selection, because the latter would not work since the changes confer no advantage until the whole system is complete.

Bubble blast

In fact, each blow is a one-two punch. Patek's team found that there were two force peaks for every strike, less than half a millisecond apart. The second one is caused by a destructive process called *cavitation*.[16] This is where high-speed water flows irregularly, causing tiny bubbles of water vapour to form. When the pressure is restored, they collapse at supersonic speeds, forming shock waves

---

12. After Sarfati, J., Shrimpy superboxer, *Creation* **30**(2):12–13, 2008; <creationontheweb.com/shrimpy>.
13. Weston, P., Creation's crustaceans, *Creation* **23**(3):10–13, 2001; <creationontheweb.com/crust>.
14. Sanders, R., Mantis shrimp may have swiftest kick in the animal kingdom, *UCBerkeley News*, <www.berkeley.edu/news/media/releases/2004/04/21_shrimp.shtml>, 2004.
15. Patek, S.N., Korff, W.L. and Caldwell, R.L., Deadly strike mechanism of a mantis shrimp, *Nature* **428**(6985):819, 2004.
16. Patek, S.N. and Caldwell, R.L., Extreme impact and cavitation forces of a biological hammer: strike forces of the peacock mantis shrimp *Odontodactylus scyllarus*, *J. Exp. Biol* **208**:3655–3664, 2005.

with huge pressures, as well as sound and even light. In fact, the cavitation forces may be almost four times those of the actual limb impact. Cavitation can destroy steel surfaces and boat propellers, and would have destroyed hard rock during Noah's Flood.[17,18] Even the shrimp's heel is not immune—though it contains tough minerals, they moult frequently to regenerate.[15]

FROGS[19]

Frogs are famous for being excellent jumpers— they can easily jump distances more than 20 times their own length.[20] The world distance record for a single leap is 5.25 m by the Mascarene rocket frog, which measures just 5 cm from nose to tail.[21] Olympic athletes can only jump around five times their body length—and that's from a running, not stationary, leap. The men's long jump world record is 8.95 m. (The high jump record is 2.45 m).

But frog leg muscles are not strong enough in themselves to explain their jumping prowess. Now, some researchers filmed bullfrogs jumping and calculated that the extra 'spring' needed to make such high-powered leaps must come from some elastic structure somewhere. So the likely explanation is that just before the frogs become airborne, their contracting leg muscles also stretch a tendon-like component. Just as the energy stored in the stretched elastic of a slingshot sends a projectile hurtling forward when released, so, too, the energy stored in the tendon helps fire a frog into the air.[22,23]

FROGHOPPERS

Even better jumpers relative to their size[20] are froghopper insects (*Philaenus spumarius*), aka 'spittle bugs'—a reference to the froth (blown out of their back ends) which covers the developing young. Froghoppers deservedly could be hailed as the champion high jumpers of the world.[24,25] These 6-mm–long insects can spring 70

17. As long as the water was fast (over 30 m/s, 70 mph) and shallow (under 10 m or 30 feet deep); Cardno, S. and Wieland, C., Clouds, coins and creation: An airport encounter with professional scientist and creationist Dr Edmond Holroyd, *Creation* 20(1):22–23, 1997; <creationontheweb.com/holroyd>.
18. Catchpoole, D., Beware the bubble's burst—Increased knowledge about cavitation highlights the destructive power of fast-flowing water, <creationontheweb.com/bubble>, 2007.
19. After Catchpoole, D., In leaps and bounds: The amazing jumping prowess of frogs and froghoppers, <creationontheweb.com/leaps>, 2007.
20. Note that relative length or height is something of a red herring, because the physics would predict that animals should be able to jump roughly the same *absolute* length or height. This is because strength or force is proportional to mass, but the acceleration is *inversely* proportional to mass, and the two cancel. So, mathematically, it is not such a surprise that a flea should be able to jump to about the same absolute height (within an order of magnitude) as a man. However, this doesn't negate at all the amazing design of their jumping machinery.
21. Mascarene rocket frog, *Ptychadena mascareniensis*, <www.calacademy.org/research/herpetology/frogs/list8.html>, 2003.
22. Roberts, T.J. and Marsh R.L., Probing the limits to muscle-powered accelerations: lessons from jumping bullfrogs, *J. Exp. Biol* 206(15):2567–2580, 2003.
23. Frogs get energy boost to leap long and high, *New Scientist* 179(2403):20, 2003.
24. Burrows, M., Froghopper insects leap to new heights, *Nature* 424(6948):509, 2003.
25. Record jumper, *New Scientist* 179(2406):20, 2003.

cm into the air—if it could be scaled up (although see note 20), it would be like a human jumping over a 210-metre–tall skyscraper.[26]

And froghoppers have relatively short and thin hind legs for jumping. So once again there is a catapult mechanism involved. This locks the legs into the cocked position until sufficient force is built up to break the lock, so they spring open in less than one millisecond. 'The legs snap open and all the force is applied at once', explained Cambridge University's Head of Zoology, Professor Malcolm Burrows, who calculated that froghoppers exert a force up to 414 times their body weight.[27] This is much higher than other jumpers such as fleas (135 times), locusts (8 times) and humans (2–3 times).

Adelaide University's Professor Russell Baudinette admitted, 'It would almost make you believe in God'. He added that the mechanism the bug uses to store the energy needed to propel itself so high is still far from understood.[28]

FLEAS

Fleas can jump a hundred times their body length because they have a catapult system called a *pleural arch* that stores energy until ready to spring. It is also very robust, because a flea can jump 600 times an hour in search of a host. Its secret is the composition of the catapult: the world's best rubber, *resilin* (see also pp. 122–3).[29]

HOW DOES A VENUS FLYTRAP TRAP?[30]

Venus flytraps have long fascinated people all around the world. But it might surprise many that they grow naturally only in a tiny part of the world, in a 1,100-km–long coastal region of North and South Carolina. They live only in humid, wet and sunny bogs, so they can't get many nutrients from the soil. They must obtain nutrition from insects. The plant is named after the pagan Roman goddess of love, and apparently by implication, seduction.

The plant grows to 20–30 cm tall, produces a round cluster of small white flowers, and leaves 8–15 cm long. The leaves include the traps which can quickly fold on their midline to snap shut on an unwary insect when it brushes against the trigger hairs.

26. So why are they not injured when they land as we would be if we fell from that height? It's physically straightforward: if you were scaled down to 1/10th of your height, your surface area would be 1/100th but your mass would be only 1/1000th of its present value. Air resistance depends on area, while gravity on mass which depends on volume, so the ratio of air resistance to gravity would be far greater. Because of this natural 'parachuting' effect, it would have a much lower terminal velocity, or the maximum speed that can be reached in free-fall. So it is not surprising that small animals can easily survive falls that would kill a man.

27. Amos, J., Garden insect is jump champion, <news.bbc.co.uk/2/hi/science/nature/3110719.stm>, *BBC News Online*, 2 September 2003.

28. Macey, R., Super bug way ahead in leaps and bounds, *Sydney Morning Herald*, 31 July 2003, p. 3.

29. Building near-perfect rubber, <www.future.org.au/news_2005/nov/building.html>, *Future Materials News*, November/December 2005.

30. After Sarfati, J., Venus flytrap: Ingenious mechanism still baffles Darwinists, *Creation* 29(4):36–37, 2007; <creationontheweb.com/flytrap>.

Then the trap snaps shut faster than we can blink, in about a tenth of a second.[31] The leaf then secretes a red sap that digests the insect in about 10 days, and opens up again when finished. After catching and digesting three or four insects, the trap withers. Matt Arnold from the UK, who is an expert on carnivorous plants, points out further ingenuity:

'The VFT begins the closing mechanism only when a creature touches two of the six hairs, or one hair twice within 20 seconds, thus helping to prevent false closing of the trap due to, say, falling plant matter.

'Should a false trigger occur, the trap will close, but not completely and will open again within 24 hours for 'business'. It takes a creature to continually trigger the hairs to cause the trap to completely seal shut and move to the digestive juice excretion stage. Thus insects that are very small will be able to escape through gaps between the teeth of the trap and the plant doesn't waste energy by eating only a 'snack', saving itself for a larger 'main course' which is worthy of the whole digestive process.'[32]

Until recently, scientists had not worked out how the trap works. But now, with a high-speed camera and clever mathematics, a team led by Lakshminarayanan Mahadevan of Harvard University has shown how.[33] The leaf changes from convex (outward-curving) to concave (inward-curving) when the trap is sprung. These researchers showed that the trap works somewhat like the way that a tennis ball cut in half can quickly flip inside out when pushed beyond a certain energy barrier.[31] This elegant geometrical model makes accurate predictions..

With the flytraps, the snapping depends entirely on finely tuned geometry. If a certain ratio is too small,[34] the trap will close too smoothly and not snap; if too large, then the energy barrier is too high and the leaf will take too long to snap and not trap the insect. Closure starts when the insect brushes the trigger hairs, forcing a tiny amount of water into the leaf, quickly taking it past the energy barrier. Also, the succulent leaf has lots of water between the cells, and this quickly damps vibrations that would cause damage in the long term.

Even Darwin wrote a book about plants that catch insects, and called the Venus flytrap 'one of the most wonderful in the world.'[35] The lead researcher said, 'Our study still leaves us baffled about one

31. How a Venus flytrap snaps up its victims, *New Scientist* **185**(2484):17, 2005.
32. Arnold, M., letter to *Creation* **30**(2):5, 2008; referring to *The Savage Garden* by Peter D'Amato.
33. Forterre, Y., *et al.*, How the Venus flytrap snaps, *Nature* **433**(7024):421–425, 2005.
34. A dimensionless geometric parameter $\alpha = L^4\kappa^2/h^2$, where L is leaf size, κ is curvature and h is thickness. Below a critical value $\alpha_c \sim 0.8$, the leaf closes smoothly; above it, it snaps rapidly.
35. Darwin, C., *Insectivorous Plants*, Murray, London, 1875.

question that motivated him—how did this mechanism evolve?'[31] and called plants 'nature's ultimate hydraulic engineers.'[33] Of course, there is no reason to believe they evolved at all!

Indeed, human designers are learning from this amazing plant—as we do from so many different examples in nature.[36]

PLANKTON'S POWERFUL POGO[37]

An actual pond-scum organism has an incredibly powerful spring for its size. A single-celled creature called *Vorticella convallaria* attaches itself to various things by a stalk called a spasmoneme. Back in 1676, the inventor of the microscope, Anton van Leeuwenhoek, noted that the stalk contracted sharply when the creature was disturbed.

Danielle France of the Massachusetts Institute of Technology studied this more closely.[38] The spasmoneme contracts like a stretched telephone lead springing back into its coiled shape. France showed that it can even contract against an acceleration of 10,000 g (i.e. 10,000 times the acceleration due to gravity). Thus weight-for-weight, it is more powerful than a car's engine.

This nano-superspring contains six proteins called centrins. Calcium ions from the cell trigger these, especially one called 'Centrin 5'.

France's team is trying to build artificial nano-supersprings from centrins, and believes they could be part of 'miniature probes that would deliver drugs deep inside the body'.

So 'pond scum', contrary to the popular evolutionary stereotype of its being 'primitive', is anything but 'primitive'.

BUNCHBERRY'S 'BANG'[39]

High-speed video cameras (taking 10,000 pictures per second) have catapulted the bunchberry dogwood plant (*Cornus canadensis*) into the 'natural catapult' record books. Researchers have shown that the bunchberry flower can open its petals, catapulting its pollen into the air, in *under 0.4 milliseconds*![40,41] That's faster than the leap of spittle bugs / froghoppers (0.5–1.0 milliseconds),[24,19] the strike of the mantis shrimp (2.7 milliseconds),[15,12] the opening of *Impatiens* / 'touch-me-not' fruits (2.8–5.8 milliseconds),[41] the strike

36. Venus Flytrap inspired lenses may lead to new adhesives, optics, coatings, *ScienceDaily*, 2007; <www.sciencedaily.com/releases/2007/11/071109212442.htm>.
37. .After Sarfati, J., Plankton's powerful pogo, <creationontheweb.com/pogo>, 1 August 2006, which includes an animated representation.
38. Anon., Whiplash spring hurls plankton to engineering fame, *New Scientist* **188**(2530):12, 2005.
39. After Catchpoole, D., Bunchberry bang! <creationontheweb.com/bunchberry>, 2007.
40. Angell, S., Professors record the world's fastest plant, Oberlin College News & Features, <www.oberlin.edu/news-info/05may/expflower.html>, 2006. This page features two videos filmed with high-speed cameras.
41. Edwards, J. *et al.*, A record-breaking pollen catapult, *Nature* **435**(7039):164, 2005.

of a chameleon's tongue (50 milliseconds),[3,1] and the snap of Venus flytraps (100 milliseconds).[33,30]

It happens this way. As the flowers burst open, the petals quickly (within the first 0.2 milliseconds) separate and flip back, out of the way of the pollen-bearing stamens. The stamens then unfurl and accelerate at 2,400 times that due to gravity—approximately 800 times the force astronauts experience during take-off—catapulting the pollen granules into the air.

The researchers explained that the key to this incredible launch power is in the design of the stamens: 'Bunchberry stamens are designed like miniature medieval trebuchets ...'.[41] (A trebuchet is a specialized projectile-launcher used in medieval wars.[42]) A flexible 'hinge' attaches the payload (pollen in the anther) to the throwing arm (filament) at its tip. After the petals open, the bent filaments unfold, releasing elastic energy, and the rotation of the anther about the filament tip accelerates pollen to its maximum vertical speed then releases it, flinging the pollen upward.[41]

It defies logic that each of the floral components could have come together in working synchrony through step-by-step evolution. 'Petals open independently of stamen activity,'[41] the researchers point out—but why would there have been a need for rapid petal opening if the fully-functioning stamen 'trebuchet' was not already in place? Conversely, a rapid-fire pollen launcher would be useless if the petals didn't spring open in time.

CHAPTER 7

STICKINESS

Some creatures have an amazing ability to stick to surfaces. Many of their diverse methods have only recently been discovered, including exquisite microscopic structures to take advantage of short-range chemical forces, hydraulic machinery, and glues.

GECKO FEET[1]

It's quite a sight to see geckos, small tropical lizards, running up and down walls and across ceilings, without any trouble. But what makes their feet stick? Several plausible ideas have been disproved:

Tessa Hatfield, <sxc.hu>

- **Suction?** Suction cups work because air pressure on one side is no longer counterbalanced if there is a vacuum on the other. Because normal air pressure is 100 kPa, or 14 pounds per square inch, suction can be very effective. But gecko's feet can stick in a vacuum where there is no air pressure, so suction cannot be the reason.
- **Electrostatic attraction?** This is the attraction between electrically charged objects, for example a plastic comb rubbed with cloth can pick up small pieces of paper. But when researchers zapped the surrounding air with x-rays to form charged molecules (ions), which would cause any charge to leak away, the feet still stuck.
- **Ordinary glue?** There are no skin glands to produce any.
- **Friction?** Keratin, the protein in skin, is too slippery.
- **Interlocking between rough surfaces?** Geckos can even stick to polished glass.

The best explanation seems to be that the geckos' feet can exploit the weak short-range bonds between molecules,[2] that is, they stick via *van der Waals* (vdW) *forces.*[3] But for such weak forces to work, there must be an extraordinarily close and large contact area between

---

1.	After Sarfati, J., Great gecko glue? *Creation* **23**(1):54–55, 2000; <creationontheweb.com/gecko>.
2.	Autumn, K. *et al.*, Adhesive force of a single gecko foot hair, *Nature* **405**(6787):681–681, 2000; perspective by Gee, H., Gripping feat, same issue, p. 631.
3.	VdW forces are attractions between permanent or temporary dipoles in atoms or molecules, and are the reason that even gases like helium liquefy when cold enough. They are much weaker than bonds holding atoms together in a molecule, and the attraction energy decreases markedly with distance—inversely proportional to the 6th power. That's why very fine structures are needed to make use of them.

foot and surface, so that enough individual weak forces can add up to a very strong force.

Under an electron microscope, researchers found that the feet have very fine hairs *(setae),* about $1/10^{th}$ of a millimetre (4 thousandths of an inch) long and packed at 5,000 per square mm (three million per square inch). In turn, the end of each seta has about 400–1,000 branches ending in a spatula-like structure about 0.2–0.5 μm ($<1/50,000^{th}$ inch) long. These *spatulae* provide the necessary contact area.[4]

With special instruments,[5] a team of biologists and engineers from several American universities, led by Kellar Autumn, analyzed a seta from the foot of a Tokay gecko (*Gekko gecko*). The foot pad has an area of about 100 mm² (0.16 sq. inch) and can produce 10 N of adhesive force (enough to support two pounds). But they showed that an individual seta had an attractive force 10 times stronger than expected. In fact, the force on one seta is strong enough to support an ant's weight, while a million could support a small child. So the gecko has plenty of attractive force to spare. This means it can handle the rough, irregular surfaces of its natural habitat.

Actually, the attractive force is far greater when the seta is gently pressed into the surface and then pulled along. The force also changes with the angle the hair is attached to the surface, so that the seta can detach at about 30°. The gecko exploits these elaborate properties with its 'unusually complex behaviour'[2] of uncurling its toes when attaching and unpeeling while detaching. This all means that the gecko can not only stick properly with each step, but can also avoid getting stuck, and all without using much energy.

Confirming van der Waals forces

Autumn later fine-tuned his previous work by providing confirmation that vdW forces were responsible, as opposed to other types of attraction.[6] That is, he wanted to rule out other types of attraction such as capillary attraction of water to a surface or a strongly polar surface. So he tested geckos on both a hydrophobic (water-repellent) and hydrophilic (water-loving) surface and found that the traction was strong each time. The only type of attraction in common to both these surfaces is vdW. Also, for 30 years it has been known that geckos can't stick to Teflon (polytetrafluoroethene), and this makes sense under Autumn's theory because Teflon has very weak vdW forces.[7]

---

4. The original *Creation* magazine article (Ref. 1) published some fascinating photographs, thanks to one-off permission from the head gecko researcher, Dr Kellar Autumn. Those photos and more can be seen on his website <www.lclark.edu/~autumn/private/u38j47a0t/images.html>.

5. '[A] micromachined, dual axis piezoresistive cantilever'.

6. Autumn, K. *et al.*, Evidence for van der Waals adhesion in gecko setae, *Proc. Nat. Acad. Sci. USA* **99**(19):12252–12256, 2002; 10.1073/pnas.192252799; <www.pnas.org/cgi/content/abstract/192252799v1?ijkey=seqJIlhQKZwtk>.

7. A Teflon surface has very weak vdW forces because the fluorine atoms bonded to the carbon chain have very tightly bound electrons. This means they are very hard to polarize, or form the dipoles needed for vdW

How sticky gecko feet keep clean[8]

Another amazing feature is that the gecko's feet are self-cleaning—unlike adhesive tape, to which dirt easily sticks, rendering it useless. Autumn and his colleagues have shown why.

They coated the gecko feet with dirt, yet it sloughed off completely within five steps on a clean surface. It's all to do with the geometry of the fine hairs. The particles are too small to be in contact with enough hairs to overcome the attraction to any surface. So the hairs, in effect, repel the particles towards the surface.[9]

Autumn 'is convinced the possibilities are infinite. Imagine bandages that leave no residue. Gecko-inspired climbing equipment. Cellular phones that never shatter.'[10]

One evolutionist said: 'It's great to look at how evolution has solved mechanical problems'.[11] But he never stated how evolution, via chance mutations and natural selection, could have produced the complex foot structure as well as the movement pattern needed to use the structure properly. For example, there was no explanation of how half-formed setae and spatulae and an imperfect movement would benefit the animal and thus be selected for. This seems more like blind faith for people who have ruled out a Designer by decree.

The researchers commented that designing such a structure is 'beyond the limits of human technology',[2] especially finding a material that can be split so finely 1,000 times. If the structure is 'beyond the limits of human technology', then it's reasonable to believe that it was designed by One whose intelligence is beyond our own. This conclusion will not be overturned if in the future someone manages to design an adhesive based on this design (see next section).

They also pointed out that the 'natural technology of gecko foot hairs can provide biological inspiration for future design of a remarkably effective adhesive'.[2] The researchers also commented: 'Geckos can do things that we just can't do with current robotics and adhesive technology.'[12]

So not only can we not design anything as complex as the gecko's foot, human designers are learning new things from it. This speaks of a Master Designer of the foot, who programmed the complex 'recipe' for the foot as well as the movement patterns into the gecko's DNA.

forces (Ref. 2). That's why Teflon is so slippery and chemically unreactive.
8. After: Gecko 'glue', *Creation* 27(3):9, 2005.
9. Hansen, W.R. and Autumn, K., Evidence for self-cleaning in gecko setae, *Proc. Nat. Acad. Sci. USA* **102**(2):385–389, 11 January 2005 | doi:10.1073/pnas.0408304102; <www.pnas.org/cgi/reprint/0408304102v1>.
10. O'Connor, A., Grip Minus Grime: Consider the Gecko, *New York Times*, 4 January 2005.
11. Bruce Jayne, a functional morphologist, cited in: Pennisi, E., Geckos climb by the hairs of their toes, *Science* **288**(5472):1717–1718, 2000.
12. Autumn, K., cited in *San Francisco Chronicle*, p. A4, 19 June 2000.

Gecko foot inspires adhesives[13]

Engineer Metin Sitti, of Carnegie Mellon University in Pittsburgh, USA, has managed to duplicate the gecko foot surface structure to some extent.[14] He used a very fine nanoprobe and an electron microscope to make a tiny wax mould for a resin, which solidified to form artificial hairs. Sitti points out that the shape and orientation of the hairs is important for their function. His artificial hairs are not yet strong enough to support the weight of a human, but the researchers are continually improving their technology. He aims to make robots for planetary exploration that could climb over any surface.[14]

Andre Geim, of the University of Manchester, leading a team of scientists from the UK and Russia, prepared a self-cleaning adhesive tape modelled on the gecko's foot.[15] Their tape,[16] with a contact area of only 0.5 cm² on glass, could bear a load of more than 100 grams.[17] However, the tape is not durable enough to attach and detach more than a few times, unlike the real gecko's feet. The researchers proposed using a more durable material—that which the real ones are made of, keratin.[17]

If they did, then gloves and shoes made of this might enable a real Spiderman (or should that be Geckoman?) to climb up walls of almost any surface. However, this would require training, to match the gecko's movement patterns, and one must wonder whether humans could manage this. And a planet-exploring robot would need this programmed into it. So far, the artificial gecko skin seems good only for attaching things in place.[18]

Researchers at the University of Akron, Ohio, made another gecko-inspired adhesive . They used bundles of carbon nanotubes, and managed to exceed the stickiness of the live gecko.[19]

Modelling the gecko hair

Further research into the gecko's properties comes from modelling larger replicas that stick via magnetism rather than vdW forces. This would only be useful for sticking to magnetic surfaces, but this modelling is far more manageable because the replicas are made of nylon and are 2 cm long. However, this can provide

13. After Sarfati, J., Gecko foot design—could it lead to a real 'spiderman'? *Creation* **26**(1):22–23, 2003; <creationontheweb.com/geckoman>.
14. Graham-Rowe, D., Fancy a walk on the ceiling? *New Scientist* **178**(2395):15, 2003.
15. Geim, A.K. *et al.*, Microfabricated Adhesive Mimicking Gecko Foot-Hair, *Nature Materials* 2:461–463, 2003 | doi:10.1038/nmat917; <http://onnes.ph.man.ac.uk/nano/Publications/Naturemat_2003.pdf >.
16. The tape had fibres 2 microns long, with a diameter of around 0.5 microns and spaced 1.6 microns apart, on a film of polyimide 5 microns thick. Geim and his colleagues used the advanced nanotechnology methods of electron-beam lithography and dry etching in oxygen plasma.
17. Kalaugher, L., 'Gecko tape' sticks with polymer fibres, *Physics Web*, <http://physicsweb.org/article/news/7/6/4>, 2003.
18. A more recent proposal comes from Nicola Pugno of the Polytechnic University of Turin. He proposes a branching structure of smaller and smaller carbon nanotubes to imitate the setae in geckos, as well as cables of nanotubes to imitate spider silk. Palmer, J.D., Gecko power could turn you into a spider, *New Scientist* **194**(2601):26, 2007.
19. Ge, L. *et al.*, Carbon nanotube-based synthetic gecko tapes, *Proc. Nat. Acad. Sci. USA*, 10.1073/pnas.0703505104; 2007.

useful information on the working of the gecko hair itself, in both sticking and detaching efficiently. A number of useful properties were identified, e.g. the hairs were flexible enough for compliance with rough surfaces, enabling greater contact; stiff enough for good leverage for easier detachment, a triangular rhomboidal shape of the 'footprint' that maximizes load while minimizing the peak forces needed for release, and the peeling ability where a group of hairs can be released one at a time.[20]

HOW SPIDER FEET STICK TO SURFACES[21]

Research since 'geckoman' of the previous section has shown that 'spiderman' is appropriate after all—some spiders use exactly the same principle as the geckos.

Antonia Kesel at the Institute for Technical Zoology and Bionics in Bremen and colleagues at the University of Zurich analyzed the feet of a jumping spider, *Evarcha arcuata*, under a powerful electron microscope.[22] The spiders cling to rough surfaces with claws on their feet. But on smooth surfaces, they attach with the claw tuft (scopula) on all eight legs. Like the gecko, this tuft has tiny hairs called setae. These are in turn covered by even tinier hairs called setules, whereas in the gecko the setae are subdivided into tiny spatulae.

Like gecko spatulae, the spider setules bond to almost any surface with vdW forces. *Evarcha arcuata* has over 600 thousand setules in contact with the surface, so there is a huge contact area.[23] This means the total attractive force is strong enough to support 160 times its own weight.[24]

But this is not enough—it would do the spider no good to have this amazing foot if it could only stick—it must also unstick quickly. As explained earlier, the gecko manages this with unpeeling its toes while detaching, but more research is needed on how the spider manages to detach quickly.[22] A later suggestion is that the spider lifts its leg in a way that setules can detach in turn, not all at once, so the required force is not too great.[25]

Kesel hopes that their research will help develop strong post-it notes that could stick even to wet or greasy surfaces, and to help astronauts stick to the wall of a spacecraft.[26]

20. Berengueres, J., Saito, S. and Tadakuma, K., Structural properties of a scaled gecko foot hair, *Bioinspiration and Biomimetics* **2**:1–8, 2007; doi:10.1088/1748-3182/2/1/001.

21. After Sarfati, J., Spectacular spider stickiness, *Creation* **27**(4):54–55, 2005; <creationontheweb.com/spiderstick>.

22. Kesel, A.B., Martin, A. and Seidl, T., Adhesion measurements on the attachment devices of the jumping spider *Evarcha arcuata*, *J. Exp. Biol.* **206**:2733–2738, 2003.

23. A single setule has a mean contact area of 1.7×10^5 nm². *E. arcuata* has about 624,000 setules in all legs combined, so the contact area is 1.06×10^{11} nm².

24. A single setule can produce an adhesive force (Fa) of 38.1 nN perpendicular to a surface. So the total Fa from all 624,000 setules is 23.8 mN. The spider's body mass is 15.1 mg so its weight is only 0.148 mN, $1/160^{th}$ of the force of all setules combined.

25. Spiders make best ever Post-it notes, *Institute of Physics*, <physics.iop.org/IOP/Press/PR2904.html>, 2004.

26. Dumé, B., Spiders get a grip, *Physics Web*, < physicsweb.org/article/news/8/4/9>, 2004.

MOSQUITOES: STICKY AS A GECKO AND SUPER WATER-STRIDER

A 2007 *Nature* article asked:
'What's as sticky as a gecko and walks on water better than a water strider? According to Cheng Wei Wu of Dalian University of Technology in China and co-workers, the answer is a mosquito.'[27]

These researchers studied mosquito legs under the electron microscope. They discovered that the mosquito feet were covered with setae that work much like those of geckos, enabling them to stick to any surface.

The legs are covered with specially shaped scales that repel water strongly. They form evenly spaced tiny ridges running down the legs, and equally tiny but more tightly packed cross ribs.

The fine structure of the legs and feet mean that the mosquito can also take off and land from water safely. Each leg has the water-supporting force of about 23 times the body weight of the mosquito, better than a water strider's leg that can support 'only' 15 times its body weight.[28]

The general principle of vdW attractions from fine hairs has now been shown to apply to a number of different insects. Armed with this information, materials engineers have developed a micropatterned polymer tape modelled on the foot pad surface of certain insects.[29,30] Subsequent testing revealed the vastly superior performance of the 'bio-inspired'[31] tape, relative to a commercially-available pressure-sensitive adhesive tape.

Compared to a flat PVS tape, the micropatterned tape demonstrated considerably higher adhesion in a peeling test, with a higher pull-off force per unit of apparent contact area.

What's more, the microstructured tape 'is less sensitive to contamination by dust particles than the flat tape or a regular scotch tape'. And even if the 'insect tape' is contaminated, it can be washed with a soap solution in water, *completely recovering its initial adhesive properties*.[32]

27.   Biomechanics: Top legs, *Nature* **448**(7151):228–229, 2007.
28.   Wu, C.W. *et al.*, Micronanostructures of the scales on a mosquito's legs and their role in weight support, *Phys. Rev. E* **76**, 017301, 2007 | doi:10.1103/PhysRevE.76.017301.
29.   Gorb, S. *et al.*, Biomimetic mushroom-shaped fibrillar adhesive microstructure, *Journal of the Royal Society Interface* **4**(13):271–275, 2007.
30.   The insect pad surface copied consisted of a pattern of hairs (fibres, pillars) with broad flattened tips and a narrowed flexible region just below the flattened tip. The pillars exhibit a hexagonal distribution pattern—therefore a high packing density.
31.   Gorb, S., Sinha, M., Peressadko, A., Daltorio, K., and Quinn, R., Insects did it first: a micropatterned adhesive tape for robotic applications, *Bioinspiration & Biomimetics* **2**:S117–S125, 2007.
32.   After Catchpoole, D., Walking up walls: Insects inspire a better 'sticky tape', <creationontheweb.com/

HOW ANTS AND BEES STICK[33]

How do ants and bees walk upside down, an essential skill for walking on plants? Not only must their feet be able to stick, but also become unstuck at the right time so they can move quickly. A team led by University of Massachusetts biologist Elizabeth Brainerd has now shown the amazing way they do this, using high-speed photography on honeybees and weaver ants walking on glass, and studying the foot structure under a microscope.[34,35,36]

The foot has a moist pad (*arolium*), which can stick to a surface like wet paper to a window. This is between two claws, shaped like a bull's horns. If the surface is rough, the claws can catch onto a surface, and the arolium is retracted because it's not needed, and is protected from abrasion. But on a smooth surface where the claws can't catch onto a surface, they retract *via* the claw flexor tendon, which also causes the arolium to rotate and extend into position. The tendon also connects to a plate that squeezes a reservoir of 'blood' (hemolymph), forcing the liquid into the arolium to inflate it, so it presses on the surface. When the foot needs to become unstuck, the claw flexor tendon is released, and the arolium and many of the mechanical parts are so elastic that they quickly spring back into place. The same basic mechanism applies to both bees and ants, but they have some differently shaped parts because of their different requirements.

This is a very complex mechanical and hydraulic design, but controlled very simply, without any brain input. This enables high reliability and very fast reaction times. Not surprisingly, this has intrigued designers of miniature robots for medical purposes.

MUSSEL SUPERGLUE

Underwater adhesives play a vital role in shipbuilding and repair, but do not bond indefinitely, as salt water degrades even the strongest of conventional adhesives. So engineers, in their search for underwater superglue, are investigating how mussels can cling onto rocks in some of the world's harshest surf.

To stick to a surface, the common blue mussel, *Mytilus edulis*, secretes a substance comprising modified proteins containing an amino acid called L-DOPA (3,4-**d**ihydr**o**xy-L-**p**henyl**a**lanine).[37] Jonathan Wilker, Mary Sever and their team at Purdue University

stickytape>, 2008.

33. After Sarfati, J., Startling stickiness, *Creation* **24**(2):37, 2002; <creationontheweb.com/stickiness>.
34. Walter Federle, W., *et al.*, Biomechanics of the movable pretarsal adhesive organ in ants and bees, *Proc. Nat. Acad. Sci. USA* **98**(11):6215–6220, 2001.
35. A Sticky Situation For Ants And Bees: UMass Biologist Looks At How These Insects Adhere To Various Surfaces, *University Of Massachusetts At Amherst*, <www.sciencedaily.com/releases/2001/09/010928071138.htm>
36. Schubert, C., Insects deploy sticky feet with precision, *Science News* **159**(2):341, 2001.
37. *Beyond 2000*, <www.beyond2000.com/news/story_395.html>, 2000; *Science News*, 1999, p. 5; Mussel muscle, *Creation* **22**(4):7, 2000.

(West Lafayette, Indiana) discovered that a vital component of the glue is iron ions that the mussel extracts from seawater.[38] The iron causes oxidation of the DOPA units into free radicals, allowing the proteins to cross-link, and the DOPA units to form very strong covalent bonds to the surface on which they attach.[39] In only about a minute, this hardens into an incredibly strong mesh, attaching the mussel to a new surface—even to Teflon. The bonds to the surface add up to such a strong attractive force that the threads will break before it detaches.

In addition to its long-lasting strength in seawater, the 'mussel glue' would offer other advantages over conventional adhesives. It doesn't need high temperatures to bond, and is not poisonous like standard petroleum- and tar-based glues. Wilker said, 'The biological origin of this glue and the ability to stick to nearly all surfaces invite applications such as the development of surgical adhesives.' His supervisor for his National Science Foundation award, chemist Mike Clark, stated:

> 'This discovery could lead to the creation of unusual new materials with designed plasticity, strength, and adhesiveness for household, structural, and biological uses. Perhaps, these properties could even be made dependent upon electrochemical potential thereby creating new vistas for electronic materials.'[40]

WET-DRY ADHESIVE MODELLED ON BOTH GECKOS AND MUSSELS

Researchers have made a 'geckel' nanoadhesive, which they modelled on both the fine structure of the gecko feet and the glue in mussels.[41] This comprised an array of tiny polymer pillars coated in a synthetic polymer, which imitated the adhesive proteins of the mussels. While the gecko type surface on its own was not so effective in water, the 'mussel' coating increased its stickiness almost 15 times, and was re-usable thousands of times without losing its stickiness.

38. Sever, M.J. *et al.*, Metal-mediated cross-linking in the generation of a marine-mussel adhesive. *Angewandte Chemie International Edition* **43**(4):448–450, 2004.
39. Mitchinson, A., Mussel muscle, *Nature* **442**(7105):877–8, 2006.
40. Chamot, J., Chemists crack secrets of nature's super glue, *EurekAlert!* (AAAS) <www.eurekalert.org/pub_releases/2004-01/nsf-ccs010704.php>, **2004.**
41. Lee, H., Lee, B.P. and Messersmith, P.B., A reversible wet/dry adhesive inspired by mussels and geckos, *Nature* **448**(7151):338–341, 2007 | doi:10.1038/nature05968.

CHAPTER 8

MAGNIFICENT MATERIALS

The living world has materials that surpass our own in strength and other properties such as elasticity. Materials scientists are continuing to discover, and learn from, more secrets of nature. One paper summarized, 'Biomimetic materials research is becoming a rapidly growing and enormously promising field.'[1]

CONCH SHELLS: INCREDIBLE TOUGHNESS[2]

The prestigious evolutionary journal *Nature* marvelled at the giant conch shell. It said it is 'one of nature's greatest engineering masterpieces'.[3]

Haplochromis, <wikipedia.org>

The animal grows its shell by first depositing an organic outer layer called the *periostracum*. This forms a base for tiny elongated crystals to grow, pointing at right-angles to the membrane. This layer is only one micron ($\frac{1}{25,000}$ inch) thick. So, more mineral grows on top to a thickness of a few mm.

This has a three-layered criss-crossing structure. It comprises rods of *aragonite*, a form of calcium carbonate ($CaCO_3$), held together by protein glue. This makes a shell with 99% mineral and 1% protein. The rods in each layer line up at 90° to those in the adjoining layer. Further, each rod is composed of even smaller rods, and these comprise rods that are smaller still. And so on, down to individual crystals.[4]

Roberto Ballarini, Material Science Engineer at Case Western Reserve University, investigated the shell's strength. He showed that its arrangement makes it hard for a crack to travel through the entire structure. So although aragonite is very brittle, the architecture means that it is 'one of the toughest brittle-natured composites known to man.' In fact, it's 30 times stronger and about 1,000 times tougher

1. Fratzl, P., Biomimetic materials research: what can we really learn from nature's structural materials? *J. Royal Soc.* **4**(15):637–642, 2007; 10.1098/rsif.2007.0218.
2. After Sarfati, J., Super shells, *Creation* **27**(3):19, 2005; <creationontheweb.com/conch>.
3. Daw, R., Give a shell a break, *Nature* **427**(6976):691, 2004.
4. Ballarini, R., *Cracking the Conch Conundrum: Tough Ceramics at the Seashore,* Distinguished Lecture Series, *Cornell University, 11 February 2003;* <www.tc.cornell.edu/news/events/2003/distinguishedlectures/previous.html>.

(more resistant to fracturing) than the pure mineral.[5] He hopes to be able to copy this structure 'for small electronic hardware to make it tougher and more resilient.'[4]

And the living conch does something no man-made material can do—repair itself. Ballarini's colleague Su Xiao-Wei has shown how the conch repairs holes. Within 24 hours, the conch seals a wound with a transparent membrane. Then it deposits tiny aragonite crystals, forming many fine layers. Only then, after 6–8 days, does the conch deposit the elongated crystals followed by the amazingly tough cross-layered structure.[3]

The repair process requires fine coordination of the organic and mineral layers. Su and colleagues hope that their research will show how to design tough man-made materials. However, they still need to find out how the conch controls this process at the molecular level.

ABALONE ARMOUR[6]

The abalone is a shellfish famous both for its edible flesh and the brilliant colours of its inner shell. The Maori people of New Zealand call it paua (pronounced PAH wa), and make beautiful jewellery from the shells. But materials scientists are interested in its great strength, and hope to learn how to make body armour using its techniques.

Other shells, such as the conch, also use intricately structured composite materials to produce great strength, as shown in the previous section. They are mainly made out of calcium carbonate ($CaCO_3$), with a tiny amount of protein, but it's the way this is arranged that makes the shells so much tougher than pure calcium carbonate could ever be. But the abalone has a different but equally ingenious structure of protein and calcium carbonate.

Abalone growth

The abalone shell is made of two types of calcium carbonate ($CaCO_3$): calcite for the rough outside, and aragonite for the smooth inside,[7] which is also called nacre or mother-of-pearl. Engineering researchers at the University of California, San Diego, have now found out how the abalone's inside shell grows, and why it is so strong.[8] They inserted very thin glass slides into the growing shell, which the abalone accepted as part of the shell, and grew new shell on top. Then they removed them at different time intervals to analyze the material under an electron microscope.

5. Queen conch shell suggests new structure for ceramics, <www.cwru.edu/pubaff/univcomm/conch.htm>, 30 June 2000; based on Kamat, S., Su, X., Ballarini, R. and Heuer, A.H., Structural basis for the fracture toughness of the shell of the conch *Strombus gigas*, *Nature* **405**(6790):1036–1040, 2000.

6. After Sarfati, J., Amazing Abalone Armour, <creationontheweb.com/abalone>, 2006.

7. Calcite is rhombohedral/trigonal while aragonite is orthorhombic.

8. Lin, A. and Meyers, M.A., Growth and structure in abalone shell, *Materials Science and Engineering A* **390**:27–41, 2005.

The animal grows its shell by first depositing a protein layer. Then calcite grows on top of that. Then a number of proteins turn this into aragonite, which would not normally form because it is less stable.[9] These tiny crystals all *align in the same direction*.[10] Then a specially structured protein *stops growth outwards*, otherwise they would form needles.

So instead the crystals grow *sideways* into tiles, stopped only by the neighbouring tiles. Regardless of the size of the abalone, the tiles are all about 0.5 microns thick and 10 microns in diameter. Then a protein layer forms to separate one tile layer from the next. A new layer starts before the previous layer is filled in, which makes the growing shell look like a forest of Christmas trees.[8]

Structure and strength

The tiles end up as irregular stacks, and they refract light to give the typical mother-of-pearl appearance. However, the tile *layers* are regular, and separated by a protein layer about 10–20 microns thick. This protein bonds the layers together strongly, but also allows the tiles within the layer to slip apart. This slippage absorbs the energy of a heavy impact. Man-made laminates (layered materials) lack this slippage, so when a layer breaks, the whole structure is weakened.[11]

The protein layers also have an important part to play. They strongly hinder cracks from going through the shell. Also, although nacre is only 5% protein, this is enough to enable the mineral components to lay down spontaneously. Pupa Gilbert, a physicist at the University of Wisconsin-Madison, said:

> 'Ninety-five percent of the mass of this biomineral is self-assembled, while only 5 percent is actively formed by the organism. It is one of the most efficient mechanisms you can think of.'[12]

Design or chance?

In the first paragraph of their scientific paper,[8] the researchers paid the seemingly compulsory homage to the wonders of evolution by natural selection over millions of years. But the rest of the paper made no mention of how evolution could invent such fine coordination of chemical processes. So evolution provided no insights whatever.

Instead, they analyzed the shell-making as if it were an engineering design for toughness. Indeed, they said, '...even the simplest bio-induced structures are currently impossible to synthesize.'[8] Thus it

---

9. Thompson, J.J. *et al.*, Direct observation of the transition from calcite to aragonite growth as induced by abalone shell proteins, *Biophysical J.* **79**(6):3307–3312, 2000.
10. The c-axes of the crystals are perpendicular to the protein layer.
11. Graham, R., Uncovering secrets of abalone body armor, *PhysOrg.com*, <www.physorg.com/news2694.html>, 2005.
12. Mother-of-pearl—Classic beauty and remarkable strength, *PhysOrg.com*, <www.physorg.com/news102610698.html>, 2007.

makes good practical scientific sense to believe it really was designed by a Master Designer whose ability far outshines our own.

FINGERNAILS: FIBRE ARRANGEMENTS PROVIDE GREAT STRENGTH[13]

Scientists have now identified just what you always wanted to know—why fingernails, when nibbled or torn, tend to tear across the nail rather than downwards towards the nail bed. University of Manchester researcher, Roland Ennos, is a habitual nail biter. Maybe that's why he (along with other researchers) tested the toughness of snippets from students' fingernails.[14] They found it takes twice the energy to cut them lengthwise as it does crosswise.

And that's just as well, says Ennos. 'Otherwise, we would be in agony throughout our lives, because every tear would damage our nail bed, inflicting great pain and incurring infection.'

Fingernails are unique to humans and primates. They not only protect the top of our fingertips, but also help keep the skin at the tips of our fingers in place, making it easier for us to hold and manipulate objects.

Now Ennos and his colleagues analyzing nails under the electron microscope have identified why nails don't tear toward the nail bed. Nails comprise three layers of tissue containing the protein keratin. The central layer was found to have keratin fibres parallel to the half moon at the base of the nail. These stop breaks from running down the nail. The two outer layers have randomly arranged keratin fibres, and they provide strength.

How much strength? 'The energy needed to cut our nails is as much as what's needed for horse's hoofs [*sic*]', says Ennos. 'It's quite amazing.'[15]

So, fingernails are as strong as horses' hooves! Zoologist John Gosline, of the University of British Columbia, has seen the same orientation of cracks in horses' hooves as in human fingernails. 'Nails and hoofs are external structures that experience a mechanically stressful environment', he explains. 'In the case of a horse, a crack in the wrong direction and infection may lead to laming and death.'

SPIDER SILK: THE STRONGEST FIBRE IN THE WORLD[16]

While Kevlar is the 'gold medallist'[17] of man-made fibres because of its bullet-stopping abilities, it's overshadowed in many

13. After Sarfati, J. and Catchpoole, D., Why nail biters don't cry, *Creation* 27(3):36, 2005; <creationontheweb.com/nails>.
14. Sanides, S., Nails and hooves: designed for wear and tears, *The Scientist* 18(4):12, <www.the-scientist.com>, 2nd March 2004.
15. Fingernails have the strength of hooves, *New Scientist*, 181(2433):19, 2004.
16. After Sarfati, J., God's webspinners give chemists free lessons, *Creation* 23(2):20–21, 2001; <creationontheweb.com/spidersilk>.
17. Fox, D., The Spinners, *New Scientist* 162(2183):38–41, 1999.

ways by the humble spiderweb.[17] 'Spider silk is stronger and more elastic than Kevlar, and Kevlar is the strongest man-made fibre', according to Danish spider expert Fritz Vollrath.[18] Dragline silk, the main support for its web, is a hundred times stronger than steel—a cable of silk a little thicker than a garden hose could support the weight of two full Boeing 737 aircraft.[19] It can also stretch to 40% of its length,[17] while the flagelliform silk in web spirals can stretch to over 200%.[19]

Silk in web spirals can stretch to over 200% of its length.[19]

Also, the manufacture of Kevlar requires harsh conditions, including boiling sulfuric acid and leaving dangerous chemicals behind that are expensive to dispose of.[17] But spiders need only ordinary temperatures, and a much milder acid bath produced by special ducts.[18] And spiders can make silk at different speeds—up to 10 times faster when dropping to escape a predator—unlike most industrial chemical processes that would make gunk if the speed was varied by that much. Spider silk is even environmentally friendly—spiders eat their own webs when they are finished with them.[18]

Complexity of fibres

Spider silk owes its amazing strength and elasticity to its 'complexity that makes synthetic fibres seem crude.'[17] Man-made fibres are usually just simple strands of material, but a silk fibre has a core surrounded by concentric layers of nanofibrils (tiny threads). Some layers contain nanofibrils aligned parallel to the axis, while other layers contain nanofibrils coiling like a spiral staircase. The coiled ones allow the silk to be stretched, because they simply straighten up rather than break.

The nanofibrils themselves are very complicated, containing tiny protein crystals in an amorphous (lacking a regular structure) matrix of tangled protein chains. These nanocrystals contain electrical charges that stop the chains from slipping, so providing strength, while the amorphous material is rubbery and allows the fibre to stretch.

Heat resistant

David Knight of Oxford University and the company Oxford Biomaterials tested silk strands of the large orb-weaving spider *Nephila edulis* from -60–150°C (-76–302°F). From icy cold to very hot, the strands could still stretch to at least 20% before breaking.

18. How spiders make their silk, *Discover* **19**(10):34, October 1998.
19. Stokstad, E., Spider genes reveal flexible design, *Science* **270**(5457):1378, 2000.

They did weaken above 150°C, but didn't disintegrate till 370°C (700°F).[20]

Knight suggests that spider silk would make excellent material for stitching nerves and tendons, especially as it can be heat-sterilized first.[21]

Spinning and liquid crystals

Some researchers have tried to make silk by forcing a solution of silk proteins, called spidroin, through tiny holes, but the fibres are less than half as strong as produced by the spider. It seems that the spider produces the high complexity required by making the spidroin go through a liquid crystal phase, where rod-shaped molecules align in parallel (Kevlar manufacture also uses a liquid crystal phase). Christopher Viney of Heriot-Watt University in Edinburgh believes that this enables them to flow more easily, thus saving energy.[17] The liquid state also aligns the protein molecules so they can form the nanocrystals and coiled nanofibrils. This seems to occur in the spider's long converging spinning canal (or S-duct), where water is both squeezed and pumped out. This brings hydrophobic (water-repelling) parts of the proteins to the outside and forms the nanocrystals and enables the fibres to form.

Thomas Scheibel and his team at Technical University of Munich provided further insight into the importance of the hydrophobic (alternatively, lipophilic = fat-friendly) and hydrophilic (water-friendly) properties of the proteins in silk spinning.[22] The crucial step for thread formation involves linking a few proteins into aggregates called *oligomers*, from Greek ολίγος *oligos*, few. The silk protein is also very rich in salt (NaCl), which suppresses oligomerization until needed.[23]

The pH is also crucial. The silk gland is quite alkaline, while the spinning duct is mildly acidic. This is very important: the alkaline conditions remove protons from the tyrosine groups in the proteins, leaving them negatively charged and thus repulsive, which prevents premature clumping.[23]

Could spider silk processing have evolved?

An informative review article in *Nature*[24] covered a number of important issues in detail, e.g., the high strength, stress *vs* strain analysis, the composition of spidroins including some non-essential amino acids, liquid crystal spinning, the particular type of liquid crystal called the nematic phase where the rod-like molecules are aligned parallel to each other (the phase used in image display

20. Y. Yang, *et al.*, Toughness of spider silk at high and low temperatures, *Advanced Materials*, **17**(1):84–88, 2005.
21. Silk surprise, *New Scientist*, **185**(2483):16, 2005.
22. Exler, J.H., Hümmerich, D. and Scheibel, T. The Amphiphilic Properties of Spider Silks Are Important for Spinning, *Angewandte Chemie International Edition* **46**(19), 2007 | doi: 10.1002/anie.200604718.
23. Fascinating Spider Silk, *PhysOrg.com*, <www.physorg.com/news94919225.html>, April 2007.
24. Vollrath, F. and Knight, D., Liquid crystalline spinning of spider silk, *Nature* **410**(6828):541–548, 2001.

devices), the conventional external drawdown used in industrial spinning as well as the advanced internal spinning technology so far not duplicated in man-made processes. The review also discusses how we can learn much from the spider's design, e.g. the hyperbolic geometry of the S-duct so that the material elongates at a constant rate, preventing disclinations (a weakening defect analogous to dislocations in solid crystals). The structural complexity of silk is even greater than previously thought! Alas, there is the usual homage to evolution as the designer without the slightest evidence.

BONES: SELF-REPAIRING GIRDERS[25]

The following is an overview of the main points of this technical section

- Bones are dynamic supports, constantly rebuilding to cope with changing stresses.
- Bone shape is a delicate balance of bone deposition and resorption.
- Bone strength is largely from the mineral hydroxyapatite (HA).
- One vital component for bone growth is the small, highly conserved protein osteocalcin.
- Large fragments of this protein have been found in dinosaur bones 'dated' over 100 million years old, although measured rates of breakdown mean that nothing should have survived that long.
- Vitamin K is essential to modify three amino acid residues of osteocalcin, otherwise it can't bind calcium at all.
- The recent discovery of osteocalcin's crystal structure shows that it binds calcium in exactly the right geometry to add it to a certain crystal face of HA.
- Thus bone construction is irreducibly complex.
- The above points collectively explain why there is no fossil intermediate between invertebrate and vertebrate.

Bones rebuild to match stresses

Bones provide most of the structure and support in vertebrates. They are analogous to girders in the building industry, but bones have a huge advantage over man-made girders, in that they are constantly rebuilding and redesigning themselves to cope with changing stress directions.[26]

This involves a fine balance of the activity of bone-depositing cells (*osteoblasts*) and bone-resorbing cells (*osteoclasts*). It's been recently shown that thyroid-stimulating hormone (TSH), best known for what its name says—stimulating the production of hormones in the thyroid gland—has an important role in this, too. It oversees both types of cells—without it, bones have osteoporosis in some parts (too little bone, so very weak), and are too dense in other patches.[27]

---

25. After Sarfati, J., Bone building: perfect protein, *J. Creation* **18**(1):11–12, 2004; <creationontheweb.com/bone>.

26. Wieland, C., Bridges and bones, girders and groans, *Creation* **12**(2):20–24, 1990; <creationontheweb.com/bones>.

27. Tromans, A., Foreman in the bone factory, *Nature* **425**(6961):909, 2003.

Osteocalcin and hydroxyapatite

The strength of bones mainly comes from the hexagonal mineral hydroxyapatite (HA, formula $Ca_5(PO_4)_3OH$).[28] But this must be built up in the right patterns. In vertebrate bones, this is built up with a special protein called *osteocalcin* (OC). It is a small protein, 49 amino acids long (5.8 kDa), and is 'highly conserved', meaning that its sequence is almost identical among vertebrates. Human OC has the sequence Tyr-Leu-Tyr-Gln-Trp-Leu-Gly-Ala-Pro-Val-Pro-Tyr-Pro-Asp-Pro-Leu-Gla-Pro-Arg-Arg-Gla-Val-Cys-Gla-Leu-Asn-Pro-Asp-Cys-Asp-Glu-Leu-Ala-Asp-His-Ile-Gly-Phe-Gln-Glu-Ala-Tyr-Arg-Arg-Phe-Tyr-Gly-Pro-Val.[29]

Like all proteins, the instructions for OC are in the DNA (see p. 160 ff) but there is more to its manufacture than simply decoding / translating the code and synthesizing the OC on a ribosome. Firstly, the transcription (DNA→mRNA) is regulated by 1,25-dihydroxy-Vitamin D_3, one reason that Vitamin D is so important for healthy bones. It is then first decoded (translated) as a preproosteocalcin, 98 amino acids long. This comprises three parts: a 23-residue signal protein that is cleaved during translation, a 26-residue target propeptide, and the 49-residue mature protein.[30]

Even this does not complete the process; this requires another vitamin—K. Vitamin K_1 or phylloquinone, best known for its vital role in the blood clotting cascade, is an essential co-factor in γ-carboxylation. That is, the specific glutamyl residues (Glu, from the amino acid glutamic acid) at positions 17, 21 and 24 have a second carboxyl group (COOH) added to form γ-carboxyglutamyl residues (Gla). This changes the structure and stabilizes the α-helical portion of the protein.[30]

Even now, the OC protein is fairly shapeless. But when OC meets calcium ions, it folds to a special structure.[31] The two carboxyl groups on the γ-carboxyglutamyl residues *chelate*[32] to the Ca^{2+} ions, as shown by Fourier-Transform Infrared spectroscopy (FTIR).[33] There was no spectral change when Ca^{2+} was added to decarboxylated OC (i.e. as it would be before converted by Vitamin K), showing that the carboxylation is necessary for binding.[33]

Amazingly (for those who believe in millions of years), enough osteocalcin to produce an immune reaction was found in bones of

---

28. Space group $P6_3/m$ (C_{6h}^2), unit cell dimensions a = b = 9.432 Å, c = 6.881 Å; Kay, M.I., Young, R.A. and Posner, A.S., The crystal structure of hydroxyapatite, *Nature* 204:1050–1052, 1964.

29. American Peptide Company, Inc., Osteocalcin (1-49), Human <www.americanpeptide.com/>, 2002.

30. Lee, A.J., Hodges, S. and Eastell, R., Measurement of osteocalcin, *Annual of Clinical Biochem.* 37:432–436, 2000; <www.leeds.ac.uk/acb/annals/annals_pdf/July00/432.PDF>.

31. Hoang, Q.Q. *et al.*, Bone recognition mechanism of porcine osteocalcin from crystal structure, *Nature* 425(6961):977–980, 2003.

32. To chelate means one ligand bonds in two or more places to one metal ion, like a claw (Greek χηλή *chēlē*).

33. Mizuguchi, M., *et al.*, Fourier-Transform Infrared Spectroscopic Study of Ca^{2+}-Binding to Osteocalcin, *Calcified Tissue Int.* 69(6):337–342, 2001; <www.springerlink.com/app/home/contribution.asp? wasp=343 91yd8qh3wng498eeq&referrer=parent&backto=searcharticlesresults,9,353>.

an *Iguanodon* 'dated' to 120 Ma,[34] yet proteins could not last for millions of years. And the fact that it's a bone protein shows it can't be contamination from outside.

Osteocalcin's crystal structure

Now, pig OC's crystal structure has been discovered, using a type of X-ray diffraction. This provides new insights into how finely designed it must be to work.[31] The active site has a negatively charged region that binds the positively charged Ca^{2+} ions. Five Ca^{2+} ions are coordinated by three special Gla residues and an Asp at position 30. But not in just any old way—five calcium ions are bound in the same arrangement as in the exposed face of a HA crystal, parallel to the c axis. So the OC can dock on the HA and add the calcium, and thus grow the crystal, making the bone grow in the area needed. To do this, OC's building blocks, the amino acids, must be in a very precise sequence. For example, there is a tightly packed core involving the hydrophobic residues Leu 16, Leu 32, Phe 38, Ala 41, Tyr 42, Phe 45 and Tyr 46. There is also hydrogen bonding to stabilize the connection between different α-helices, Asn 26 in the helix α1– α2 linker and Tyr 46 in α3. The helices α1 and α2 form a V-shaped arrangement stabilized by a disulphide bridge between Cys 23 and Cys 29.

SPONGE'S FIBRE-OPTICS[35]

Optical fibres are very fine fibres of glass about 120 microns in diameter (a human hair is 50–70 microns thick). They comprise a core plus a cladding made from a different type of glass, so if light is shone into one end of the fibre, the cladding reflects light back into the fibre without escaping (called total internal reflection). Therefore they act as wave guides which can transmit light along the length of the fibre.[36]

Such fibres have revolutionized the telecommunications industry, because they can conduct signals of voice or computer data in the form of light pulses for 50 km without a repeater to boost signals. While copper wires conduct the same information (but in the form of electrical impulses), optical fibres have many advantages. They are much lighter, require less power, can carry far more information, are immune to electromagnetic interference and are harder to hack into without being detected.[36]

34. Embery G., *et al.*, Identification of proteinaceous material in the bone of the dinosaur Iguanodon, *Connect Tissue Res.* **44 Suppl. 1:**41–6, 2003; <www.ncbi.nlm.nih.gov/entrez/query.fcgi?cmd=Retrieve&db=PubMe d&list_uids=12952172&dopt=Abstract>. The abstract says: 'an early eluting fraction was immunoreactive with an antibody against osteocalcin.'
35. After Sarfati, J., Fantastic fibre-optics—sponge's super spicules, *Creation*, **26**(2):52, 2004; < www. creationontheweb.com/sponge>.
36. *Fibre Optic Technology: Introduction*, Bell College of Technology, UK, <http://floti.bell.ac.uk/ MathsPhysics/introduction.htm>, 2003.

The deep-sea sponge *Euplectella*, or the Venus flower basket, grows attractive glassy fibres, called spicules. Now, researchers led by Joanna Aizenberg (who had also discovered the brittlestar eye—see p. 34) have shown that these are superb optical fibres.[37]

The sponge's fibres are 5–15 cm long, and 40–70 microns in diameter, about the thickness of human hair, so are finer than man-made fibres. They have an elaborate structure: a core of pure silica glass 2 microns in diameter surrounding an ultra-thin organic filament, and a finely layered shell.

The shell works as optical cladding just like in man-made fibres, making them excellent wave guides. They conduct light very well because they contain small amounts of sodium ions. The sponge adds these ions in a controlled way using organic molecules at ordinary temperatures. But artificial optic fibres are made at temperatures high enough to partially melt glass, and adding controlled amounts of sodium ions is a real challenge because it makes the fibres lose their glassiness.[37]

The sponge's fibres are far more flexible than man-made ones—you can even tie a knot with them without them breaking. Man-made fibres break because once a small crack starts it spreads easily through a brittle material like glass. This is a major cause of outages in commercial optical fibres, and requires costly repairs.[38] But the boundaries between the fine layers of the shell of the sponge fibres stop the crack from spreading.[37]

Geri Richmond of the University of Oregon said, 'It's such a wonderful example of how exquisite nature is as a designer and builder of complex systems.'[39] Aizenberg herself said, 'We're in the stone age compared to nature.'[39]

RESILIN: INSECTS' SUPER-RUBBER

The stretchiest rubber in the world, resilin, comes from insects. It is responsible for the super-jumping abilities of fleas and the deafening chirps of cicadas, and also has an important role in insect wings. In fact, it was first found in dragonfly wings about 40 years ago.

Resilin must also be stable enough to last an insect's lifetime, because the adult insect does not manufacture it. Chris Elvin, a molecular biologist at CSIRO Livestock Industries in Queensland, Australia, stated:

Dorte Jensen, <sxc.hu>

---

37. Sundar, V.C., Yablon, A.D., Grazul, J.L., Ilan, M. and Aizenberg, J., Fibre-optical properties of a glass sponge, *Nature* **424**(6951):899–890, 2003.

38. Grad, P., Inspirational sponge, *Engineers Australia* **75**(11):30, 2003.

39. Cited in: McCall, W., Sponge has natural glass fiber optics, *San Francisco Chronicle*, 8 August 2003, p. A2.

'The resilin gene is turned off in adult insects, so there is no way of renewing their supplies. If you consider the number of contraction and extension cycles that resilin must accomplish during the course of an insect's life, the fatigue lifetime of the material is extraordinary.

'Spinal disc implants need to last for 100 million cycles, which is roughly how many times we move our back in a lifetime, and we know resilin can last that long.'[40]

Now Elvin's team has reproduced this super-rubber.[41] However, they didn't really invent anything, but in effect copied already-existing instructions. The resilin gene had been found within the fruit fly genome in 2001, so they copied the gene into common gut bacteria, *Escherichia coli*. Then the bacteria were made to follow the instructions to produce the raw protein.

But this is not enough—the resilin gene controls only the amino acid sequences of the protein chains, but they must also be linked together in very specific ways to produce the super-rubber. So insects require not only the instructions for the protein, but also instructions for processing the proteins. As one article said, 'The living world puts human engineering to shame.'[42] Elvin's team used bright light with a ruthenium metal catalyst to make the proteins link in the right way.

This artificial resilin was as good as the natural insect rubber. It was 'almost perfectly elastic', with only 3% of the energy stored in stretching lost as heat when the resilin contracts. By comparison, even polybutadiene 'superballs' lose 20% of their energy with each bounce. And resilin can 'stretch to three times its unstressed length without breaking.'[42] Elvin states that this is 'as close to a perfect rubber as is found anywhere.'[42]

SUMMARY

A recent paper in the *Journal of the Royal Society* (UK) pointed out that materials scientists are learning from the materials in nature, and this knowledge is growing quickly:

'Nature provides a wide range of materials with different functions and which may serve as a source of bio-inspiration for the materials scientist. ... A thorough analysis of structure-function relations in natural tissues must precede the engineering of

---

40. Building near-perfect rubber, <www.future.org.au/news_2005/nov/building.html>, *Future Materials News*, Nov./Dec. 2005.
41. Elvin, C.M., *et al.*, Synthesis and properties of crosslinked recombinant pro-resilin, *Nature* **437**(7061): 999–1002, 2005.
42. Nature's super-rubber made in lab, *ScienceNow*, <http://sciencenow.sciencemag.org/cgi/content/full/2005/1012/1>, 2005.

new bio-inspired materials. There are, indeed, many opportunities for lessons from the biological world: on growth and functional adaptation, about hierarchical structuring, on damage repair and self-healing. Biomimetic materials research is becoming a rapidly growing and enormously promising field.'[1]

PLANT POWER

The best known features of design involve animals. But without plants, animals would not exist. Plants capture energy from the sun to make food, and this is the basis of the food chain.

Recent discoveries on this process, photosynthesis, point to its intricate design and irreducible complexity. The process involves splitting the water molecule, and this occurs in four steps; if one step is missing, the process cannot work at all. Human designers are researching plants to try to develop ways of capturing solar energy as efficiently.

Another important design feature is flat leaves. We don't usually think about the flatness of leaves, but they maximize the collection of energy. And growing a flat surface from a point is surprisingly difficult, because the natural tendency is growing in a curve. Flatness is produced by balancing opposite curvatures.

IMPORTANCE OF PLANTS: PHOTOSYNTHESIS[1]

Even now, plants are the basis of the food chain, because they don't require their own food but make it from sunlight. In the process, they also produce the oxygen (O_2) we breathe, so life couldn't survive long without them. The process of making food from sunlight and releasing oxygen is called *photosynthesis*, one of the most important chemical reactions on earth. If we could duplicate this, it would probably solve all the world's energy problems. But even the most ingenious chemists have yet to match the ingenious machinery of the humble plant.

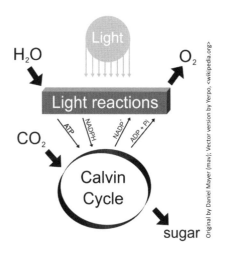

Water blasting problem

The key to photosynthesis is breaking up a molecule of water into hydrogen and oxygen. The hydrogen can then combine with

1.   After Sarfati, J., Green power: God's solar power plants amaze chemists, *J. Creation* **19**(1):14–15, 2005; <creationontheweb.com/greenpower>.

CO_2 from the air to make sugars, which the plant (and animals that eat them) can use for food. All this occurs in molecules called *chlorophylls*, which are responsible for the greenness of plants.

But how can you break up water? This requires an enormous amount of energy. Just think of the Hindenburg disaster of 1937, where a Zeppelin airship caught fire, and burned the hydrogen gas into water. To break up water, this amount of energy has to be 'put back'.

One problem is the very nature of light itself. Light is a form of energy, but it comes in 'packets' called *photons*. If the photon energy is not large enough to break the water molecule, then it won't matter how many of them there are (i.e. how bright the light is). But a photon that is energetic enough[2] to break water would also shatter most biological molecules in the process. Yet we don't see exploding leaves!

A few years ago, two chemists from Yale University, Gary Brudvig and Robert Crabtree, made an artificial system that managed to produce oxygen.[3] However, they had not worked out how to use light energy, so instead they used the chemical energy of powerful bleaches.[4] And even then, it produced only 100 O_2 molecules before being destroyed. Yet it was a great achievement, by human standards, to make something that didn't fall apart immediately.[5]

Ingenious solution

It turns out that in leaves there is a special assembly called Photosystem II (named because it was discovered second). A photon strikes this, and it is channelled into a type of chlorophyll called P680. There it knocks out an electron from an atom, and this energetic electron eventually helps make sugars from CO_2. But then, the P680 must replenish the lost electron. This is a big problem for artificial photosynthesis— chemists have so far been unable to produce a system that replenishes the electrons knocked out by the photons. Photosynthesis would have quickly ground to a halt without this, so how are the electrons replaced?

They come from a special *catalytic core*, which removes the required electrons from water, again with the help of light. The light breaks two molecules of water into a molecule of oxygen, four electrons and two hydrogen ions.

The core has a unique arrangement of atoms, with an unusual cube of three atoms of manganese (Mn), one calcium (Ca) and four

---

2.   The energy E is related to the frequency v (*nu*) by $E = hv$, where h = Planck's constant = 6.6262×10^{-34} Js. A photon energetic enough to break water would be in the ultraviolet region of the electromagnetic spectrum, i.e. more energetic than visible light photons.

3.   Burke, M., Green miracle, *New Scientist* **163**(2199):27–30, 1999.

4.   Interestingly, humble single-celled organisms in the root nodules of legumes use a far better chemical energy mechanism to break apart the nitrogen molecule, even tougher than water. See Demick, D., The molecular sledgehammer, *Creation* **24**(2):52–53, 2002.

5.   Plant energy miracle, *Creation* **22**(1):9, 1999.

oxygen (O), attached to a single Mn. This core builds up enough energy, in the form of redox potential, *in stages* by absorbing four photons.

The redox potential of water is +2.5 V, while each photon raises the catalytic core's redox potential by 1 V.[6] So after the third stage, there is enough energy for the single Mn to remove an electron from a water molecule, leaving an OH radical and H[+] ion. Then the catalytic core gets to the fourth stage, and provides the Mn atom with enough power to attack the OH radical and leaves a highly reactive O atom and another H[+] ion. At this moment, the Ca atom in the cube plays its essential role. It is holding another water molecule in just the right place, so it can be attacked by this O atom, producing an O_2 molecule, two more H[+] ions and two electrons.

The unique Mn_3CaO_4–Mn arrangement is present in all plants, algae and cyanobacteria, which suggests that this arrangement is essential. This is not surprising, because it has to be able to store the energy from four photons, and hold water molecules in just the right positions. This structure had to be complete from the start otherwise it would not work at all—in splitting water and replenishing electrons. Therefore it could not be built up gradually by small changes via mutations and natural selection. This is because an incomplete intermediate system is no use at all, so it would not be selected.

And even this core would be useless without many other coordinated features. For example, as already mentioned, the energy involved is damaging for biological structures. Yet there are key proteins required, which must be constantly repaired, so these mechanisms must be in place too. In fact, this instability made it hard to work out the core's structure.[7]

SOLAR CELL BASED ON PHOTOSYNTHESIS[8]

Scientists have long sought (so far unsuccessfully) to duplicate photosynthesis. Now a team of electrical and biomedical engineers, nanotechnology experts and biologists has managed to incorporate a protein complex derived from spinach chloroplasts (in leaf cells) into a solid-state electronic device that they hope may one day power laptop computers and mobile phones.

But why prefer a 'spinach sandwich' device rather than a conventional solar cell? A press release explained: 'Plants' ability to generate energy has been optimized by evolution, so a spinach plant

---

6. Redox (reduction/oxidation) potential measures how strongly a molecule or ion attracts electrons. The more electron-loving, the more positive; the more electron-releasing, the more negative. Redox potential is measured in volts. Water's redox potential is high, so it needs a very strong electron remover, such as an oxygen atom, to remove one of its electrons.

7. By X-ray crystallography—see Zouni, A. and six others, Crystal structure of photosystem II from *Synechococcus elongatus* at 3.8 Å resolution, *Nature* **409**(6821):739–743, 2001.

8. After: Spinach power, *Creation* **27**(4):7, 2005.

is extremely efficient, churning out a lot of energy relative to its size and weight.'[9] Certainly, the photosynthetic protein complex is tiny, as around 100,000 of these protein complexes would fit on the head of a pin—'the smallest electronic circuits I know of', observed one researcher. But the article didn't explain *how* evolution is supposed to have created or even optimized this process.

HOW ARE FLAT LEAVES PRODUCED?[10]

Most leaves are flat, because this shape enables the greatest area for light capture in return for a given amount of material, so the leaf can capture the most sunlight energy. But, surprising though it might seem, flatness is actually a puzzle to explain. It requires that the leaf's growth be *carefully coordinated*, as plant physiologists point out:

> '[I]t is more difficult to make a flat leaf than to make a curved one because growth of central regions of the leaf must be coordinated with growth at the leaf edges.'[11]

So flatness is produced by balancing two different growth rates, which researchers recently discovered are regulated by genes.[12] We can see what happens if a mutation disrupts this coordination: instead of the 'zero curvature' of flatness, there are curves. If cells near the leaf edge grow more slowly than those in the centre, the leaf will end up 'positively curved', i.e. cup-shaped. Conversely, when cells near the leaf margin grow more quickly than those in the central region, 'negative curvature' will result, i.e. the leaf will buckle into a shape with a wavy edge, similar to a horse-riding saddle. Precise balance is remarkable, because there are many more ways that growth could be unbalanced:

> 'Although such flatness is often taken for granted, the probability of this happening

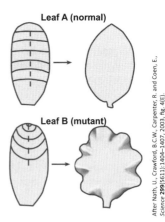

Leaf A (normal)

Leaf B (mutant)

After Nath, U., Crawford, B.C.W., Carpenter, R. and Coen, E., *Science* **299**(5611):1404–1407, 2003, fig. 4(E).

When the arrest front progressing down the developing leaf is weakly convex (Leaf A), an elliptical final leaf shape results with zero Gaussian curvature. But in mutants, a concave arrest front (Leaf B) produces greater growth at the leaf margins, resulting in a broader leaf with negative curvature.

9. Green, leafy spinach may soon power more than Popeye's biceps, <http://web.mit.edu/newsoffice/2004/spinach-0915.html>. 2004.
10. After Catchpoole, D., Flat leaves—a curly problem, *J. Creation* **19**(1):8, 2005; <creationontheweb.com/flatleaf>.
11. McConnell, J.R. and Barton, M.K., Leaf development takes shape, *Science* **299**(5611):1328–1329, 2003.
12. Nath, U., *et al.*, Genetic control of surface curvature, *Science* **299**(5611):1404–1407, 2003.

by chance is low because there are many more ways for a structure to adopt negative or positive curvature than zero curvature.'[12]

The precision is even more remarkable since it must control individual cell division. Growth occurs by cell division, where each cell divides into two daughter cells, and these daughter cells divide in turn, and so on. In normal (flat) leaves, cells at the tip stop dividing and become mature (differentiate) before those in the base of the leaf.

The recent research shows that the cell division is stopped when a 'wave' or 'arrest front' passes. The arrest mechanism involves snippets of RNA stopping genes from producing certain proteins,[13] which makes the cells mature, stopping cell division. But the wave must be timed and shaped precisely.

In normal leaves, the front is slightly convex and descends from tip to base. So at a given distance from the leaf tip, cells at the edges receive the arrest signal before cells in the centre of the leaf. There is also a gene, *CIN*, that codes for a protein, *TCP*, that seems to make cells more sensitive to an arrest signal, especially in marginal regions.[12] This results in an ellipse-shaped leaf with zero curvature (see diagram, Leaf 'A').

But in snapdragon plants with a certain genetic mutation, the arrest front is concave and moves more slowly than in normal leaves. So the cells in the centre receive the arrest signal before cells near the edge. Thus the cells in the centre of the leaf stop dividing before cells near the leaf margins, giving greater growth in edge regions, resulting in a broader leaf with negative curvature (Leaf 'B' in diagram).

The same problem applies to the membranous wings of insects. Evidently, there is much control of the growth rate here, too. This is shown by mutations that result in crinkly wings, just as mutations can result in crinkly leaves. But with insects, flatness is even more critical, because it is essential for the aerodynamics of flight.

Origin of flatness?

Since flatness is the result of precisely controlled growth rates, it is not surprising that the researchers admit that 'the probability of this happening by chance is low'.[12] So where did flat leaves come from? Neo-Darwinian theory invokes small mutations and natural selection. However, flatness requires highly coordinated changes in growth rates, so it's impossible to explain simply by cumulative selection of one continuous variable in Dawkinsian fashion. It might be possible to fine-tune an existing system of control, but not create it.

13.   Benfrey, P.N., Molecular biology: MicroRNA is here to stay, *Nature* **425**(6955):244–245, 2003 | doi:10.1038/425244a.

CHAPTER 10

MOTORS

The living world surprisingly contains real electrical rotary motors. Surprising, that is, for evolutionists who predicted that wheels could not exist, because they could not have evolved gradually. The motors in the living world epitomize the ultimate nano-technology.

The living world also has a variety of linear motors, which are equally problematic for evolution.

Some cutting edge research involves using biological motors to assist man-made nanotechnology, which at present is primitive compared to the machines in the living world.

THE EVOLUTIONARY CONUNDRUM

As noted before (p. 86), J.B.S. Haldane claimed in 1949 that evolution could never produce 'various mechanisms, such as the wheel and magnet, which would be useless till fairly perfect.'[1]

<wikipedia.org>

J.B.S. Haldane, 1914

Therefore such machines in organisms would, in his opinion, prove evolution false. These molecular motors have indeed fulfilled one of Haldane's criteria. Also, as shown in the chapter on navigation, the multitude of creatures that use magnetic sensors for navigation fulfil Haldane's other criterion. Once again, I wonder whether Haldane would have had a change of heart if he had been alive to see these discoveries. Many evolutionists rule out intelligent design *a priori*, so the evidence, overwhelming as it is, would be dismissed automatically.

MOTORS

Motors are irreducibly complex, because they need many parts working together to function. For example, an electric motor needs a power source, fixed stator, movable rotor, and a commutator or slip rings.

The more parts needed for a machine, the harder it is to make it smaller. Miniaturization is such a vital part of the computer industry, and the best human minds constantly work at it. And though miniaturized motors would be very useful, e.g. for unblocking clogged arteries and blood cleaning, the number of parts makes it

---

1. Dewar, D., Davies, L.M. and Haldane, J.B.S., *Is Evolution a Myth? A Debate between D. Dewar and L.M. Davies vs. J.B.S. Haldane*, p. 90, Watts & Co. Ltd / Paternoster Press, London, 1949.

difficult to make them below a certain size. But ingenious scientists are making them smaller all the time.[2]

THE WORLD'S TINIEST MOTOR: ATP SYNTHASE[3]

A landmark paper published in *Nature,* March 1997, announced the discovery of the tiniest known motor in the universe.[4] A commentary in the same journal was appropriately entitled 'Real Engines of Creation'.[5]

Hiroyuki Noji *et al.* directly observed the rotation of the enzyme F_1-*ATPase*, a subunit of a larger enzyme, *ATP synthase*.[6] The F_1 subunit stands off the membrane, but the other part is within the membrane, called F_O—see diagram (below).[7]

Rotational energy had earlier been suggested as the mechanism for the enzyme's operation by Paul Boyer—i.e. that the enzyme worked as a motor.[8] Structural determination by X-ray diffraction by a team led by John Walker had supported this theory.[9] A few months after Noji *et al.* published their work, it was announced that

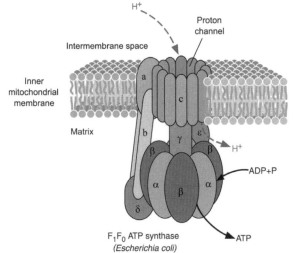

ATP synthase, after John Walker, one of the 1997 Nobel laureates.

2. Hogan, H., 1996. Invasion of the micromachines. *New Scientist* **150**(2036):28–33.
3. Updated from Sarfati, J., Design in living organisms (motors), *J. Creation* **12**(1):3–5, 1998; <creationontheweb.com/motor>, written not long after the original work on the motor was published.
4. Hiroyuki Noji *et al.*, Direct observation of the rotation of F1-ATPase, *Nature* **386**(6622):299–302, 1997.
5. Block, S. Real engines of creation, commentary on Noji, Ref. 4, *Nature* **386**(6622):217–219, 1997.
6. Wu, C., Molecular motor spins out energy for cells, *Science News* **151**(12):173, 1997.
7. Note that it is a subscript letter O not the number zero, for historical reasons: from 'oligomycin binding fraction'.
8. Boyer, P., *Biochim. Biophys. Acta* **1140**:215–250, 1993.
9. Abrahams, J.P. *et al.*, Structure at 2.8 Å resolution of F1-ATPase from bovine heart mitochondria, *Nature* **370**(6491):621–628, 1994; comment by Cross, R.L. Our primary source of ATP, same issue, pp. 594–595.

Boyer and Walker had won a half share of the 1997 Nobel Prize for Chemistry for their discovery.[10]

The F_1-ATPase motor has nine components—five different proteins ($\alpha,\beta,\gamma,\delta,\varepsilon$) with three of α, three of β and one each of γ, δ and ε. In cattle mitochondria, they contain 510, 482, 272, 146 and 50 amino acids respectively. F_1-ATPase is a flattened sphere about 10 nm across by 8 nm high—so tiny that it would take 10^{17} (that's a one with 17 zeroes following it!) to fill the volume of a pinhead. This has been shown to spin 'like a motor' to produce ATP, a chemical which is the 'energy currency' of life (see below, p. 134).

This motor produces an immense torque (turning force) for its size—in the experiment of Noji *et al.*, it rotated a strand of another protein, *actin*, 100 times its own length, sufficiently to enable observation of the rotary motion with a powerful microscope. Also, when driving a heavy load, it probably changes to a lower gear, as any well-designed motor should. Without this load it rotates at about 10,000 rpm.

Unlike man-made motors, which are powered by negatively charged current (electrons through a wire), ATP synthase is powered by positively charged current, i.e. a flow of protons (hydrogen ions). ATP synthase also contains the membrane-embedded F_0 subunit that acts as a proton channel. The protons flowing through the channel somehow turn a wheel-like structure on F_1-ATPase, as water turns a water wheel.

ATP synthase is the central enzyme in energy conversion in mitochondria (they are embedded into the *cristae*, folds in the mitochondrion's inner membrane), chloroplasts and bacteria.

How rotation produces the ATP

One rotation produces *three* new ATP molecules. In turn, ten protons are used for every rotation, which means there must be *exactly* ten 'c' subunits in the rotor of the F_0 unit (bottom of diagram) or it won't work.[11] This 10:3 ratio means there is another layer of complexity for evolution to explain, and the authors didn't try:

> 'This noninteger H^+/ATP (10:3) ratio means that one molecule of ATP is produced by transport of three protons on one occasion but four protons on another occasion. Therefore, microscopic couplings between events at F_0 and those at F_1 cannot be strict like a meshed gear but rather "permissive"; consecutive transports of three protons at F_0, for example, do not

10. Service, R.F., Awards for High-Energy Molecules and Cool Atoms, *Science* **278**(5338):578–579, 1997. The third winner was Jens Skou of the University of Aarhus in Denmark. Forty years previously, he was the first to identify an enzyme that moves substances through cell membranes (in this case, sodium and potassium ions). This is a key function of all cells.
11. Mitome, N. *et al.*, Thermophilic ATP synthase has a decamer c-ring: Indication of noninteger 10:3 H+/ATP ratio and permissive elastic coupling, *Proc. Nat. Acad. Sci. USA* **101**(33):12159–12164 | 10.1073/pnas.0403545101.

necessarily require to accompany three corresponding elementary catalytic steps of ATP synthesis at F_1. It is easily understood that the microscopic coupling should be permissive if the central rotorshaft twists during rotation, as described in the previous paragraph. Here, we report the permissive nature of the coupling between proton transport and ATP synthesis of F_0F_1, but such nature of the coupling can be general among other biological motor systems to connect critical well tuned microscopic events in the large domain motions.'[11]

The synthesis depends on three chemically identical regions that each have three conformations (arrangements in space) of the catalytic sites: loose (L), tight (T), and Open (O). L can hold the two reactants reversibly.[12] In the T configuration, the reactants are bound so tightly that ATP is formed. But in the O configuration, the binding is weak enough to release the ATP already formed in the T state.

So, production of the ATP involves changing the conformation at any given site from L to T to O, then back to L to begin again. This is achieved by the rotation of the asymmetrical central stalk, which rotates in 120° steps (⅓ turn),[13] and causes internal shifting that changes the conformation. At any part of the rotation, the three sites have different conformations.[14]

Unlike most enzymes, where energy is needed to link the building blocks, ATP synthase uses energy to link them to the enzyme, and to throw off the newly formed ATP molecules. Separating the ATP from the enzyme needs much energy.

Proton-motive force

The force driving the protons is another layer of complexity. Chemical energy in food is released via oxidation in the complex *Krebs cycle*. This releases high-energy electrons, and their energy is captured by specialized molecules in the *electron transport chain*. This energy produces an electrochemical gradient, much like a battery. But in this case, instead of driving electrons around a circuit, the energy is released by driving protons across the membrane, which is necessary to create the proton gradient that drives the ATP synthase. The whole system is needed!

---

12. The overall equation is: $ADP^{3-} + HPO_4^{2-} + H^+ + nH^+_{out} \leftrightarrow ATP^{4-} + H_2O + nH^+_{in}$ where subscripts 'out' and 'in' refer to the protons in the outer (positively charged) and the inner (negatively charged) side of the membrane, respectively.

13. ATP Synthase: an interpretation by Donald Nicholson, Department of Biochemistry and Microbiology, University of Leeds (UK), <www.iubmb-nicholson.org/atpase.html>; this site contains an animated diagram showing the motion.

14. Bianchet, M.A. *et al.*, The 2.8-Å structure of rat liver F1-ATPase: Configuration of a critical intermediate in ATP synthesis/hydrolysis, *Proc. Nat. Acad. Sci. USA* **95**(19):11065–11070, 1998.

Vital for life

ATP stands for **a**denosine **tri**phosphate. It is a high energy compound, and releases this energy by losing a phosphate group to give ADP, **a**denosine **di**phosphate. Energy is essential for life, and all life uses ATP as its energy currency.[15] Even bacteria and archaeans have ATP synthase motors. This probably makes ATP synthase the most ubiquitous protein on Earth.

In fact, the human body generates about its own weight of ATP every day, generated by trillions of these motors. And it is consumed very quickly to power vital biochemical reactions, including DNA and protein synthesis, muscle contraction, transport of nutrients and nerve impulses. An organism without ATP is like a car without gasoline. Cyanide is so toxic precisely because it stops ATP production.

Evolution of ATP synthase?

This motor has many components that need to be fully together before it can work at all. In particular, the 10-fold symmetry of the F_0 carousel has no function by itself. And the three-fold symmetry of the F_1 'mushroom cap', with just the right molecular arrangements to give the three possible conformations, would be useless without the rotating stalk to change the conformations. And the motor would not run without the proton channel in the right place. The motor works only because its components are *organized correctly*. Similarly, the existence of electrical wiring, brushes and magnets does not explain how they were organized specifically to form a motor.

Some evolutionists have speculated that the F_1 sector could have arisen via a certain helicase, the enzyme that separates the two DNA strands (see pp. 163–4). The rationale is some shared homology and the fact that research has shown that helicase 'is an active unwinding motor',[16] where supposedly the DNA chain is analogous to the γ-subunit of the ATP synthase. However, the operation of helicase *itself* uses ATP copiously, *currently supplied by ATP synthase,* so how could these supposed precursors operate at all?

Also, because energy is vital for life, life could not have evolved before this motor was fully functional. This is an even more foundational problem: natural selection by definition is differential reproduction, so requires self-reproducing entities at the start (see chapter 11). Yet self-reproduction requires ATP to supply the energy! So does the expression of the information that is selected. So even if a series of gradual steps could be imagined up this peak of 'Mount Improbable',[17] there would be no natural selection to enable that

---

15. Bergman, J., ATP: The perfect energy currency for the cell, *Creation Res. Soc. Q.* **36**(1):2–10, 1999; <www.creationresearch.org/crsq/articles/36/36_1/atp.html>.
16. Researchers solve mystery of how DNA strands separate, *Physorg.com*, <http://www.physorg.com/news102663442.html>, 2007.
17. After Richard Dawkins' book *Climbing Mount Improbable* (1996); see review by Sarfati, J., *J. Creation* **12**(1):29–34, 1998; <creationontheweb.com/dawkins>.

climb. This is because all the hypothetical intermediates would be lacking energy and thus *dead*.

BACTERIAL FLAGELLUM: POWERED BY AN ELECTRIC MOTOR

Your large intestines are full of bacteria, for example *Escherichia coli*. This microbe is only 2 μm long (0.002 mm), with a cell wall only about 30 nm thick, and its mass is only 1 picogram, and comprises about 70% water.[18] No wonder the biologists in Darwin's time dismissed such cells as mere blobs of jelly.

However, every living organism is an astronomically complex self-reproducing machine (see chapter 11). The code for the instructions to build *E. coli*, its genome, compromises 4,639,221 base pairs specifying 4,288 genes, most of which encode proteins.[14]

Outboard motors

The germ moves with the aid of real electrical outboard motors, only 45 nm in diameter. [14] These motors are connected to long, thin,

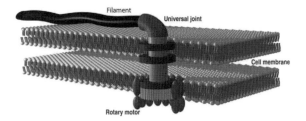

Bacterial flagellum with rotary motor, with the following features:
• Self assembly and repair
• Water-cooled rotary engine
• Proton motive force drive system
• Forward and reverse gears
• Operating speeds of up to 100,000 rpm
• Direction-reversing capability within 1/4 of a turn
• Hard-wired signal transduction system with short-term memory

whip-like helical filaments several times as long as the germ, via a universal joint. This converts the rotary motion into wavelike motions in the filament. The motor comprises a stator, rotor, drive shaft and bushing that guides the driveshaft out through the cell wall. 'The assemblage of motor and filament is called a *flagellum*.'[14] The cell has several flagella, and their concerted motion enables the cell to swim at 35 cell lengths per second. [14]

---

18. A good summary is by Howard Berg, a professor of molecular and cellular biology, and of physics, at Harvard University: Motile Behavior of Bacteria, *Physics Today*, 1999; <http://www.aip.org/pt/jan00/berg. htm>.

Like ATP synthase, the flagellar motor is powered by proton flow, this time from the outside to the inside of the cell (except for marine bacteria and bacteria that live in very alkaline conditions (i.e. low concentration of protons), where sodium ions are used instead). The protons are driven by either an electrical or pH gradient, and the energy to generate this gradient is from the oxidation of its food. The proton flow changes the shape of one of the stator proteins, which exerts a force on one of the rotor proteins, thereby driving the rotor.[14]

Could it have evolved?

Scientific American, in an article specifically attacking creationists and design theorists, tried to explain the origin of this amazing miniature motor by evolution, by claiming that the parts were 'co-opted' from other functions, in particular the type III secretory system (TTSS) of some disease germs:

> 'The sophisticated components of this flagellum all have precedents elsewhere in nature …

> 'In fact, the entire flagellum assembly is extremely similar to an organelle that *Yersinia pestis*, the bubonic plague bacterium, uses to inject toxins into cells. …

> 'The key is that the flagellum's component structures … can serve multiple functions that would have helped favor their evolution.'[19]

Right organization

Scientific American's argument, which comes from Kenneth Miller,[20] and has been parroted by Richard Dawkins,[21] is like claiming that if the components of an electric motor already exist in an electrical shop, they could assemble by themselves into a working motor. However, the right *organization* is just as important as the right components.

Scott Minnich of the University of Idaho, a world expert on the flagellar motor, disagrees with *Scientific American* and Miller (Minnich points out that Miller, unlike him, has no experience in the area). He says that his belief that this motor has been intelligently designed has given him many research insights. Minnich points out that the very process of assembly in the right sequence requires other regulatory machines.[22] He also points out that only about 10 of the

---

19. Rennie, J., 15 Answers to Creationist Nonsense, *Scientific American* **287**(1):78–85, 2002; see refutation, Sarfati, J., 15 ways to refute materialistic bigotry: A point by point response to *Scientific American*, <creationontheweb.com/sciam>, 20 June 2002.

20. A more recent version of Miller's argument is Miller, K.R., The Flagellum Unspun: The Collapse of 'Irreducible Complexity'; in: Dembski, W.A. and Ruse, M., eds., *Debating Design: From Darwin to DNA*, Cambridge University Press, 2004.

21. Dawkins, R., Inferior Design, *New York Times*, 1 July 2007; see refutation, Sarfati, J., Misotheist's misology: Dawkins attacks Behe but digs himself into logical potholes, <creationontheweb.com/dawkbehe>, 13 July 2007.

22. *Unlocking the Mystery of Life*, DVD, Illustra Media, 2002.

40 components can possibly be explained by co-option, but the other 30 are brand new.

Finally, Dr Minnich's research shows that the flagellum won't form above 37°C; instead, some secretory organelles form from the same set of genes. But this secretory apparatus, as well as the plague bacterium's drilling apparatus, are a *degeneration* from the flagellum. Minnich says that although the flagellum is more complex, it came first, so it couldn't have been derived from the secretory apparatus.[23] This makes sense: The flagellum assembly mechanism is designed to punch out the proteins required for the flagellum in a very orderly way. If this is *disabled*, it can punch out proteins (including toxins) in a *haphazard* way, as the TTSS does.

For example, the flagellum is formed base-first. Then an export apparatus forms to make a hole in the cell wall, then expel the right proteins in the right place through a hollow tube, and these proteins must be labelled to distinguish them from non-flagellar proteins. Some of these proteins must be shepherded by other proteins called chaperones.

Then the 'hook' or universal joint must form. This requires a 'hook cap' protein to keep the components in place as the hook is built. Then the cap detaches and floats away.

Finally, the actual whip must form. This is a hollow tube comprising tens of thousands of copies of the protein, *flagellin*. This must be sent by the export apparatus and squeezed through the growing tube. But before this, a filament cap must be sent through. This is composed of five protein parts, so the whole is shaped something like a starfish on stilts.[24]

The flagellum itself comprises 11 strands, while the legs of the cap can fit in a crease between every other strand. But with only five legs, there is one crease unfilled. But this is all part of the coordination. When a flagellin arrives, having travelled inside the developing flagellum to the growing tip, the cap stops it from floating away and allows it to fold into its functional shape, and is then directed to the unfilled space. This filling rotates the cap so that the next available slot is now unfilled by one of the legs. So the next flagellin also arrives at the right spot. This process repeats tens of thousands of times, so each flagellin is automatically directed to the right spot.[25]

Evolutionary propagandists out of step with evolutionary experts!

Another problem for this evolutionary 'explanation' is that it is inconsistent with their own theory! Evolution teaches that bacteria

---

23. Minnich, S <www.idurc.org/yale-minnich.html>, 2003.
24. Using Michael Behe's description of the shape and process in *The Edge of Evolution*, Appendix C: Assembling the bacterial flagellum, Free Press, NY, 2007.
25. See animation at *Protonic Nanomachine Project*, Japan,

evolved before the plants and animals that they could parasitize. So it makes sense that the swimming machinery preceded the secretion machinery that would be needed only once multicellular life evolved. Indeed, evolutionary specialists agree that the flagellum preceded the TTSS:

> 'It seems plausible that the original type III secretion system for virulence factors evolved from those for flagellar assembly.'[26]

> 'We suggest that the flagellar apparatus was the evolutionary precursor of Type III protein secretion systems.'[27]

So the Miller explanation is totally without merit, not only objectively but also within his own evolutionary framework. It is highly disingenuous for Miller to propose an explanation that *defies even the best evolutionary theories*, without telling his readers.[28]

OTHER MOTORS

This chapter majors on the rotary motors, because they specifically fulfil Haldane's criterion for falsification of evolution (p. 131). But there are other types of motors as well.

Kinesin

This is a miniature *linear motor* that transports large molecules and components through a cell. They 'walk' in one direction along microtubule tracks, and use one molecule of the energy currency ATP per step. Each step is only 8 nm, or 125,000 steps per mm!

Kinesin is a protein dimer comprising of two heavy chains and two light chains. The heavy chains each terminate in a globular 'head', which is attached to the tubule. The heads are connected to the light chains that intertwine to form the 'tail' that attaches to the cargo, a vesicle (bag of proteins).

It is most likely that they use the 'hand-over-hand' mechanism, where the kinesin heads step over each other, taking turns in binding to the tubule as they alternate the lead position. One expert wrote:

> 'Kinesin, an essential motor protein that moves intracellular cargo along microtubules, walks like a person. When we walk, our feet exchange roles with each step, one moving and one remaining stationary. The moving foot travels twice as far as our torso during a single step, and our body alternates between two configurations (left vs. right leg leading). Recent work shows that kinesin shares all three of these hallmarks of bipedal

26. Mecsas, J., and Strauss, E.J., Molecular Mechanisms of Bacterial Virulence: Type III Secretion and Pathogenicity Islands, *Emerging Infectious Diseases* 2(4), October–December 1996; <www.cdc.gov/ncidod/EID/vol2no4/mecsas.htm>.

27. Nguyen L. *et al.*, Phylogenetic analyses of the constituents of Type III protein secretion systems, *J. Mol. Microbiol. Biotechnol.* 2(2):125–44, April 2000.

28. See also Dembski, W.A., Still spinning just fine: a response to Ken Miller, <www.designinference.com/documents/2003.02.Miller_Response.htm>, 17 February 2003.

walking. The challenge now is to determine how the gait of this lilliputian biped is coordinated.'[29]

Kinesins are also now known to be vital for cell division itself, without which life is impossible.

Dynein

Kinesins move towards the 'plus end' of the microtubule, which is normally from the centre of the cell outwards. To move the other way, linear motors called dyneins move towards the 'minus end', usually inwards towards the centre.

Cilia

The above is called *cytoplasmic dynein*. Another type of motor protein called the *axonemal dynein* powers cilia—an *axoneme* is the 'skeleton' of these whiplike appendages that line the lungs (bronchi) and fallopian tubes, for example.

Cilia are powered by dynein, but instead of walking on a single tubule, the two heads walk up adjacent tubules. This would cause the tubules to slide past each other, except that there is a flexible linking protein, called *nexin*. Thus instead of sliding away, the tubules are forced to bend. This results in the regular 'beating' motion of the cilia (see diagram, right).[30]

Each cilium comprises a ring of nine double microtubules surrounding two central single microtubules. The dynein motions must be precisely coordinated, and this is likely achieved by the radial spokes (see diagram, below).

Cilia are vital in many aspects of life. Their coordinated beating helps move gunk from our lungs, and in the fallopian tubes of female mammals, they guide the fertilized ovum to the uterus, preventing it lethally implanting in the tube.

The complexity of the cilium has recently been shown to be even greater. Within the cilium, there is a precisely coordinated system of *intraflagellar transport* (IFT). This involves kinesins running up and dyneins running down an internal trackway. This is essential both to build and maintain the cilium. These carry an *IFT particle*,

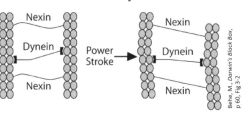

Behe, M., *Darwin's Black Box*, p 60, Fig 3-2

Schematic drawing of part of a cilium. The power stroke of the motor protein, dynein, attached to one microtubule, against subfibre B of a neighbouring microtubule causes the fibres to slide past each other. The flexible linker protein, nexin, converts the sliding motion to a bending motion.

29. Asbury, C.L., Kinesin: world's tiniest biped, *Curr. Opinion Cell Biol.* **17**:89–97, 2006.
30. Behe, M., Molecular Machines: Experimental Support for the Design Inference, *Access Research Network*, <www.arn.org/docs/behe/mb_mm92496.htm>, 1997.

a container made up of a 16-protein complex. This grabs the necessary proteins and releases them at the right time and place.

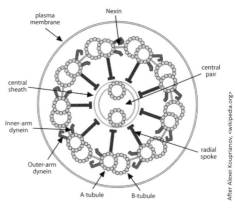

Axoneme cross section.

Myosin and actin

This motor system is responsible for muscle contraction. Myosin is another motor that contains two heads that 'walk', but with special tail regions. The tail regions enable the myosins to combine in a thick filament where the heads stick out.

In skeletal muscle contraction, the myosin molecules 'walk' down actin filaments. These are attached to two *Z-discs* of the basic unit of the muscle fibril, the *sarcomere*. (In cross-section under an electron microscope, the Z-discs form dark lines. This is why skeletal muscles are also known as striped or striated muscles). The myosin's walk results in the filaments sliding past each other, drawing the two Z disks closer, resulting in muscle contraction—this is the *sliding filament model* of muscle contraction (see diagram below).

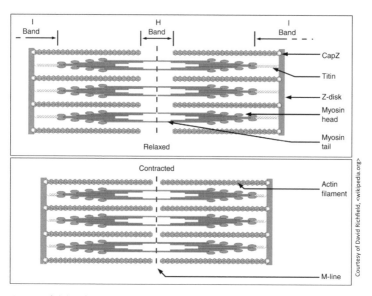

Diagram of sliding filament model of muscle contraction, from Wikipedia

VIRUS MOTOR FOR WINDING DNA[31]

Viruses are particles too tiny to see under an ordinary light microscope, needing an electron microscope. Viruses come in many different sizes, shapes and designs, and they operate in diverse ways. They are composed of DNA (or RNA in the case of RNA viruses, including retro-viruses) and protein.

They are not living organisms because they cannot carry out the necessary internal metabolism to sustain life, nor can they reproduce themselves. They are biologically inert until they enter into host cells. Then they start to propagate using host cellular resources. The infected cell produces multiple copies of the virus, often bursting to release the new viruses so the cycle can repeat.[32]

One of the most common types is the bacteriophage (or simply 'phage') which infects bacteria. It consists of an infectious tailpiece made of protein, and a head capsule (capsid) made of protein and containing DNA packaged at such high pressure that when released, the pressure forces the DNA into the host cell to infect it.

How does the virus manage to assemble this long information molecule at high pressure inside such a small package, especially when the negatively charged phosphate groups of the DNA repel each other? It has a special *packaging motor*, more powerful than any molecular motor yet discovered, even those in muscles. Douglas Smith, an assistant professor of physics at UCSD, explained the challenge:

> 'The genome is about 1,000 times longer than the diameter of the virus. It is the equivalent of reeling in and packing 100 yards of fishing line into a coffee cup, but the virus is able to package its DNA in under five minutes.'[33]

Smith and some colleagues at UCSD joined researchers from the American Catholic University (Washington, DC) to solve the problem.[34] They analyzed the bacteriophage T4—a virus that infects *E. coli* bacteria, the type that inhabit human intestines—using 'laser tweezers' to hold onto a single molecule of DNA, and measure the force exerted upon it by the virus's packaging motor.

They showed this motor exerts a force of more than 60 piconewtons. This sounds small (6×10^{-11} N), but for its size, it's twice as powerful as a car engine. So the motor, a terminase enzyme complex, 'can capture and begin packaging a target DNA molecule within a few seconds.'[30] Such a powerful motor must use a lot of

31. After Sarfati, J., Virus has powerful mini-motor to pack up its DNA, *J. Creation* **22**(1):15–16, 2008; <creationontheweb.com/virusmotor>.
32. See also ch. 13, pp. 205 ff, about why a Designer would design pathogenic viruses.
33. Powerful Molecular Motor Permits Speedy Assembly of Viruses, Physorg.com, 2007; <www.physorg.com/news112896152.html>.
34. Fuller, D.N., *et al.*, Single phage T4 DNA packaging motors exhibit large force generation, high velocity, and dynamic variability, *Proc. Nat. Acad. Sci., USA* **104**(43):16868–16873, 2007; <www.pnas.org/cgi/content/abstract/104/43/16868>.

energy, and in one second, this one goes through over 300 units of life's energy currency, ATP, which itself is generated by a remarkable molecular motor, ATP synthase (see pp. 132–6). The virus has a complementary motor-enzyme, ATPase, built into its packaging engine, to release the energy of the ATP.[35]

And not only is the packing motor powerful, it can change its speed as if it had gears. The researchers say that this is important, because the DNA fed to it from the cell is likely not a straightforward untangled thread. Dr Smith said:

'Just as it is good for a car to have brakes and gears, rather than only being able to go 60 miles per hour, the DNA-packaging motor may need to slow down, or stop and wait if it encounters an obstruction.'[33]

A report said:

'It may permit DNA repair, transcription or recombination—the swapping of bits of DNA to enhance genetic diversity—to take place before the genetic material is packaged within the viral capsid.'[33]

USING THE CELL'S MACHINES IN MAN-MADE NANOTECHNOLOGY?

An interesting recent article[36] stated in its abstract:

'The biological cell is equipped with a variety of molecular machines that perform complex mechanical tasks such as cell division or intracellular transport. One can envision employing these biological motors in artificial environments. We review the progress that has been made in using motor proteins for powering or manipulating nanoscale components. In particular, kinesin and myosin biomotors that move along linear biofilaments have been widely explored as active components. Currently realized applications are merely proof-of-principle demonstrations. Yet, the sheer availability of an entire ready-to-use toolbox of nanosized biological motors is a great opportunity that calls for exploration.'

I.e. the technology of living things is a great inspiration for human designers, but practical applications are not yet available. The article starts by acknowledging the amazing machines for life, but gives the usual vacuous homage to evolution, which provides nothing of practical benefit:

---

35. Sun. S. *et al.*, The Structure of the ATPase that Powers DNA Packaging into Bacteriophage T4 Procapsids, *Molecular Cell* **25**:943–949, 2007.
36. van den Heuvel, M.G.L. and Dekker, C., Motor Proteins at Work for Nanotechnology, *Science* **317**(5836):333–336, 2007 | DOI: 10.1126/science.1139570.

'A huge amount of biological research in recent decades has spurred the realization that the living cell can be viewed as a miniature factory that contains a large collection of dedicated protein machines. Consider the complicated tasks that a single cell can perform: It can create a full copy of itself in less than an hour; it can proofread and repair errors in its own DNA, sense its environment and respond to it, change its shape and morphology, and obtain energy from photosynthesis or metabolism, using principles that are similar to solar cells or batteries. All this functionality derives from thousands of sophisticated proteins, optimized by billions of years of evolution. At the moment, we can only dream of constructing machines of similar size that possess just a fraction of the functionality of these natural wonders.

'One particular class of proteins is formed by molecular motor enzymes, which are catalytic proteins that contain moving parts and use a source of free energy to direct their motion. Upon studying these motors, their resemblance to machines becomes more and more clear. We find rotary motors that comprise shafts and bearings, as well as linear motors that move along tracks in a step-by-step fashion. We find motors that are powered by chemical energy, derived from hydrolyzing adenosine triphosphate (ATP) molecules (the cell's major energy currency), and motors that employ a gradient of ions, using both electric and entropic forces.'

Of course, since these motors resemble our machines on such a fundamental level, and obviously our machines are designed, it is reasonable to treat living motors as likewise designed. Indeed, design theory is likely to provide more of an incentive to try to find out the functions of the parts, while assertions of evolution provide nothing of value to using them as machines. The authors continue:

'It is of interest to ponder whether we can employ these biological nanomachines in artificial environments outside the cell to perform tasks that we design to our benefit. Or, at the very least, can these proteins provide us with the inspiration to mimic biocomponents or design artificial motors on comparable scales?'

The rest of the paper gives a number of promising examples, then concludes:

'The small size and force-exerting capabilities of motor proteins and the range of opportunities for specific engineering give them unique advantages over current human-made motors. Upon studying and using biomotors, we will gather a lot of knowledge that is of interest to biology, material science, and chemistry, and it is reasonable to expect spin-offs for medicine, sensors, electronics, or engineering. The exploration of biomotors in technology will thus remain an interdisciplinary playground for many years to come.'

SUMMARY

Man-made motors exhibit obvious design that no-one would doubt. Indeed, earlier biologists thought that wheels, and *a fortiori* motors, could not be found in living organisms because evolution could not build them. Yet recent research has discovered many examples of exquisite miniature motors. In particular, the ATP synthase motor produces the vital energy currency for life, which could thus not exist without it.

CHAPTER 11

THE ORIGIN OF LIFE

Even the simplest life is incredibly complicated. As scientists investigate the cell, they discover ever more amazingly complex machinery. The origin of life by chemical evolution remains intractable. And natural selection can't help, because this presupposes self-reproduction so can't explain the origin of self-reproduction.

There are three main sections of this chapter. The first explains why the origin of life is a vital area for design vs evolution. The second explains the enormous complexity of even the simplest conceivable life (p. 151). The third explains why undirected chemistry in a primordial soup would have no chance of achieving even this minimal complexity (p. 170). The conclusion cites leading researchers admitting that chemical evolution is accepted because of a materialistic faith.

There is currently a million-dollar prize for anyone who proposes a chemically plausible naturalistic origin-of-life scenario, but it is thus far unclaimed.

1. ORIGIN OF LIFE AND EVOLUTION

Many evolutionists now claim that origin of life from non-living chemicals has nothing to do with evolution, and claim that 'abiogenesis' is the correct term for the former. However, evolutionist Prof. Gerald Kerkut (1927–2004) of the University of Southampton (UK) defined the 'General Theory of Evolution' as 'the theory that all the living forms in the world have arisen from a single source which itself came from an inorganic form.'[1] Also, the September 1978 issue of *Scientific American* was specially devoted to evolution, and one major article was 'Chemical Evolution and the Origin of Life'.[2] This stated:

> 'J.B.S. Haldane, the British biochemist, seems to have been the first to appreciate that a reducing atmosphere, one with

NASA-Ames Research Center, <wikipedia.org>

The Miller-Urey experiment attempted to recreate the chemical conditions of the primitive Earth in the laboratory, and synthesized some of the building blocks of life.

---

1. Kerkut, G.A., *Implications of Evolution*, Pergamon, Oxford, UK, p. 157, 1960. He continued: 'the evidence which supports this is not sufficiently strong to allow us to consider it as anything more than a working hypothesis.'
2. Dickerson, R.E., Chemical Evolution and the Origin of Life, *Scientific Amer.* **239**(3):62–102, September 1978.

no free oxygen, was a requirement for the *evolution of life from non-living organic matter.*' [Emphasis added]

And an old stalwart of origin-of-life theories, Cyril Ponnamperuma (1923–1994), co-authored a paper with the same title, and his affiliation was the **Laboratory of Chemical Evolution**, Chemistry Department, University of Maryland.[3]

Also, many biology textbooks include discussions of the origin of life as part of their evolutionary sections. And a number of Richard Dawkins' books defending atheistic evolution include origin-of-life scenarios (often contradicting each other, but he doesn't seem to realize that, possibly because he is not a chemist).

Dr Cyril Ponnamperuma analyzing a moon sample.

CAN NATURAL SELECTION HELP?

Many of the examples of design in this book might be explained (away!) by natural selection (although I aim to show that it's inadequate). However, this won't work for the origin of *first* life. Theodosius Dobzhansky (1900–1975) was one of the leading evolutionists of the 20th century, and an ardent materialist, despite a Russian Orthodox upbringing.[4] In commenting on the origin of life, he firmly rejected theorists who invoked natural selection as an explanation, because *this requires pre-existing life*:

'In reading some other literature on the origin of life, I am afraid that not all authors have used the term [natural selection] carefully. *Natural selection is differential reproduction, organism perpetuation. In order to have natural selection, you have to have self-reproduction or self-replication and at least two distinct self-replicating units or entities. ...* I would like to plead with you, simply, please realize you cannot use the words 'natural selection' loosely. *Prebiological natural selection is a contradiction of terms.*'[5]

So the origin of life is a big problem for materialists: if evolution by natural selection could not have started in the first place, it's

3. Pleasant, L.G. and Ponnamperuma, C., Chemical evolution and the origin of life, *Origins of Life and Evolution of Biospheres* **10**(1), 1980; <www.springerlink.com/content/m185944813n42138/>
4. See documentation by O'Leary, D., *Darwinist Theodosius Dobzhansky was* **not** *an orthodox Christian believer!* <http://post-darwinist.blogspot.com/2006/09/darwinist-theodosius-dobzhansky-was.html>, 8 September 2006.
5. Dobzhansky, T.G., Discussion of Synthesis of Nucleosides and Polynucleotides with Metaphoric Esters, by George Schramm, in Fox, S.W., ed., *The Origins of Prebiological Systems and of Their Molecular Matrices*, Proc. Conference at Wakulla Springs, Florida, pp. 309–310, 27–30 October 1963, Academic Press, NY, 1965. Emphases added.

dead in the water. *It's pointless to talk about selection between two runners if both are dead on the starting line!*

The famous philosopher Antony Flew (1923–), until recently known as a leading proponent of atheism, abandoned this belief by considering the design of a cell. He explains:

'It seems to me that Richard Dawkins constantly overlooks the fact that Darwin himself, in the fourteenth chapter of *The Origin of Species*, pointed out that his whole argument began with a being which already possessed reproductive powers. This is the creature the evolution of which a truly comprehensive theory of evolution must give some account.

'Darwin himself was well aware that he had not produced such an account. It now seems to me that the findings of more than fifty years of DNA research have provided materials for a new and enormously powerful argument to design.'[6]

CHEMICAL EVOLUTION: EVIDENCE OR BLIND FAITH?

The non-creationist information theorist Hubert Yockey (1916–) made a very revealing comment 30 years ago:

'Research on the origin of life seems to be unique in that the conclusion has already been authoritatively accepted … . What remains to be done is to find the scenarios which describe the detailed mechanisms and processes by which this happened.'[7]

This is important to keep in mind when reading popular accounts of evolution, or in response to those who claim that believers in design are 'biased'.

Dr Yockey finished his paper with:

'One must conclude that, contrary to the established and current wisdom a scenario describing the genesis of life on Earth by chance and natural causes which can be accepted on the basis of fact and not faith has not yet been written.'[7]

The Origin-of-Life Foundation, Inc. currently offers a $1 million prize to anyone providing a chemically plausible naturalistic solution for the origin of the genetic code and life. The website states:

'"The Origin-of-Life Prize"® (hereafter called "the Prize") will be awarded for proposing a highly plausible *mechanism* for the spontaneous rise of *genetic*

---

6. My Pilgrimage from Atheism to Theism: an exclusive interview with former British atheist Professor Antony Flew by Gary Habermas, *Philosophia Christi*, Winter 2005; <www.illustramedia.com/IDArticles/flew-interview.pdf>.

7. Yockey, H.P., A calculation of the probability of spontaneous biogenesis by information theory, *J. Theoretical Biol.* **67**:377–398, 1977; quotes from pp. 379, 396.

instructions in nature sufficient to give rise to life. To win, the explanation must be consistent with empirical biochemical, kinetic, and thermodynamic concepts as further delineated herein, and be published in a well-respected, peer-reviewed science journal(s).'[8]

Thus far, there have been no awards.[9]

Life from outer space?

To emphasize the desperation of chemical evolutionary theories, some researchers have seriously proposed that aliens seeded life on earth. E.g., one of the co-discovers of the DNA double helix, Francis Crick (1916–2004), said:

> 'What is so frustrating for our present purpose is that it seems almost impossible to give any numerical value to the probability of what seems a rather unlikely sequence of events... An honest man, armed with all the knowledge available to us now, could only state that in some sense, the origin of life appears at the moment to be almost a miracle, so many are the conditions which would have had to have been satisfied to get it going. ...

> 'Every time I write a paper on the origin of life, I determine I will never write another one, because there is too much speculation running after too few facts.'[10]

But since he was a staunch antitheist, he, along with leading chemical evolutionist Leslie Orgel (1927–2007), resorted to 'Directed Panspermia'.[11] This proposes that intelligent aliens seeded life on Earth.[12]

Crick later thought that an 'RNA world' idea might solve his problems, although this has its own enormous problems (see p. 167). But more recent researchers have realized that there are still major problems with chemical evolution on Earth, and are driven to accept panspermia at least as a possibility.

Life arose too quickly on Earth, so must have been seeded?

Martin Line, a microbiologist in Tasmania, in an overview[13] admits that 'there remain numerous unsolved "chicken and egg" problems' (cf. p. 151). But his major problem is the *timing*. That is, there is far too short a time interval, even according to evolutionary

8.   <www.us.net/life/>.
9.   Smith, Calvin, Who wants to be a millionaire? $1 million prize offered for scientific proof of 'natural-process' origin of life, <creationontheweb.com/lifeprize>, 2007.
10.   Crick, *Life Itself, Its Origin and Nature*, pp. 88, 153, Simon and Schuster, 1981.
11.   Crick, F. and Orgel, L.E., Directed Panspermia, *Icarus* **19:**341–346, 1973.
12.   See also Bates, G., *Designed* by aliens? Discoverers of DNA's structure attack Christianity, *Creation* **25**(4):54–55, 2003; <creationontheweb.com/aliens>.
13.   Line, M.A., The enigma of the origin of life and its timing, *Microbiology* **148:**21–27, 2002, <http://mic.sgmjournals.org/cgi/content/full/148/1/21>.

'dates', between the earth becoming habitable and being inhabited. Earth was allegedly fit for life about 3.8. billion years ago, but 'all basic types of bioenergetic processes probably existed 3·5 billion years ago and the biogeochemical cycling of carbon, nitrogen and sulfur was established as we know it today...'.[14]

> 'Hence the enigma: an origin of life on Earth appears highly improbable, an origin elsewhere is highly conjectural. While this conundrum has been identified in various forms for several decades, its magnitude has dramatically increased over the last five years as new constraints are placed on the timing of the primary divergence of the domains of life. ...

> 'If Earth was the cradle for life, the time interval between its origin and the existence of the LCC [Last Common Community, cf. p. 140] appears incomprehensibly short. In view of the apparent complexity of the LCC, particularly in terms of biochemistry, it would be reasonable to allow perhaps 4 gigayears for its evolution from the primordial cell.'[13]

Thus he concludes:

> 'Acceptance of such an extended period of evolution must however lead to the conclusion of an extra-terrestrial origin for life on Earth. ... The concept of interstellar panspermia has been a philosophical luxury; it may soon become a necessity if constraints of evolutionary theory continue to conspire against an origin of life in our solar system.'[13]

Problems with panspermia

1. It merely pushes the problem back a step. I.e. instead of choosing between creation and evolution for life on earth, we have to decide whether the hypothetical alien life was created or evolved.
2. Many evolutionists claim creation is unscientific because it postulates a Creator who can't be tested in the lab. But exactly the same objection applies to aliens!

2. THE COMPLEXITY OF LIFE

THE SIMPLE CELL?

In Darwin's day, many people swallowed the theory of spontaneous generation—that life arose from non-living matter. It was somewhat easier to believe then because the cell's structure was almost unknown. Ernst Haeckel, Darwin's popularizer in Germany,

---

14. Fenchel, T. and Finlay, B.J., Anaerobic environments; in: *Ecology and Evolution in Anoxic Worlds*. pp. 1–31. Ed. May R.M. and Harvey, P.H., Oxford University Press, 1995; cited in Line, Ref. 13.

claimed that a cell was a 'simple lump of albuminous combination of carbon.'[15] (Haeckel was also a notorious fraudster—he forged embryonic diagrams to bolster the erroneous idea that the embryo's development recapitulated (re-traced) its alleged evolutionary ancestry).[16]

The molecular biological revolution of the last half century has shown how the cell requires both high *information* and a means to pass this information on to the next generation (*reproduction*).

The cell's information content

All the cell's machinery is programmed on the famous double-helix molecule DNA (deoxyribonucleic acid). This recipe has an enormous *information content*, which is transmitted from one generation to the next, so that living things reproduce 'after their kinds' (cf. Genesis 1, 10 times). Richard Dawkins admits:

> '[T]here is enough information capacity in a single human cell to store the *Encyclopaedia Britannica*, all 30 volumes of it, three or four times over.'[17]

The printed page stores information via the 26 letters of the alphabet, which are arrangements of ink molecules on paper. However, the information is not contained in the ink molecules, but in the way they are arranged into letters, words and sentences. A translation into another language, even one with a different alphabet, need not change the information content, but simply the way the ink molecules are arranged.

However, a computer hard drive stores information in a totally different way—an array of magnetic 'on or off' patterns on a ferromagnetic disk, and again the information is in the patterns, the arrangement, not the magnetic substance.

Totally different media can carry exactly the same information. An example is this book you're reading—the information is exactly the same as that on my computer's hard drive, but my hard drive looks vastly different from this page.

In DNA, the information is stored as sequences of four types of DNA bases, A,C,G and T. These could be called chemical 'letters' because they store information in an analogous way to printed letters.[18] There are huge problems for evolutionists explaining how even the 'letters' themselves could come from a primordial soup, as explained later (see p. 174, 181ff). But even if this were solved, it would be as meaningless as getting a bowl of alphabet soup, because the letters would not spell anything.

15. Behe, M.J., *Darwin's Black Box: The Biochemical Challenge to Evolution*, p. 24, The Free Press, New York, 1996.
16. Grigg, R., Ernst Haeckel: Evangelist for evolution and apostle of deceit, *Creation* **18**(2):33–36, 1996; <creationontheweb.com/haeckel>.
17. Dawkins, R., *The Blind Watchmaker*, p. 115, W.W. Norton, New York, 1986.
18. Adenine, cytosine, guanine and thymine. They are part of building blocks called nucleotides, which comprise the sugar deoxyribose, a phosphate and a base. In RNA, uracil (U) substitutes for thymine and ribose substitutes for deoxyribose.

Is the DNA message the result of chemistry?

No. There is nothing in the bases themselves that would make them join up in predetermined ways, any more than forces between ink molecules make them join up into letters and words. Michael Polanyi (1891–1976), a former chairman of physical chemistry at the University of Manchester (UK) who turned to philosophy, confirmed this:

'As the arrangement of a printed page is extraneous to the chemistry of the printed page, so is the base sequence in a DNA molecule extraneous to the chemical forces at work in the DNA molecule. It is this physical indeterminacy of the sequence that produces the improbability of any particular sequence and thereby enables it to have a meaning—a meaning that has a mathematically determinate information content.'[19]

CELL: 'SUPREME TECHNOLOGY AND BEWILDERING COMPLEXITY'

Molecular biologist Michael Denton, writing as a non-creationist skeptic of Darwinian evolution, explains some of the cell's complexity that modern biology has discovered. This shows that Darwin and Haeckel were naïve in the extreme:

'Perhaps in no other area of modern biology is the challenge posed by the extreme complexity and ingenuity of biological adaptations more apparent than in the fascinating new molecular world of the cell ... To grasp the reality of life as it has been revealed by molecular biology, we must magnify a cell a thousand million times until it is twenty kilometres in diameter and resembles a giant airship large enough to cover a great city like London or New York. What we would then see would be an object of *unparalleled complexity and adaptive design*. On the surface of the cell we would see millions of openings, like the port holes of a vast space ship, opening and closing to allow a continual stream of materials to flow in and out. If we were to enter one of these openings we would find ourselves in a *world of supreme technology and bewildering complexity*.'

'Is it really credible that random processes could have constructed a reality, the smallest element of which—a functional protein or gene—is complex beyond our own creative capacities, a reality which is the very antithesis of chance, which excels in every sense anything produced by the intelligence of man? *Alongside the level of ingenuity and complexity*

19. Polanyi, M., Life's irreducible structure, *Science* **160**:1308, 1968.

exhibited by the molecular machinery of life, even our most advanced artefacts appear clumsy. ...

'It would be an illusion to think that what we are aware of at present is any more than a fraction of the full extent of biological design. In practically every field of fundamental biological research ever-increasing levels of design and complexity are being revealed at an ever-accelerating rate.'[20]

THE SIMPLEST LIFE?

Given the basic requirements of information and reproduction just explained, what is the minimum amount of information required for a self-reproducing cell? Modern science has discovered vast quantities of complex, specific information in even the simplest self-reproducing organism.

Mycoplasma

Mycoplasma genitalium has the smallest known genome of any free-living organism—a virus doesn't count because it can't reproduce without hijacking the machinery of more complex cells. *Mycoplasma* contains 482 genes comprising 580,000 bases.[21] Of course, these genes are only functional with pre-existing translational and replicating machinery (see pp. 166–9), a cell membrane, etc. But *Mycoplasma* has no cell walls, and can only survive by parasitizing more complex organisms (e.g. the respiratory system and urogenital tract of humans) which provide many of the nutrients it cannot manufacture for itself. Indeed, this organism seems to have arisen by loss of genetic information, making it dependent on its host.[22]

LUCA

Since the simplest forms of life are obligate parasites, evolutionists must posit a more complex first living organism with even more genes. Much research concerns a hypothetical creature called LUCA or Last Universal Common Ancestor, supposedly the ancestor of all creatures living today (i.e. of all three 'domains' of life: archaebacteria, eubacteria and eukaryotes). A recent study concluded that LUCA must be much more complex than parasites like *Mycoplasma* and would need to be as complex as free-living bacteria. LUCA would need thousands of genes and the full set of tRNA synthetases and tRNAs. One research paper said:

'Therefore, the common belief that the hypothetical genome of LUCA should resemble those of the smallest extant genomes

20. Denton, M., *Evolution: A Theory in Crisis*, Adler and Adler, Maryland, 1986, pp. 328, 342; emphasis added. This book greatly influenced leaders of the modern Intelligent Design movement such as Phillip Johnson and Michael Behe. The explosion in knowledge since 1986 has amply vindicated Denton's perspective.

21. Fraser, C.M. *et al.*, The minimal gene complement of *Mycoplasma genitalium*, *Science* **270**(5235):397–403, 1995; perspective by Goffeau, A., Life with 482 Genes, same issue, pp. 445–446. Other reports have a different number, but all within the same ball park.

22. Wood, T.C., Genome decay in the Mycoplasmas, *Impact* **340**, 2001; <http://www.icr.org/pubs/imp/imp-340.htm>

of obligate parasites is not supported by recent advances in computational genomics. Instead, a fairly complex genome similar to those of free-living prokaryotes, with a variety of functional capabilities including metabolic transformation, information processing, membrane/transport proteins and complex regulation, shared between the three domains of life, emerges as the most likely progenitor of life on Earth ...'[23]

And the genetic code of LUCA would need to be almost as old as the earth is alleged to be,[24] which leaves far too little time for its posited evolution.

Bacteria

According to evolution, bacteria (and other prokaryotes, or cells without a nucleus) are 'primitive' organisms, while the cells of complex (eukaryotic) organisms like humans have a much higher level of sub-cellular organization.

However, recent research[25] by University of California (Los Angeles) biochemists led by Todd Yeates 'blurs the distinction between eukaryotic cells and those of prokaryotes by showing that bacterial cells are more complex than scientists had imagined.'[26]

The researchers have identified how microcompartments—the 'mysterious' molecular machines present in a wide variety of bacteria—are able to close in three dimensions, forming a protective shell around enzymes.

The key principle is that a large number of hexagons are combined with 12 strategically located pentagons to create a structure which is completely closed—a principle well understood by architects and soccer ball manufacturers.[27]

Artificial life?

A decade ago, Eugene Koonin, a researcher interested in making artificial biological organisms, tried to calculate the bare minimum required for a living cell. He based this on mycoplasmas, and estimating how many genes even these simple cells could do without. His team came up with a result of 256 genes.[28]

But they doubted whether such a hypothetical bug could survive, because such an organism could barely repair DNA damage, could no longer fine-tune the ability of its remaining genes, would lack the ability to digest complex compounds, and would need a comprehensive supply of organic nutrients in its environment.

23. Ouzounis, C.A. *et al.*, A minimal estimate for the gene content of the last universal common ancestor— exobiology from a terrestrial perspective, *Res. Microbiol.* **157**:57–68, 2006.
24. Eigen, M. *et al.*, How old is the genetic code? Statistical geometry of tRNA provides an answer, *Science* **244**(4905)673–679, 1989.
25. Tanaka, S. *et al.*, Atomic-Level Models of the Bacterial Carboxysome Shell, *Science* **319**(5866):1083–1086, 2008.
26. Biochemists reveal details of mysterious bacterial microcompartments, *Physorg.com*, <www.physorg.com/news122826699.html>, 2008.
27. From: Bacteria 'more complex than imagined', *Creation* **30**(3):9, 2008.
28. Wells, W., Taking life to bits, *New Scientist* **155**(2095):30–33, 1997.

So it is not surprising that follow-up research, led by Hamilton Smith at the J. Craig Venter Institute in Rockville, has revised this number significantly upwards. This new minimum genome consists of 387 protein-coding and 43 RNA-coding genes.[29]

PROTEINS: THE MACHINES OF LIFE[30]

To perform their right function, the protein machines must be folded correctly into specific, complex three-dimensional shapes. This is essential so that each one fits its target molecule, much as a key fits a lock.

Molecular surface of several proteins showing their comparitive sizes.

But predicting the right shape from a given sequence is one of the hardest problems for a supercomputer to solve. IBM built the world's most powerful supercomputer (dubbed *Blue Gene*, completed in 2005) to tackle the protein folding problem. The IBM website explains why:

> 'The scientific community considers protein folding one of the most significant "grand challenges"—a fundamental problem in science … whose solution can be advanced only by applying high-performance computing technologies.

> 'Proteins control almost all cellular processes in the human body. Comprising strings of amino acids that are joined like links of a chain, a protein folds into a highly complex, three-dimensional shape that determines its function. Any change in shape dramatically alters the function of a protein, and even the slightest change in the folding process can turn a desirable protein into a disease.'[31]

However, despite the enormous computing power, they estimated that it would still take about a year for *Blue Gene* to finish its calculations and model the folding of a simple protein. But the cell takes less than a second!

29. Glass, J.I., *et al.*, Essential genes of a minimal bacterium, *Proc. Nat. Acad. Sci. USA* **103(2):**425–430, 2006 | 10.1073/pnas.0510013103.

30. After Heinze, T., Did God create life? Ask a protein, *Creation* **28**(3):50–52, 2006; <creationontheweb.com/proteins>.

31. IBM and Department of Energy's NNSA partner to expand IBM's Blue Gene Research Project, <www.research.ibm.com/bluegene/press_release.html>, 28 November 2003.

As one IBM researcher had earlier noted, 'It's absolutely amazing, the complexity of the problem and the simplicity with which the body does it every day.'[32]

EXCELLENT ENZYMES[33]

One vital class of proteins is enzymes, which are *catalysts*, i.e. they speed up chemical reactions without being consumed in the process. Without them, many reactions essential for life would be far too slow for life to exist.[34]

Speeding up a reaction quintillion-fold

Enzyme expert Richard Wolfenden, of the University of North Carolina, showed in 1998[35] that a reaction '"absolutely essential" in creating the building blocks of DNA and RNA would take 78 million years in water', but was speeded up 10^{18} times[36] by an enzyme.[37]

The enzyme has a special shape, a *TIM-barrel*. This binds the substrate at the open end of the barrel, while protein loop movements almost totally surround the substrate. The enzyme has amino acid residues in just the right places to interact with the functional groups on the substrate.[38]

Sextillion-fold acceleration: new record

In 2003, Wolfenden found another enzyme that exceeded even this vast rate enhancement. A *phosphatase*, which catalyzes the hydrolysis (splitting) of phosphate bonds, magnified the reaction rate by a thousand times more than even that previous enzyme—10^{21} times. This enzyme allows reactions vital for cell signalling and regulation to take place in a hundredth of a second. Without the enzyme, this essential reaction would take a trillion years—almost a hundred times even the supposed evolutionary age of the universe (about 15 billion years)![39]

32.	Lohr, S., IBM plans a supercomputer that works at the speed of life, *New York Times*, 6 December, 1999, p. C1.

33.	After Sarfati, J., *J. Creation* 19(2):13–14, 2005; <creationontheweb.com/enzymes>.

34.	Catalysts do not affect the equilibrium, but only the *rate* at which equilibrium is reached. They work by lowering the activation energy, which means decreasing the energy of a transitional state or reaction intermediate.

35.	Miller, B.G., *et al.*, Anatomy of a proficient enzyme: The structure of orotidine 5'-monophosphate decarboxylase in the presence and absence of a potential transition state analog, *Proc. Nat. Acad. Sci. USA* 97(5):2011–2016, 2000; <www.pnas.org/cgi/content/full/97/5/2011>.

36.	Cited in Lang, L.H., Without enzyme catalyst, slowest known biological reaction takes 1 trillion years, Biocompare Life Science News, <http://news.biocompare.com/newsstory.asp?id=10433>, 2003.

37.	This was orotidine 5'-monophosphate decarboxylase, responsible for *de novo* synthesis of uridine 5'-phosphate, an essential precursor of RNA and DNA, by decarboxylating orotidine 5'-monophosphate (OMP).

38.	One lysine provides a positive charge to interact with the increasing negative charge as the substrate reacts, and provides a proton which replaces the carboxylate group at C-6 of the product. And the enzyme is structured so that some hydrogen bonds form and delocalize negative charge in the transition state, lowering the energy. Interactions between the enzyme and the phosphoribosyl group anchor the pyrimidine within the active site, helping to explain the phosphoribosyl group's remarkable contribution to catalysis despite its distance from the site of decarboxylation. Still other interactions hold the pyrimidine within the active site, which also contributes greatly to the catalysis, although it is far from the site of decarboxylation.

39.	Lad, C., Williams, N.H. and Wolfenden, R., The rate of hydrolysis of phosphomonoester dianions and the exceptional catalytic proficiencies of protein and inositol phosphatases, *Proc. Nat. Acad. Sci. USA*

Implications

Wolfenden said:

> 'Without catalysts, there would be no life at all, from microbes to humans. It makes you wonder how natural selection operated in such a way as to produce a protein that got off the ground as a primitive catalyst for such an extraordinarily slow reaction.'[36]

Of course, as pointed out on pp. 148–9, natural selection could not have been operational until there was life, while as he says, life could not have functioned without these enzymes to speed up vital reactions enormously.

COULD INFORMATION HAVE ARISEN BY CHANCE?

Having touched upon the complexity of even the simplest life, and including its amazing machinery, could this information have arisen by time and chance—since natural selection is not available without life? Yockey calculated that given a pool of pure, activated biological amino acids, the total amount of information which could be produced, even allowing 10^9 years as evolutionists posit, would be only a single small polypeptide 49 amino acid residues long.[40] This is about 1/8 the size (therefore approximate information content) of a typical protein, yet the hypothetical simple cell above needs at least 387 proteins. And Yockey's estimate generously presupposes that the many chemical hurdles can be overcome, which is a huge assumption, as will be shown on pp. 170 ff.

Alternatively, one could calculate the probability of obtaining all these proteins in the right sequence. Certainly, in many proteins, some substitutions are permissible, but not around the *active sites*. However, in other proteins there is hardly any leeway, e.g. the histones that act as spools around which DNA wraps in chromosomes. Other examples are ubiquitin, which is *ubiquitous* in organisms apart from bacteria and essential for marking unwanted proteins for destruction,[41,42] and calmodulin, the ubiquitous calcium-binding protein which has almost all of its 140–150 amino acids 'conserved' (the same in all organisms).

Even evolutionary writers implicitly concede that some sequences are essential, but they call them 'conserved'—i.e. the sequence was so vital that natural selection conserved it by eliminating variants. As the following conservative calculation shows, even making

100(10):5607–5610, 2003; <www.pnas.org/cgi/content/full/100/10/5607>.

40. Yockey, H.P., A Calculation of the probability of spontaneous biogenesis by information theory, *J. Theor. Biol.,* **67:**377–398, 1977.

41. Truman, R., The ubiquitin protein: chance or design? *J. Creation* **19**(3):116–127, 2005.

42. Aaron Ciechanover, Avram Hershko and Irwin Rose won the Nobel Prize in Chemistry in 2004 'for the discovery of ubiquitin-mediated protein degradation', <http://nobelprize.org/nobel_prizes/chemistry/laureates/2004/press.html/>.

generous assumptions to the evolutionists (e.g. ignoring the chemical problems), the origin of life from non-life still defies probability.

- 20 amino acids
- 387 proteins for the simplest possible life
- 10 conserved amino acids on average
- $\therefore$ the chance is $20^{-3870} = 10^{-3870.\log 20} = \mathbf{10^{-5035}}$
- This is one chance in one followed by over 5000 zeroes. So it would be harder than guessing a correct 5000-digit PIN on the first go!

Is time really 'the hero of the plot'? No:

- 10^{80} atoms in the universe
- 10^{12} atomic interactions per second
- 10^{18} seconds in the universe, according to the fallacious big bang theory
- $\therefore$ only 10^{110} interactions possible. This is a huge number, but compared with the tiny chance of obtaining the right sequence, it is absurdly small: only 10^{-4925}.

The former atheist Sir Fred Hoyle (1915–2001)[43] abandoned this view when he considered the absurdly small probabilities:

'Imagine 10^{50} blind persons each with a scrambled Rubik cube, and try to conceive of the chance of them all simultaneously arriving at the solved form. You then have the chance of arriving by random shuffling of just one of the many biopolymers on which life depends.

'The notion that not only the biopolymers but the operating program of a living cell could be arrived at by chance in a primordial organic soup here on the Earth is evidently nonsense of a high order.'[44]

Advanced probability calculation

Alternatively, we could do the calculations on the coding material. Since the RNA World hypothesis is popular (but see pp. 180–5 for the intractable problems), Dermot Mullan calculated the probability of forming an RNA molecule that coded for the necessary proteins. Even allowing for considerable flexibility, he concluded:

'In order to illustrate the consequences of the finite value of nr [number of relevant chemical reactions], we make some extremely minimalist assumptions about cells. We consider a cell composed of $Np = 12$ proteins, each containing $Na = 14$ amino acids. We refer to the minimum (Np, Na) set as a $(12–14)$ cell. Such a cell is smaller than some modern viruses. ...

TECHNICAL DETAILS

---

43. See Hoyle's obituary, Demme, G. and Sarfati, J., Big-bang critic dies, *J. Creation* **15**(3):6–7, 2001, <creationontheweb.com/hoyle>.
44. Hoyle, Sir Fred, The Big Bang in Astronomy, *New Scientist* **92**:521–527, 19 November 1981.

TECHNICAL DETAILS

'We find that, even assigning the minimum possible specificity (m = 1), the probability Pr of assembling the RNA of a (12–14) cell by random processes in 1.11 billion years using triplet codons is no more than one in 10^{79}. And if the protein tasks are even marginally specific (with m = 2–3, say), the chances of random assembly of RNA for the first cell decreases to less than one in 10^{100}. ...

'In order to improve the chances of random assembly of the first cell, we consider a situation which might have existed in the young Earth. We suppose that proteins could be constructed using a smaller set (numbering Naa) of distinct amino acids: we consider the case of Naa = 5 (instead of the modern 20). If, in these conditions, the number of bases in DNA remained as large as 4, then doublet codons sufficed to encode protein production with the same amount of error protection as occurs in the modern (triplet) genetic code. In such conditions, the probability of randomly assembling the RNA for the first cell in 1.11 b.y. improves. However, it is still small: the optimal probability is no more than one in 10^{63}. ...

'We stress that our assumptions about a (12–14) cell are minimalist in the extreme. In the real world, it is not obvious that a protein containing only 14 peptides will be able to fold into a stable 3-dimensional shape at the temperatures where water is liquid. And in the real world, a cell probably requires as many as 250 proteins to function. ...

'Our calculations refer only to the assembling of a cell in which the genetic code is already at work. We do not address the origin of the genetic code itself.'[45]

GENETIC CODE

The cell's information technology

The instructions to make all of an organism's proteins are stored on its DNA. DNA is by far the most compact information storage system in the universe. While we might think that our 100 gigabyte hard drive is advanced technology, a pinhead of DNA could hold 40 *million* times more information.

---

45.   Mullan, D.J., Probabilities of randomly assembling a primitive cell on Earth, *Progress in Complexity, Information, and Design* 1(4), October–December 2002.

Overview
- The encyclopedic information content of living things is stored and transmitted to the next generation as a message on DNA 'letters,' but the message is in the arrangement, not the letters themselves.
- The message requires decoding and transmission machinery, which itself is part of the stored 'message.'
- The choices of the code and even the letters are optimal.
- Therefore, the genetic coding system is an example of irreducible complexity.
- There are other codes super-imposed on the DNA.

Triplet code

A group (codon) of three DNA 'letters' codes for one protein 'letter' called an amino acid (AA, see diagram, right), and the conversion requires *transcription* and *translation* (see p. 167). Since even one mistake in a protein can be catastrophic, it's important to decode correctly. Think again about a written language—it is only useful if the

How the DNA 'letters' (codons) code for amino acids in proteins.

reader is familiar with the language. For example, a reader must know that the letter sequence f-i-s-h codes for an aquatic creature with fins and scales. But consider the sequence g-i-f-t—in English, it means a present; but in German, it means poison. Understandably, during the anthrax scare shortly after the 9-11 terrorist attack, some German postal workers were very reluctant to handle packages marked 'Gift.'

The *Origin of Life Foundation* asks, and provides no answer:

'How does an algorithmically complex sequence of codons arise in nature which finds phenotypic usefulness only after translation into a completely different language (AA sequence)?'[8]

They also reinforce what Dobzhansky pointed out (p. 148); that natural selection cannot explain it:

'The problem is that natural selection works only at the phenotypic level, not at the genetic level. Neither physicochemical forces nor environmental selection choose the next nucleotide to be added to the biopolymer. Mutations occur at the genetic level. But environmental selection occurs at the folding (functional) level, after-the-fact of already strongly set sequence, and after-the-fact of already established algorithmic function of the folded biopolymer.'[5]

Not universal

Many evolutionists claim that the DNA code is universal, and that this is proof of a common ancestor. But this is false—there are exceptions, some known since the 1970s. An example is *Paramecium*, where a few of the 64 (4^3 or 4x4x4) possible codons code for different amino acids. More examples are being found constantly. Also, some organisms code for one or two extra amino acids beyond the main 20 types.[46] But if one organism evolved into another with a different code, all the messages already encoded would be scrambled, just as written messages would be jumbled if computer keys were switched. This is a huge problem for the evolution of one code into another.

However, there is substantial consistency in the code, which is not surprising, since there is one Creator—one Mind behind it all. And the inconsistencies are sufficient to throw a spanner into evolutionists' attempts to explain the code.

Optimal code

Our DNA code has built-in redundancy: there are 64 possible DNA triplets to the 20 amino acids plus one stop codon. There are an astronomical number of possible codes linking the 64 to the 20—1.51×10^{84}—so why is ours *almost* universal, and why is there redundancy?

It turns out that ours, or something almost like it, is optimal for protecting against errors.[47] With the redundancy, there is more likelihood that a mutation will not change the amino acid at all. And the particular code means that a change is more likely to result in a chemically similar amino acid (acidic to acidic, basic to basic, hydrophobic to hydrophobic).

The redundancy also allows *variable translation speed* because the special adaptor molecules, called *tRNAs* (see p. 167) are present in different amounts. I.e. if a lot of protein is needed, a codon with a high concentration of the corresponding tRNA would be used for a particular amino acid. [48] But if the cell requires a small amount of protein, then the same amino acid would be coded by another codon corresponding to a rarer tRNA. This means that the construction of the protein must wait till the rare tRNA lands in the right place. The cell controls this by maintaining different amounts of the enzymes needed to form the tRNAs.

Natural selection cannot explain this code optimality, since there is no way to replace the first functional code with a 'better' one

---

46. Certain Archaea and eubacteria code for 21st or 22nd amino acids, selenocysteine and pyrrolysine—see Atkins, J.F. and Gesteland, R., The 22nd amino acid, *Science* **296**(5572):1409–10, 2002; commentary on technical papers on pp. 1459–62 and 1462–66.

47. Knight, J., Top translator, *New Scientist* **158**(2130):15, 1998.

48. Sharp, P.M., *et al.*, Codon usage: mutational bias, translational selection of both? *Biochem. Soc. Trans.* **21**:835–841, 1993.

without destroying functionality.[49] And the probability of hitting on the optimal code by chance, even if a naturalistic origin of a code were possible, is so small as to be considered impossible.

Source of information

Just as the *Britannica* had intelligent writers to produce its information, as do the documents on my hard drive, so it is reasonable and even scientific to believe that the information in the living world likewise had an original compositor/sender. Indeed, wherever we *know* the source of any sequence of information that corresponds to a language convention, whether books or computer code, the source is always an intelligence. The coding portions of the DNA have exactly these properties. There is no known non-intelligent cause that has ever been *observed* to generate even a small portion of the literally encyclopedic information required for life.

DNA and reproduction

The 'letters' of DNA have another vital property due to their structure, which allows information to be transmitted: *A* pairs only with *T*, and *C* only with *G*, due to the chemical structures of the bases—the pair is like a rung or step on a spiral staircase. This means that the two strands of the double helix can be separated, and new strands can be formed that copy the information exactly. The new strand carries the same information as the old one, but instead of being like a photocopy, it is a little like a photographic negative.

Editing machinery

The copying is far more precise than pure chemistry could manage—only about 1 mistake in 10 billion letters, because there is editing (proof-reading and error-checking) machinery, again encoded in the DNA. But how would the information for editing machinery be transmitted accurately before this editing machinery was in place? Lest it be argued that the accuracy could be achieved stepwise through selection, note that a high degree of accuracy is needed to prevent 'error catastrophe'—the accumulation of 'noise' in the form of junk proteins. Again there is a vicious circle, a 'Catch-22' (more irreducible complexity).

Separating the double helix

For replication, the two strands must be separated so a copy can be made. The strands are separated by a molecular motor called *helicase*. This is a ring-shaped molecule that lies on the replication fork, where the two strands separate. Helicase pulls one strand though its hole, while the other strand is shuttled away.[50]

---

49. Truman, R. and Borger, P., Genetic code optimisation: Part 1, *J. Creation* **21**(2):90–100, 2007.
50. Mechanism of T7 Primase/Helicase (includes animation), <www.scianafilms.com/html/animation/features/t7/index.htm>.

Helicase also doesn't need to wait passively for the fork to widen; rather, researchers from Cornell University show that it opens the fork *actively*.[51] One of them, Michelle Wang, said, 'Basically, it is an active unwinding motor.'[52] However, the unwinding is much faster in cells than in the test tube, so she suggested that 'accessory proteins are helping the helicase out by destabilizing the fork junction.'[51]

All this activity would be impossible without the universal energy currency of life, ATP (adenosine triphosphate), made by the world's tiniest motor (see ch. 10, p. 133–6)—something else that has to be functioning at the time the first cell came together.

Since replication is vital for life, helicases are vital to all living organisms. Wang's colleague Smita Patel pointed out also, 'Helicases are involved in practically all DNA and RNA metabolic processes'. Furthermore, 'Defects in helicases are associated with many human diseases, ranging from predisposition to cancer to premature aging.' So the origin of such elaborate machinery and the energy source is just one more problem for chemical evolution to solve.

Why these letters?

Would there not be any other chemical letters that could do the job of base-pair matching? Actually, even the choice of the letters A, T, G and C now seems to be based on minimizing error during reproduction. Evolutionists usually suppose that these letters happened to be the ones in the alleged primordial soup, but research shows that C (cytosine) is extremely unlikely to have been present in any such 'soup' (see p. 174). Rather, Dónall Mac Dónaill of Trinity College Dublin suggests that the letter choice is like the advanced error-checking systems that are incorporated into ISBNs on books, credit card numbers, bank accounts and airline tickets. Any alternatives would suffer error catastrophe.[53]

Decoding the information on DNA

The genetic code is not an outcome of raw chemistry, any more than the computer ASCII code is the result of the properties of semiconductors. Rather, both are the result of elaborate decoding machinery.

In living organisms, the decoding has two main steps. DNA is not read directly, but first the cell makes a copy (actually more analogous

51. Johnson, D.S., Bai, L., Smith, B.Y., Patel, S.S., Wang, M.D., Single-molecule studies reveal dynamics of DNA unwinding by the ring-shaped t7 helicase, *Cell* **129**(7):1299–1309, 2007.

52. Researchers solve mystery of how DNA strands separate, *Physorg.com*, <www.physorg.com/news102663442.html>, 2007.

53. Bradley, D., The genome chose its alphabet with care, *Science* **297**(5588):1789–91, 2002. Mac Dónaill's theory involves *parity bits*, an extra 1 or 0 added to a binary string to make it add up to an even number (e.g. when transmitting the number 11100110, add an extra 1 onto the end (11100110,1), and the number 11100001 has a zero added (11100001,0). If there is a single error changing a 1 to a 0 or vice versa, the string will add up to an odd number, so the receiver knows that it has not been transmitted accurately. Mac Dónaill found that he could treat certain structural features of the DNA 'letters' as a four-digit binary number, with the fourth digit a parity bit. He found that these DNA letters all have even parity, while 'alphabets composed of nucleotides of mixed parity would have catastrophic error rates.'

to a photographic negative) in a very similar molecule called RNA (ribonucleic acid), specifically 'messenger RNA' (mRNA). This is called *transcription* (more on p. 166). Then the mRNA is transported to a machine called the *ribosome* (more on p. 166–8), where the information is decoded into the proteins—*translation.*

Chicken and egg problem

Remarkably, this decoding machinery is itself encoded in the DNA, which is a real 'chicken and egg' problem. The noted philosopher of science Sir Karl Popper (1902–1994) pointed out (emphasis added):

> 'What makes the origin of life and of the genetic code a *disturbing riddle* is this: the genetic code is without any biological function unless it is translated; that is, unless it leads to the synthesis of the proteins whose structure is laid down by the code. But ... the machinery by which the cell ... translates the code consists of at least fifty macromolecular components *which are themselves coded in the DNA*. Thus the code can not be translated except by using certain products of its translation.

> 'This constitutes a *baffling circle; a really vicious circle*, it seems, for any attempt to form a model or theory of the genesis of the genetic code.

> 'Thus we may be faced with the possibility that the origin of life (like the origin of physics) becomes an impenetrable barrier to science, and a residue to all attempts to reduce biology to chemistry and physics.'[54]

So, such a system must be fully in place before it could work at all, a property called *irreducible complexity*. This means that it is impossible for natural selection to build it working with small incremental changes.

Although Popper wrote this over 30 years ago, the origin of the genetic code remains as much an enigma now as it was then. Trevors and Abel admit:

> 'Thus far, no paper has provided a plausible mechanism for natural-purpose algorithm-wiring.'[55]

Uncoiling the DNA

The DNA is bound in the double helix, which is itself wound into nucleosomes, the positioning of which is governed by another

54. Popper, K.R., Scientific Reduction and the Essential Incompleteness of All Science. In Ayala, F. and Dobzhansky, T., eds., *Studies in the Philosophy of Biol.*, University of California Press, Berkeley, p. 270; emphasis added, 1974.
55. Trevors, J.T. and Abel, D.L., Chance and necessity do not explain the origin of life, *Cell Biol. Int.* **28**:729–739, 2004.

code (see p. 169). Then this is coiled further, then supercoiled around scaffold proteins to form the chromosomes visible under a microscope at cell division. So to read the DNA information, it must be uncoiled in various stages.[56]

Transcription and the scrunching machine

Even the copying of the correct section of the DNA to mRNA requires intricate machinery. This involves an enzyme called *RNA polymerase*, comprising four protein chains. And another protein tells the RNA polymerase where to start reading the DNA template. Then the enzyme complex moves along the DNA strand, adding the matching RNA letters one at a time, and then stops in the right place.

Richard Ebright and his team from Rutgers University have discovered more intricacies in this process of *transcription*.[57,58,59] Indeed, it is this transcribed mRNA that is translated into proteins in the complex machines known as ribosomes.

DNA is double-stranded and only one strand is copied, so it must be unwound for copying. The copying machine, called RNA polymerase (RNAP), first locks on to the start of the gene (i.e., protein-coding sequence). The anchored RNAP then reels in the DNA—*scrunching*.[60] This unwinds the double strand so the mRNA copy can be formed off one of them. Also, the unwinding stores energy; like winding the rubber band of a rubber-powered airplane. And just like the toy plane, this energy is eventually released, with the machine then breaking free of its starting point and shooting forward. This also rewinds the unwound DNA ('unscrunching') which then escapes from the back of the machine.

Ebright states that this research should enable them to develop antibacterial agents that target the bacterial version of this machine.[57]

READING THE INFORMATION

Ribosome

This is the vital machine of the cell that reads the information on the mRNA, producing proteins. Even in a 'simple' bacterium such as *E. coli*, which lives in your intestines, ribosomes comprise 50 different proteins and three different ribosomal RNAs (rRNAs).

56. Williams, A., Astonishing DNA complexity update, <creationontheweb.com/DNAupda >, 2007.
57. *PhysOrg.com*, Nanotech tools yield DNA transcription breakthrough, <www.physorg.com/news82910354. html>, 2006.
58. Revyakin, A., *et al.*, Abortive initiation and productive initiation by RNA Polymerase involve DNA scrunching, *Science* **314**(5802):1139–1143, 2006.
59. Kapanidis, A.N., *et al.*, Initial transcription by RNA polymerase proceeds through a DNA-scrunching mechanism, *Science* **314**(5802):1144–1147, 2006.
60. Roberts, J.W., RNA Polymerase, a Scrunching Machine, *Science* **314**(5802):1139–1143, 17 November 2006 (comment on refs 58 and 59).

In more complex organisms with cell nuclei (eukaryotes), there are 73 different proteins involved and four rRNAs. One expert said:
'The ribosome, together with its accessories, is probably the most sophisticated machine ever made. All of its components are active and moving, and it is environmentally friendly, producing only GDP and phosphate.'[61]

The ribosome also makes sure that a protein grows *linearly*. Outside a machine, a growing peptide chain would easily form undesirable *side branches*, where side groups react with each other (e.g. the extra –COOH of aspartic and glutamic acids could react with the extra $–NH_2$ groups of lysine and arginine). In industrial peptide synthesis, the side groups must be blocked by *protecting groups*, then unblocked when synthesis is finished by removing those groups.

Transfer RNA

Transfer RNA (tRNA) molecules are vital adaptors, shaped like a four-leafed clover, and are responsible for carrying individual amino acids to the site where they are added to a new protein. They comprise about 80 nucleotide 'letters', three of which are called the *anticodon*. The anticodon links to the corresponding codon on the mRNA, which in turn relays the correct code from the DNA. Thus the tRNAs can transfer the right amino acids to the right place in the growing peptide chain, as coded in the mRNA.

Also, each amino acid is *activated*, to overcome the energy barrier to linking up to the adjacent amino acid in the growing protein (see p. 178–180), and the energy comes from ATP (cf. p. 164). Then a special enzyme called *aminoacyl-tRNA synthetase* (aaRS) bonds each amino acid in two steps to the correct tRNA. . There have to be a minimum of 20 aaRSs—at least one for each type of amino acid. Any failure here would destroy the message, and thus the whole purpose of the genetic code.

The adaptor molecules must have exactly the right geometry to hold the amino acids in a position where they can form a peptide bond and also place the anticodon in the right place on the mRNA. But correct geometry of the adaptors is unlikely to be sufficient outside the ribosome. Also, hypothetically evolving adaptors are likely to tangle with each other and the mRNA.[49]

Furthermore, the adaptors must be detachable once the amino acid has been joined. The ribosome moves the mRNA along like a ratchet, and energy for detachment comes from GTP (guanosine triphosphate).[49]

Double-sieves: advanced chemical machines[62]

These aaRSs perform amazing chemistry. They can even distinguish between amino acids that are very chemically similar, e.g. leucine and isoleucine—one text book said, 'Leucine and isoleucine are particularly difficult to separate.'[63] But their small difference can still mean the difference between life and death—even a single mutation substituting one for the other can be detrimental in ribonuclease T_1, chymotrypsin inhibitor 2 and human lysozyme, and can increase susceptibility to lung cancer.

Yet the aaRS for isoleucine manages to distinguish them extremely well, with an error rate of only 1 in 40,000. It achieves this with a *double-sieve* mechanism: one sieve rejects amino acids too large, while the other rejects those too small.[64]

Chaperones

Even the protein chain that forms in the ribosome is not the finished product. To perform its function in a cell, including the enzymes on p. 157, a protein must be folded correctly into its own complex three-dimensional shape (see p. 156). The final protein configuration that results from a particular DNA sequence is mainly determined by cellular machines called *chaperones* or *chaperonins*, themselves barrel-shaped proteins that help other proteins to fold. Without chaperones, an important protein might mis-fold into a deadly prion. This is the likely cause of the fatal brain conditions Creutzfeldt–Jakob disease and bovine spongiform encephalopathy (BSE), also known as mad cow disease.

There is yet another vicious circle here: the chaperones fold correctly because they have chaperones of their own! So how did the first *chaperones* ever fold correctly without pre-existing chaperones?[65] Evolution has to explain such impossibilities.

MORE THAN JUST A SUPER HARD DRIVE

Actually, DNA is far more complicated than simply coding for proteins, as we are discovering all the time.[1] For example, because the DNA letters are read in groups of three, it makes a huge difference which letter we start from. E.g. the sequence GTTCAACGCTGAA … can be read from the first letter, GTT CAA CGC TGA A … but a totally different protein will result from starting from the second letter, TTC AAC GCT GAA …

This means that DNA can be an even more compact information storage system. This partly explains the surprising finding of the

---

62. After Sarfati, J., Decoding and editing designs: double-sieve enzymes, *J. Creation* **13**(1):5–7, 1999; <creationontheweb.com/doublesieve>.
63. Karlson, P., (tr. Doering, C.H.), *Introduction to modern biochemistry*, 4th ed., Academic Press, NY, London, pp. 145–146, 113, 1975.
64. Nureki, O., *et al.*, Enzyme structure with two catalytic sites for double-sieve selection of substrate, *Science* **280**(5363):578–82, 1998; Perspective by A.R. Fersht, Sieves in sequence, same issue, p. 541.
65. Aw, S.E., The Origin of Life: A critique of current scientific models, *J. Creation* **10**(3):300–314, 1996.

Human Genome Project that there are 'only' about 25,000 genes, when humans can manufacture over 100,000 proteins.[66]

ADDITIONAL CODE

In the cell, the DNA double helix is wound into spools called *nucleosomes*. These contain eight proteins called *histones*, which are almost invariant among different species—pea and cow histones differ by only two amino acids out of 102. Each nucleosome has 1.65 loops of DNA; 147 bases. So human cells need 20 million nucleosomes.

They likely protect the DNA from unwanted transcription; e.g. skin cells have all the information to make bone, but it would be harmful for bone to grow where skin is supposed to be. However, in the living cell, when a gene must be transcribed, the nucleosome is free to move away from it.

Now Eran Segal of the Weizmann Institute in Israel and Jonathan Widom of Northwestern University in Illinois and their colleagues have found *another DNA code beyond genetics* that *controls the positioning of the nucleosomes*.[67] Instead of a triplet code, this code operates over a much larger scale, where there are certain regions of DNA that can bend more sharply and thus bind to the nucleosome more strongly. Their 'results demonstrate that genomes encode an intrinsic nucleosome organization.' From these sequences, the scientists were able to predict the positions of about 50% of the nucleosomes. This is an important role of the alleged 'junk DNA' (see chapter 12 pp. 210–217).

The origin of one code by chance is hard enough; the origin of two superimposed codes is much harder still. They can probably co-exist because the nucleosome position code allows some flexibility, and the genetic code has some redundancy, so this is another reason for the latter. But this new code explains the reason why the histone sequence must be precise: so the nucleosomes can find the right positions on the DNA.[68]

This extra 'epigenetic code' is still a mystery for evolutionists, as one researcher admitted:

> 'While the role of epigenetic inheritance in development is becoming a major subject of biological research, **the study of its implications for evolution is lagging far behind**.'[69] (emphasis added)

---

66. Batten, D., Discoveries that undermine the one gene→one protein idea, *Creation* **24**(4):13, 2002; <creationontheweb.com/one_gene>.
67. Segal, E., *et al.*, A genomic code for nucleosome positioning, *Nature* **442**(7104):772–778, 17 August 2006; DOI: 10.1038/nature04979.
68. Wade, N., Scientists Say They've Found a Code Beyond Genetics in DNA, *New York Times*, 25 July 2006.
69. Jablonka, E., The evolution of the peculiarities of mammalian sex chromosomes: an epigenetic view, *BioEssays* **26**:1327–1332, 2004; White, D., The Genetic Puppeteer, *Creation* **30**(2):42–44, 2008; <creationontheweb.com/puppet>.

3. CHEMICAL EVOLUTIONARY THEORIES *VS* THE FACTS OF CHEMISTRY[70]

Evolutionists believe that all life came from a chemical soup. That is, somehow the building blocks for life formed by themselves, then linked in the right way on their own. However, there are many chemical problems that chemists well know.

Indeed, the more we understand about biochemistry, the more we learn how different it is from other chemistry. The laws are the same, but chemistry outside the living world is always 'dirty' mass action chemistry, while biochemistry is pure single-molecule chemistry.[71]

The term 'dirty' comes from chemical evolutionist and Nobel laureate Christian de Duve. It is merely a statement of fact that chemistry in the non-living world involves many molecules at a time, and invariably includes contaminants.[72] The theistic evolutionary paleontologist Simon Conway Morris called the product of typical 'origin-of-life' experiments 'muck', 'goo' and 'gunk',[73] echoing chemical evolutionist Graham Cairns-Smith's term 'grossly contaminated gunks'.[74]

Indeed, modern industrial chemistry, with carefully planned processes, can't normally achieve purities above 99.99%. This is largely because it deals with huge numbers of molecules at a time. But biochemistry can achieve better, because each enzyme manipulates the right substance one molecule at a time, then its products are taken care of by the next enzyme, in the right shape and right place.

Oparin and Haldane: chemical evolution pioneers

The Russian biochemist, Alexander Ivanovich Oparin (Александр Иванович Опарин, 1894–1980), originated the modern form of chemical evolution in 1924.[75] He stated:

'Engels' materialistic philosophy shows that the origin of life could have only followed a single path. It could not have existed eternally, nor could it have arisen [instantaneously]. It must, therefore, have resulted from a long evolution of matter.'

70. One of the best books about the problems with chemical evolution is Thaxton, C.B., Bradley, W.L. and Olsen, R.L., *The Mystery of Life's Origin,* Philosophical Library Inc., New York, 1984. The basic principles of chemistry have not changed in a quarter of a century, although chemical evolutionists continue to invent new ways to try to work around them. Some chapters are available online at <www.ldolphin.org/mystery/index.html>.

71. Williams, A., Life's irreducible structure—Part 1: autopoesis, *J. Creation* 21(2):116–122, 2007.

72. De Duve, C., *Singularities: Landmarks on the Pathways of Life,* Cambridge University Press, 2005; see review by Williams, A., Great minds on the origin of life, *J. Creation* 21(1): 38–42, 2007.

73. Conway Morris, S., *Life's Solution: Inevitable humans in a lonely universe,* Cambridge University Press, Chs 3–4, 2003; see review by ReMine, W., Evidence for Message Theory, *J. Creation* 20(2):29–35, 2006.

74. Cairns-Smith, A.G., *Genetic Takeover and the Mineral Origins of Life,* Cambridge University Press, New York, 1982.

75. Oparin, A.I., *Proiskhozhdyeniye Zhizny* (Происхождение жизни), Izd. Moskovskii Rabochii, Moscow, 1924; *Origin of Life,* trans. S. Morgulis, Macmillan, NY, 1938.

It's interesting to note the logical chain in his argument: materialistic philosophy (a philosophical belief, not a scientific one) … therefore chemical evolution.

A few years later, the British biologist, J.B.S. Haldane, thought of a similar idea independently.[76] He was also a devoted Communist for many years, writing frequently for the Party newspaper, *The Daily Worker*.

Their idea, with some modifications, is taught today by most biology textbooks. The idea is that various energy sources would generate organic compounds from a primitive reducing atmosphere (one rich in hydrogen-containing compounds). They reasoned that as there were no microbes to feed on those chemicals, they would accumulate in the oceans, forming what Haldane called a 'hot dilute soup'. These compounds would react further to form enzymes and other important biochemicals. Eventually, these would form a self-reproducing cell. Then the stage is set for neo-Darwinian evolution.

Miller–Urey experiments[77]

The Oparin–Haldane model was thought to have received a big boost from these experiments. Stanley Miller (1930–2007), was a graduate student of Harold Urey (1893–1981), who had won the 1934 Nobel Prize for Chemistry for discovering deuterium (heavy hydrogen).[78] They filled a sealed glass apparatus with the gases that Oparin had speculated were necessary to form life—namely methane, ammonia and hydrogen. There was also a flask of boiling water, to supply water and drive the gases to circulate past a 60,000-volts sparking device to simulate lightning. Then the gas mixture passed though a water-cooled condenser that cooled and condensed the products so they could be collected by falling into a water trap below.

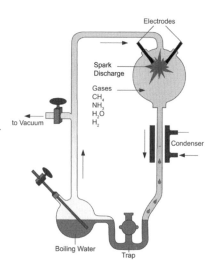

---

76. Haldane, J.B.S., The Origin of Life, *Rationalist Annual*, p.148, 1928.
77. See Bergman, J., Why the Miller–Urey research argues against abiogenesis, *J. Creation* **18**(2):74–84, 2002.
78. < http://nobelprize.org/nobel_prizes/chemistry/laureates/1934/urey-bio.html>.

After a week, they found a red stain in the trap. Most of this was an insoluble toxic carcinogenic mixture called 'tar' or 'resin', a common product in organic reactions, including burning tobacco. Using recently developed analysis tools (2D chromatography), they found a small amount of amino acids.[79,80]

However, they were mainly the simplest amino acids glycine and alanine.[81] And the yields were a tiny 1.05% and 0.75% respectively. Miller admitted, 'The total yield was small for the energy expended.'[79] Yet there is no evidence that the situation would improve with longer time—the tiny yields of simple products seem to be as much as the simulation could ever achieve. There are many other problems:

Wrong atmosphere

There is almost universal agreement among specialists that earth's primordial atmosphere contained no methane, ammonia or hydrogen—'reducing' gases. Rather, most evolutionists now believe it contained carbon dioxide and nitrogen.

'... the accepted picture of the earth's early atmosphere has changed: It was probably O_2-rich with some nitrogen, a less reactive mixture than Miller's, or it might have been composed largely of carbon dioxide, which would greatly deter the development of organic compounds.'[82]

The oxygen dilemma

Miller–Urey models exclude oxygen, because

1. No amino acids can form in the Miller-type experiments if even a trace of oxygen is present.
2. Free oxygen would destroy any organic molecules rapidly.

However, there is no evidence that the Earth's atmosphere was ever oxygen-free. Indeed, some chemical evolutionists claim that the strongest 'evidence' for an oxygen-free atmosphere is that chemical evolutionary theories require it![83]

Sunlight can split water vapour into oxygen and hydrogen, and the latter escapes Earth's gravity, leaving the oxygen.[84] Also, there is evidence for photosynthetic organisms very soon after the earth

79. Miller, S.L., A production of amino acids under possible primitive earth conditions, *Science* **117**:528–529; p. 528, 1953.
80. Miller, S.L., Production of some organic compounds under possible primitive earth conditions, *J. Amer. Chem. Soc.* **77**:2351–2361, 1955.
81. Yockey argued in *Nature* (**415**(6874):833, 2002) that Stanley Miller wasn't the first. There were earlier experiments of Walther Löb (1913), Oskar Baudisch (1913), Edward Bailey (1922) and Harold Urey (1928,29). Yockey suggested that Miller merely augmented these previous experiments with modern separation and detection techniques such as two-dimensional paper chromatography. Coincidentally, the significance of these techniques was emphasized by my organic chemistry professor. A reply by Jeffrey Bada and Antonia Lazcano *Nature* (**416**(6880):475) defended the significance of Miller's experiments for chemical evolution, while Löb showed no interest in this.
82. Flowers, C., *A Science Odyssey: 100 Years of Discovery*, William Morrow and Company, New York, p. 173, 1998.
83. Walker, J.C.G., 'reasons' this way in *Evolution of the Atmosphere*, Macmillan, NY 1977.
84. Brinkmann, R.T., Dissociation of water vapour and the evolution of oxygen in the terrestrial atmosphere, *J. Geophys. Res.* **74**:5355–5366, 1969.

had formed, something that is difficult for chemical evolutionary theories to explain (see chapter 10). A 2004 paper argues from uranium geochemistry that there were oxidizing conditions, thus photosynthesis, at 3.7 evolutionary billion years ago.[85] But according to evolutionary dating, the earth was being bombarded by meteorites up to 3.8 billion years ago. So even granting evolutionary presuppositions, this latest research shows that life existed almost as soon as the earth was able to support it, not 'billions and billions of years' later.

But if there were no oxygen (O_2), then there would be no ozone (O_3), which shields Earth from short-wave radiation, so ultraviolet light would destroy any biochemicals. This is a real 'catch-22'. Another one is that the hydrogen cyanide (HCN) polymerization that is alleged to lead to adenine (an essential DNA/RNA base) can occur only in the *presence* of oxygen.[86]

Missing primordial soup

Although the idea of a primordial soup is part of popular culture, most would be surprised that there is not the slightest evidence that one ever existed. Such a soup was supposed to be the source of the essential nitrogen-containing amino acids and nucleotides. So if it existed, then evolutionary geologists should find some massive deposits rich in nitrogen in what they claim are very early rocks. Yet there is hardly any nitrogen in what they call the earliest organic materials—only about 0.015%. Two geochemists point out:

'If there ever was a primitive soup, then we would expect to find at least somewhere on this planet either massive sediments containing enormous amounts of the various nitrogenous organic compounds, acids, purines, pyrimidines, and the like; or in much metamorphosed sediments we should find vast amounts of nitrogenous cokes. In fact *no such materials have been found anywhere on earth.*' [87]

Unrealistic traps

All energy sources that produce the biochemicals destroy them enormously faster. On the hypothetical primordial earth, the destructive UV radiation is both more plentiful than the constructive UV radiation, and also more effective. This amounts to two strikes, so that the destructive effects are about 10^4–10^5 stronger than the constructive ones.[88]

85. Rosing, M.T. and Frei, R., U-rich Archaean sea-floor sediments from Greenland—indications of >3700 Ma oxygenic photosynthesis, *Earth and Planetary Science Letters* **217**:237–244, 2004.
86. Eastman/ M.P., *et al.*, Exploring the Structure of a Hydrogen Cyanide Polymer by Electron Spin Resonance and Scanning Force Microscopy, *Scanning* **2**:19–24, p. 20.
87. Brooks, J., and Shaw, G., *Origins and Development of Living Systems*, Academic Press, London and New York, 1973 (emphasis added).
88. Hulett, H.R., Limitations on Prebiological Synthesis, *J. Theoret. Biol.* **24**:56–72, 1969.

The Miller–Urey experiments used strategically designed traps to isolate the biochemicals as soon as they formed, so that the sparks or UV radiation did not destroy them. Without the traps, even the tiny amounts obtained would not have survived. But this is not a realistic simulation of the primordial soup, which lacks a plausible prebiotic mechanism for rescuing the amino acids from the UV by quickly removing them from the atmosphere and even exposure to water. Note that you can be badly sunburned on a cloudy day and even under water—UV penetrates even tens of metres of liquid water.[89] So the traps were *an unacceptable level of interference from intelligent investigators.*

Lack of production and stability of vital building blocks[90]

Evolutionary propaganda understates the difficulty of a naturalistic origin of life. Production of traces of 'building blocks' is commonly equated with proving that they could have built up the required complicated molecules under natural conditions.

The instability of 'building blocks' in non-biotic environments is usually glossed over. In particular, the high temperatures proposed in many modern chemical evolution theories would quickly destroy them.[91] A team including the famous evolutionary origin-of-life pioneer Stanley Miller found that the half life ($t_{1/2}$) of ribose is only 44 years at pH 7.0 (neutral) and 0°C. It's even worse at high temperatures—73 minutes at 100°C.[92] Elsewhere Miller pointed out that the RNA bases are destroyed very quickly in water at 100°C—adenine and guanine having half lives of about a year, uracil about 12 years, and cytosine only 19 days.[93]

Spark discharge experiments do not produce the RNA/DNA base cytosine. And cytosine itself, even if it could be made, is too unstable to accumulate over alleged geological 'deep time', as its half life for decomposition is 340 years at 25°C.[94]

The proposed conditions for prebiotic production of complex polymers are chemically unrealistic because the alleged precursors are unlikely to be concentrated enough, and they would undergo side reactions with other organic compounds, or hydrolyze.

89. UV-B penetrates 65 metres deep in clear Antarctic waters, according to Gieskes, W.C. and Kraay, G.W., Transmission of ultraviolet light in the Weddell Sea: Report on the first measurements made in Antarctic, *Biomass Newsl.* **12**:12–14, 1990.

90. Sarfati, J., Origin of life: instability of building blocks, *J. Creation* **13**(2):124–127, 1999; <creationontheweb.com/blocks>.

91. Sarfati, J., Hydrothermal origin of life? *J. Creation* **13**(2):5–6, 1999; <creationontheweb.com/hydrothermal>.

92. Larralde, R., Robertson, M.P. and Miller, S.L., Rates of decomposition of ribose and other sugars: Implications for chemical evolution, *Proc. Nat. Acad. Sci. USA* **92**:8158–8160, 1995.

93. Levy, M and Miller, S.L., The stability of the RNA bases: Implications for the origin of life, *Proc. Nat. Acad. Sci. USA* **95**(14):7933–38, 1998.

94. Shapiro, R., Prebiotic cytosine synthesis: A critical analysis and implications for the origin of life, *Proc. Nat. Acad. Sci. USA* **96**(8):4396–4401, 1999.

Left and right hands[95]

Many of life's chemicals come in two forms, 'left-handed' and 'right-handed'. Life requires polymers with all building blocks having the same 'handedness' (homochirality)—proteins have only 'left-handed' amino acids (see diagram, right), while DNA and RNA have only 'right-handed' sugars.

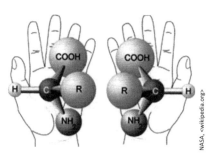

A 'chiral' molecule is one that is not superimposable with its mirror image. Like left and right hands that have a thumb, fingers in the same order, but are mirror images and not the same, chiral molecules have the same things attached in the same order, but are mirror images and not the same.

Living things have special molecular machinery to produce homochirality. But ordinary undirected chemistry, as in the hypothetical primordial soup, would produce equal mixtures of left- and right-handed molecules, called *racemates*. Racemic polypeptides could not form the specific shapes required for enzymes; rather, they would have the side chains sticking out all over the place. Also, a wrong-handed amino acid disrupts the stabilizing α-helix, a common structure in proteins. DNA could not be stabilized in a helix if even a tiny proportion of the wrong-handed form was present, so it could not form long chains. This means it could not store much information, so it could not support life.[96] A small fraction of wrong-handed molecules terminates RNA replication.[97] A world conference on 'The Origin of Homochirality and Life' made it clear that the origin of this handedness is a complete mystery to evolutionists.[98]

Do meteorites show that chirality could have arisen spontaneously?

Many evolutionists claim that meteorites have produced some excess of one handedness, although nothing like the 100% required. The evolutionary expert on amino acid racemization, Jeffrey Bada urged caution:

> 'There is, indeed, a reported excess of L-alanine in the Murchison meteorite.[99] Is this evidence of an extraterrestrial origin of homochirality? In my view, it is dangerous to rely on enantiomeric ratios

95. Sarfati, J., Origin of Life: The chirality problem, *J. Creation* **12**(3):263–266, 1998; <creationontheweb. com/chirality>.
96. Thiemann, W., ed., *International Symposium on Generation & Amplification of Asymmetry in Chemical Systems*, Jülich, Germany, pp 32–33, 1973; cited in: A.E. Wilder-Smith, *The Natural Sciences Know Nothing of Evolution*, Master Books, CA, 1981.
97. Joyce, G.F., *et al.*, Chiral selection in poly(C)-directed synthesis of oligo(G), *Nature* **310**:602-4, 1984.
98. Cohen, J., Getting all turned around over the origins of life on earth, *Science* **267**:1265–1266, 1995.
99. Citing Engel, M.H., Macko, S.A. and Silfer, J.A., *Nature* **348**, 47–49, 1990.

of protein amino acids because of the omnipresent problem of terrestrial contamination. In fact, the non-protein alpha-dialkyl amino acids in Murchison, such as isovaline, which are not prone to contamination problems, are racemic.'[100]

Bada commented that this latter type of amino acid, 'has not been reported to occur in terrestrial matter', supposedly ruling out terrestrial contamination. But other researchers claimed that a small chiral excess (2–9%) of other amino acids was found in the meteorite.[101] Bada pointed out that a mechanism to generate this excess 'if verified' is not known.[102] He cautioned further about the unknowns in this discovery and any application to chemical evolution, and we should also note the lots of 'may haves' and 'somehows' in this:

> 'Whether exogenous delivery could have provided sufficient amounts of organic compounds necessary for the origin of life, or to sustain life once it started, is largely unknown, although extraterrestrial organic compounds, including racemic (within the precision of the measurements) isovaline, have been detected in deposits associated with impact events [ref.]. The reported L amino acid excesses are very small and would need to be amplified by some process in order to generate homochirality. Even if this did take place, the L amino acid homochirality would be associated with α-dialkyl amino acids, which are not major players in protein biochemistry. If α-dialkyl amino acids had an important role during the origin of biochemistry, then initially life may have been based on a different protein architecture because peptides made primarily of these amino acids tend to form 3_{10}-helical structures rather than the α-helical conformation associated with proteins made of α-hydrogen amino acids [refs.]. Finally, the homochirality of α-dialkyl amino acids would need to be somehow transferred to the α-hydrogen protein amino acids either during the origin or early biochemical evolution of life on Earth.'[102]

More recently, a paper presented at the *Seventh Conference on Chemical Evolution and the Origin of Life*, September 2003, reinforced Bada's caution about the chiral excess coming from contamination from earth. The abstract reads:

100. Bada, J.L., Origins of homochirality, *Nature* **374**(6523):594–595, 1995.
101. Cronin, J.R. and Pizzarello, S., Enantiomeric excesses in meteoritic amino acids, *Science* **275**(5302):951–955, 1997.
102. Bada, J.L., Extraterrestrial handedness [comment on Cronin and Pizzarello, Ref. 101] *Science* **275** (5302):942–3, 1997.

TECHNICAL DETAILS

'We are investigating *one possible and seemingly plausible chemical explanation* for the significant and very curious L-enantiomeric excesses being reported [refs.] for the amino acid complements extracted/derived from (especially) Murchison material. Given that reported analyses among the chiral small-molecule inventories of carbonaceous chondritic materials are necessarily limited by both sample size/availability and by these precious samples' curatorial/custodial histories, and given that terrestrially-derived contaminants (many of which in fact contain asymmetric centers) have recently been shown [refs.] to have entered into the free/extractable organic component of Orgueil material, *it would seem chemically reasonable now to suppose that imported terrestrial and chirally-biased molecular information will necessarily have 'impressed' itself during the effective 'titration' of available prochiral functionalities contained*, perhaps, in native meteoritic macromolecular material; and that such a situation will obtain both during various wet extractive protocols in the lab, and over the longer-term (storage time) during *in situ* mineral-surface-mediated organic reactions (e.g. slow hydrolyses, ammonolyses, reductions, etc.). In our experimental attempt to *at least qualitatively illustrate the essential feasibility of such an explanation* in terms of known physical organic chemistry, stereochemistry, and the various methods of achieving variable degrees of stereo- and enantio-controls during organic syntheses, we are attempting to show that the 'titration' of prochiral functionalities (e.g. alkenyl and amidine-type functions) in a ^{13}C-labelled 'HCN-polymer' material (prepared at PSU/NAI, and modeling here for general hydrolysable meteoritic macromolecular material, GHMMM) can be informationally/chirally-biased during typical chemical derivatisations (especially hydrolyses) made in the deliberate presence of an unreactive chiral auxiliary and solvating species, which is commercially-available in both (essentially pure) enantiomeric forms, and which stands as proxy for *general terrestrial chiral contamination*. While oligomeric HCN compounds, $(HCN)_x$, are certainly too N-rich to stand as realistic model materials for

GHMMM, this is actually of secondary concern in the present investigations, as is specific knowledge of the exact nature of the prochiral functions contained.'[103]

In other words, these researchers think that the reported small bias in handedness was due to changes during storage of the samples and/or the processing and measurement techniques; it was not real.

The problem of making long molecules[104]

Life requires many *polymers*, large molecules built from many simple *monomers*. Polymerization requires *bifunctional* monomers (i.e., they combine with two others), and is stopped by a small fraction of *unifunctional* monomers (that can combine with only one other, thus blocking one end of the growing chain). All 'prebiotic simulation' experiments produce *at least three times more* unifunctional molecules than bifunctional molecules.[105]

Formic acid (HCOOH) is by far the commonest organic product of Miller–Urey-type simulations. Indeed, if it weren't for evolutionary bias, the abstracts of the experimental reports would probably state nothing more than: 'An inefficient method for production of formic acid is here described ...' Formic acid has little biological significance except that it is a major component of ant (Latin *formica*) stings.

A realistic prebiotic polymerization simulation experiment should begin with the organic compounds produced by Miller-type experiments, but the reported ones always exclude unifunctional contaminants.

Water is the enemy!

Also, the chemistry goes in the wrong direction! Biological polymerization reactions *release* water (so are called *condensation* reactions), so by the well-known *law of mass action*, excess water *breaks up* polymers. The long ages postulated by evolutionists simply make the problem worse, because there is more time for water's destructive effects to occur. While living cells have many ingenious repair mechanisms, DNA cannot last very long in water outside a cell.[106] Condensing agents (water absorbing chemicals) require acidic conditions and they could not accumulate in water. Heating to evaporate water tends to destroy some vital amino

103. Platts, S.N., On the apparently consistent L-biased enantiomeric excesses in meteoritic extracts as representing a form of attenuated forensic stereochemical evidence of chiral information derived from terrestrial contamination, *Life in the Universe: From the Miller experiment to the search for life on other worlds—Seventh Conference on Chemical Evolution and the Origin of Life*, 15–19 September 2003 (emphasis added).

104. Sarfati, J., Origin of life: the polymerization problem, *J. Creation* 12(3):281–284, 1998; <creationontheweb. com/polymer>.

105. Dickerson, Ref. 2. A chart on p. 67 shows a typical yield from one of Miller's experiments. 59,000 mmol carbon in the form of methane yielded as the main unifunctional products: 2,330 mmol formic acid, 310 mmol lactic acid, 150 mmol acetic acid and 130 mmol propionic acid. Four amino acids found in modern proteins were produced: 630 mmol glycine, 340 mmol alanine, 6 mmol glutamic acid, and 4 mmol aspartic acid.

106. Lindahl, T., Instability and decay of the primary structure of DNA, *Nature* 362(6422):709–715, 1993.

acids, racemize all the chiral amino acids, and requires geologically unrealistic conditions. Also, heating amino acids with other gunk inevitably present in the hypothetical primordial soup would destroy them.

A recent article in *New Scientist* described the instability of polymers in water as a 'headache' for researchers working on evolutionary ideas on the origin of life.[107] The writer also showed his materialistic bias by saying this was not 'good news'.

Thus even if the 'building blocks' could be formed, the evidence is strongly against them actually building anything!

Wächtershäuser's pyrite theory

A German patent attorney and organic chemist, Günter Wächtershäuser, has tried to overcome the problem of polymerization by proposing that the surface of pyrite, a mineral, catalyzed the reaction.[108] However, there are many problems with this idea—one of their most highly touted experiments managed to link only two or three amino acids together.[109] Even more damaging, according to an overview on chemical evolution in *Scientific American*, the grand old man of chemical evolution, Stanley Miller, denounced Wächtershäuser's theory as 'paper chemistry'.[110] This also reports, 'Wächtershäuser himself admits that his theory is for the most part "pure speculation".'[111]

Wrong reactions

In a simple mixture, many of the important biochemicals would destroy each other. Living organisms are well-structured to avoid this, but the 'primordial soup' would not be. Damaged cells can display these wrong reactions, for example, the browning of heated foodstuffs. Reactions between sugars and amino acids (Maillard reactions, known to food chemists as a source of flavouring as well as a problem) cause this browning. Yet evolution requires these chemicals to form nucleic acids and proteins respectively, rather than destroy each other as per real chemistry.[112]

Fatty acids are necessary for cell membranes, and phosphate is necessary for DNA, RNA, ATP, and many other important vital molecules of life. But abundant calcium ions in the ocean would precipitate fatty acids and phosphate, making them unavailable for chemical evolution. (Remember this next time you have problems washing with soap in 'hard water'.)

---

107. Matthews, R., Wacky Water, *New Scientist* **154**(2087):40–43, 1997.
108. Huber, C. and Wächtershäuser, G., Peptides by activation of amino acids with CO on (Ni,Fe)S surfaces: implications for the origin of life, *Science* **281**(5377):670–672, 1998.
109. Sarfati, Ref. 104 extensively critiques Huber and Wächtershäuser, Ref. 108.
110. Horgan, J., In the beginning, *Scientific Amer.* **264**(2):100–109, 1991; Miller cited on p. 102.
111. Horgan, Ref. 110, p. 106.
112. Sugars contain the carbonyl (>C=O) group, so they react destructively with amino acids and other amino (–NH$_2$) compounds, to form imines (>C=N).

Heavy metal ions ruin proteins, e.g. silver, mercury and lead ions disrupt the disulfide bonds linking protein chains together. That's why silver nitrate is such a powerful disinfectant—dilute silver nitrate solution placed in the eyes of newborn babies destroys the bacteria that cause gonorrhea. Cells have machinery to protect their chemistry from the bad effects of such ions at normal concentrations, and from other harmful cross-reactions.

Faulty methodology

When analyzed in detail, the chemistry doesn't support the optimistic chemical evolutionary scenarios. Indeed, much of the populist evolutionary propaganda resembles the following hypothesis for the origin of a car:

> 'Design is an unscientific explanation, so we must find a naturalistic explanation instead. Now, experiments have shown that one of the important building blocks of the car—iron—can be produced by heating naturally occurring minerals like hematite to temperatures which are found in some locations on Earth. What's more, iron can be shown to form thin sheets under pressures which are known to occur in certain geological formations … .'

SELF-REPLICATING MOLECULES?[113]

As noted, Popper realized that the origin of the genetic code was a vicious circle: proteins are needed to read the DNA, but these proteins are themselves encoded on the DNA. The proteins are the machinery, and the DNA is the reproductive material, yet both are needed for the cell to function at all.

To try to grasp both horns of the dilemma, some evolutionists have theorized that one type of molecule could perform both catalytic and reproductive roles. The following sections address some of these proposals.

RNA world?

In 1967, Carl Woese suggested that RNA was not only reproductive, but could also act as a catalyst, thus perform both roles.[114] In the 1980s, Thomas Cech and Sidney Altman independently demonstrated that some sequences of RNA had catalytic effects. For 'discovery of catalytic properties of RNA', they received the Nobel Prize in chemistry in 1989.[115]

The discovery of such *ribozymes* has led many evolutionists to postulate an 'RNA world'. They propose that the first life consisted

---

113. After Sarfati, J., Self-replicating enzymes? *A critique of some current evolutionary origin-of-life models, J. Creation* **11***(1):4–6, 1997;* <*creationontheweb.com/replicating*>.
114. Woese, C., *The Genetic Code*, Harper and Row, NY, 1967.
115. <http://nobelprize.org/nobel_prizes/chemistry/laureates/1989/press.html>.

mainly of RNA, which could not only reproduce but also carry out many of the functions now carried out by enzymes. But this model has enormous problems:

1. As shown in the next section, RNA is actually a very complex molecule, and it's a flight of fantasy to claim that it could have arisen in a primordial soup.
2. Even if such polymers *could* form, they would then have to be able to *replicate* themselves.
3. Such self-replicating RNA molecules would have to have all the functions needed to sustain (maintain) an organism.
4. How could such an RNA organism possibly give rise to a modern organism, with protein catalysts, coded on reproducing DNA? This requires a whole new layer of decoding machinery.

These postulates are all contrary to experimental evidence.[116] It is no wonder that one of the leading researchers into 'RNA World' models, Gerald Joyce, wrote:

'The most reasonable assumption is that life did not start with RNA. … The transition to an RNA world, like the origins of life in general, is fraught with uncertainty and is plagued by a lack of experimental data.'[117]

Another chemical evolutionist, Robert Shapiro, stated after showing that one of the building blocks of RNA was an implausible component of a primordial soup, said:

'the evidence that is available at the present time does not support the idea that RNA, or an alternative replicator that uses the current set of RNA bases, was present at the start of life.'[94]

Chemical evolutionist admits major problems

Graham Cairns-Smith is well known for a bizarre theory (tentatively supported by Richard Dawkins in *The Blind Watchmaker*) that the first living organisms were self-replicating clay minerals. However, according to the previously cited overview on chemical evolution in *Scientific American*:

'Cairns-Smith cheerfully admits the failings of his pet hypothesis: no-one has been able to coax clay into something resembling evolution in the laboratory; nor has anyone found anything resembling a clay-based organism in nature.'[118]

---

116. See also Mills, G.C. and Kenyon, D.H., The RNA World: A Critique, *Origins and Design*, **17**(1):9–16, 1996; <www.arn.org/docs/odesign/od171/rnaworld171.htm>.
117. Joyce, G. F., RNA evolution and the origins of life, *Nature* **338**:217–224, 1989.
118. Horgan, Ref. 110, p. 108.

But it is not so well known that he is driven to such outlandish ideas by the enormous chemical difficulties of mainstream theories of chemical evolution, such as the RNA World, and indeed any primordial soup theory, as he states in the following technical section:

The implausibility of prevital [pre-life] nucleic acid[119]

Graham Cairns-Smith:

If it is hard to imagine polypeptides or polysaccharides in primordial waters it is harder still to imagine polynucleotides. But so powerful has been the effect of Miller's experiment on the scientific imagination that to read some of the literature on the origin of life (including many elementary texts) you might think that it had been well demonstrated that nucleotides were probable constituents of a primordial soup and hence that prevital nucleic acid replication was a plausible speculation based on the results of experiments.

There have indeed been many interesting and detailed experiments in this area. But the importance of this work lies, to my mind, not in demonstrating how nucleotides could have formed on the primitive Earth, but in precisely the opposite: these experiments allow us to see, in much greater detail than would otherwise have been possible, just why prevital nucleic acids are highly implausible. Let us consider some of the difficulties:

- First, as we have seen, it is not even clear that the primitive Earth would have generated and maintained organic molecules. All that we can say is that there might have been prevital organic chemistry going on, at least in special locations.
- Second, high-energy precursors of purines and pyrimidines had to be produced in a sufficiently concentrated form (for example at least 0.01 M HCN).
- Third, the conditions must now have been right for reactions to give perceptible yields of at least two bases that could pair with each other.
- Fourth, these bases must then have been separated from the confusing jumble of similar molecules that would also have been made, and the solutions must have been sufficiently concentrated.
- Fifth, in some other location a formaldehyde concentration of above 0.01 M must have built up.
- Sixth, this accumulated formaldehyde had to oligomerise to sugars.
- Seventh, somehow the sugars must have been separated and resolved, so as to give a moderately good concentration of, for example, D-ribose.
- Eighth, bases and sugars must now have come together.

---

119. This section from Cairns-Smith, Ref. 74, list formatting added.

- Ninth, they must have been induced to react to make nucleosides. (There are no known ways of bringing about this thermodynamically uphill reaction in aqueous solution: purine nucleosides have been made by dry-phase synthesis, but not even this method has been successful for condensing pyrimidine bases and ribose to give nucleosides (Orgel and Lohrmann, 1974).)

- Tenth, whatever the mode of joining base and sugar it had to be between the correct nitrogen atom of the base and the correct carbon atom of the sugar. This junction will fix the pentose sugar as either the alpha or beta-anomer of either the furanose or pyranose forms [i.e. five- and six-membered rings]. For nucleic acids it has to be the beta-furanose. (In the dry-phase purine nucleoside syntheses referred to above, all four of these isomers were present with never more than 8 % of the correct structure.)

- Eleventh, phosphate must have been, or must now come to have been, present at reasonable concentrations. (The concentrations in the oceans would have been very low, so we must think about special situations—evaporating lagoons and such things (Ponnamperuma, 1978).)

- Twelfth, the phosphate must be activated in some way—for example as a linear or cyclic polyphosphate—so that (energetically uphill) phosphorylation of the nucleoside is possible.

- Thirteenth, to make standard nucleotides only the 5'-hydroxyl of the ribose should be phosphorylated. (In solid-state reactions with urea and inorganic phosphates as a phosphorylating agent, this was the dominant species to begin with (Lohrmann and Orgel, 1971). Longer heating gave the nucleoside cyclic 2',3'-phosphate as the major product although various dinucleotide derivatives and nucleoside polyphosphates are also formed (Osterberg, Orgel and Lohrmann. 1973).)

- Fourteenth, if not already activated—for example as the cyclic 2',3'-phosphate—the nucleotides must now be activated (for example with polyphosphate; Lohrmann, 1976) and a reasonably pure solution of these species created of reasonable concentration. Alternatively, a suitable coupling agent must now have been fed into the system.

- Fifteenth, the activated nucleotides (or the nucleotides with coupling agent) must now have polymerised. Initially this must have happened without a pre-existing polynucleotide template (this has proved very difficult to simulate (Orgel and Lohrmann. 1974)); but more important, it must have come to take place on pre-existing polynucleotides if the key function of transmitting information to daughter molecules was to be achieved by abiotic means. This has proved difficult too. Orgel and Lohrmann give three main classes of problem:

TECHNICAL DETAILS

183

1. While it has been shown that adenosine derivatives form stable helical structures with poly(U)—they are in fact triple helixes—and while this enhances the condensation of adenylic acid with either adenosine or another adenylic acid—mainly to di(A)—stable helical structures were not formed when either poly(A) or poly(G) were used as templates.

2. It was difficult to find a suitable means of making the internucleotide bonds. Specially designed water-soluble carbodiimides were used in the experiments described above, but the obvious pre-activated nucleotides—ATP or cyclic 2',3'-phosphates—were unsatisfactory. Nucleoside 5'-phosphorimidazolides, for example were more successful, but these now involve further steps and a supply of imidazole, for their synthesis (Lohrmann and Orgel, 1978).

3. Internucleotide bonds formed on a template are usually a mixture of 2'-5' and the normal 3'-5' types. Often the 2'-5' bonds predominate although it has been found that Zn^{2+}, as well as acting as an efficient catalyst for the template-directed oligomerisation of guanosine 5'-phosphorimidazolide also leads to a preference for the 3'-5' bonds (Lohrmann, Bridson and Orgel, 1980).

TECHNICAL DETAILS

- Sixteenth, the physical and chemical environment must at all times have been suitable—for example the pH, the temperature, the M^{2+} concentrations.

- Seventeenth, all reactions must have taken place well out of the ultraviolet sunlight; that is, not only away from its direct, highly destructive effects on nucleic acid-like molecules, but away too from the radicals produced by the sunlight, and from the various longer lived reactive species produced by these radicals.

- Eighteenth, unlike polypeptides, where you can easily imagine functions for imprecisely made products (for capsules, ion exchange materials, etc.), a genetic material must work rather well to be any use at all—otherwise it will quickly let slip any information that it has managed to accumulate.

- Nineteenth, what is required here is not some wild one-off freak of an event: it is not true to say 'it only had to happen once'. A whole set-up had to be maintained for perhaps millions of years: a reliable means of production of activated nucleotides at the least.

Now you may say that there are alternative ways of building up nucleotides, and perhaps there was some geochemical way on the early Earth. But what we know of the experimental difficulties in nucleotide synthesis speaks strongly against any such supposition. However it is to be put together, a nucleotide is too complex and metastable a molecule for there to be any reason to expect an easy synthesis.

You might want to argue about the nineteen problems that I chose: and I agree that there is a certain arbitrariness in the sequence of operations chosen. But if in the compounding of improbabilities nineteen is wrong as a number that would be mainly because it is much too small a number. If you were to consider in more detail a process such as the purification of an intermediate you would find many subsidiary operations—washings, pH changes and so on. (Remember Merrifield's machine: for one overall reaction, making one peptide bond, there were about 90 distinct operations required.)

A self-replicating molecule

A group led by Julius Rebek synthesized a molecule called amino adenosine triacid ester (AATE), which itself consists of two components, called pentafluorophenyl ester and amino adenosine. When AATE molecules are dissolved in chloroform with the two components, the AATE molecules act as templates for the two components to join up and form new AATE molecules.[120] There are a number of reasons why this is *irrelevant* to an evolutionary origin of life

1. This system carries vanishingly little information, in contrast to even the simplest cell.

1. The new AATE molecule binds too strongly to the parent, so no new reactants can come in and join, as Rebek himself admits.[121]

2. Replication only occurred in highly artificial, unnatural conditions.[122] A reaction in chloroform is irrelevant to living organisms. In particular, chloroform would not hinder condensation reactions as water does, as explained on p. 178.

3. The molecule reproduced **too** accurately—there is no possibility of neo-Darwinian evolution by mutation and natural selection.[118]

Did proteins come first?

With all the problems with naturalistic origins of nucleic acids, some evolutionists are investigating protein-first rather than nucleic-acid-first theories of the origin of life. But proteins do not have anything analogous to the base-pairing in nucleic acids. So there was a surprise in August 1996, when some newspapers and science journals reported a peptide that can reproduce itself. A team led by

120. Tjivikua, T., Ballester, P. and Rebek, J., Jr., 1990. A Self-Replicating System, *J. Amer. Chem. Soc.* **112**(3):1249–50.
121. Amato, I., Making molecules that copy themselves, *Science News* **137**(5):69, 1990.
122. Horgan, Ref. 110, reporting a comment by Gerald Joyce on p. 104.

Reza Ghadiri reported that a short peptide derived from part of a yeast enzyme can catalyze its own formation.[123]

They made a 32-unit-long α-helical peptide based on the leucine-zipper domain of the yeast transcription factor GCN4. They found that it catalyzed its own synthesis in a neutral, dilute water solution of 15 and 17-unit fragments. This was an ingenious experiment, but it does not help the evolutionary cause because:

- Where would the *first* 32-unit long chain of 100% left-handed amino acid residues come from? Ghadiri overestimates the ease of formation on a primordial earth (p. 172) as well as the problem of forming purely left-handed amino acids (p. 175) and joining them together (p. 178).

- Where would a supply of the matching 15- and 17-unit chains come from? Not only does the objection above apply, but what mechanism is supposed to produce the right sequences? Even if we had a mixture of the correct left-handed amino acids, the chance of getting one 15-unit peptide right is one in 20^{15} (= one in 3 x 10^{19}). If it is not necessary to get the sequences exactly right, then it would mean that the 'replication' is not specific, and would thus allow many errors.

- The 15- and 17-unit peptides must be *activated*, because condensation of ordinary amino acids is not spontaneous in water (see p. 178). Lee *et al.* used a thiobenzyl ester derivative of one peptide. As they say, this also circumvents potential side reactions (p. 179). The hypothetical primordial soup would not have had intelligent chemists adding the right chemicals to prevent wrong reactions!

Although Ghadiri's paper says, 'we suggest the possibility of protein self-replication in which the catalytic activity of the protein could be conserved,' they present no experimental proof.

Dr Ghadiri's work has excited a number of atheists, but he was much more realistic in an interview with an atheist a few years later:

> 'I asked him if it was proper to consider these molecules "life" and he shot back a resounding "No!" Nobody has even come close to creating what we would call life, according to Dr Ghadiri.'[124]

123. Lee, D.H., *et al.*, A self-replicating peptide, *Nature* **382**:525–528, 1996. See also Kauffman, S. Even peptides do it, same issue, pp. 496–497, for a perspective of the leading complexity theorist on Ghadiri's paper.
124. Self-Replicating Molecules, and the Meaning of Life, Cliff Walker interviews Dr M. Reza Ghadiri, <www.positiveatheism.org/crt/ghadiri.htm>, 1999.

And while his group first claimed that this peptide showed, in the title of a paper, 'Emergence of symbiosis in peptide self-replication through a hypercyclic network',[125] they had to publish the following correction:

> 'Although the kinetic data suggest the intermediary of higher-order species in the autocatalytic processes, the present system should not be referred to as an example of a minimal hypercycle in the absence of direct experimental evidence for the auto-catalytic cross-coupling between replicators.'[126]

Summary

Shapiro summed up the problems with the idea that life began with a self-replicating molecule:

> 'A profound difficulty exists, however, with the idea of RNA, or any other replicator, at the start of life. Existing replicators can serve as templates for the synthesis of additional copies of themselves, but this device cannot be used for the preparation of the very first such molecule, which must arise spontaneously from an unorganized mixture. The formation of an information-bearing [RNA chain or equivalent] through undirected chemical synthesis appears very improbable.'[127]

WOULD CREATION OF LIFE IN A TEST TUBE DISPROVE CREATION?

From time to time, there are reports of scientists proposing to make life in a test tube. After one origin of life paper,[108] a report stated, 'WA Museum evolutionary biologist Ken McNamara said if life could be created artificially, it could emerge naturally given the right conditions.'[128] The atheistic anti-creationist Ian Plimer also made this same blooper in the context of creating a self-reproducing RNA molecule.[129] And in 2002, one heading about one research proposal was 'Scientists Planning to Make New Form of Life.'[130] Almost as soon as the news broke, we received a gloating email basically saying that we should be so frightened that we may as well disband our creationist ministry, saying:

---

125. Lee, D.H., *et al.*, Emergence of symbiosis in peptide self-replication through a hypercyclic network, *Nature* **390**:591–594, 1997.

126. Lee, D.H., *et al.*, Erratum: Emergence of symbiosis in peptide self-replication through a hypercyclic network, *Nature* **394**:101, 1998.

127. Shapiro, R., A replicator was not involved in the origin of life, *IUBMB Life* (A Journal of the International Union of Biochemistry and Molecular Biology) **49**:173–175, 2000.

128. *The West Australian*, 12 August 1998.

129. See Sarfati, J, More nonsense from Professor Plimer, <creationontheweb.com/nonsense>, 2001.

130. Gillis, J., *Washington Post*, 21 November 2002, Page A01.

'New life forms can now be produced in a dish. So much for saying man can't create life. Keep defending your deep seated belief though, people depend on you.'

The most obvious response to the last report is that the scientists have not actually produced these new life forms, just *hoped* or *planned* to. Most importantly though, our claim has never been that man can't create life, but that only *intelligence* can generate the encyclopaedic quantities of information required. So, as illustrated by the cartoon above, if scientists succeed, it would actually *reinforce* our claim! They rely on meticulous, intelligent planning, not just throwing a few 'building blocks' into something resembling the hypothetical primordial soup.

Evolutionist admits that chemical evolution is a failed paradigm

As Yockey said, this whole edifice of chemical evolution is a failed paradigm:

> 'Although at the beginning the paradigm was worth consideration, now the entire effort in the primeval soup paradigm is self-deception on the ideology of its champions.'

> 'The history of science shows that a paradigm, once it has achieved the status of acceptance (and is incorporated in textbooks) and regardless of its failures, is declared invalid only when a new paradigm is available to replace it. Nevertheless, in order to make progress in science, it is necessary to clear the decks, so to speak, of failed paradigms. This must be done even if this leaves the decks entirely clear and no paradigms survive. It is a characteristic of the true

believer in religion, philosophy and ideology that he must have a set of beliefs, come what may (Hoffer, 1951). Belief in a primeval soup on the grounds that no other paradigm is available is an example of the logical fallacy of the false alternative. In science it is a virtue to acknowledge ignorance. This has been universally the case in the history of science as Kuhn (1970) has discussed in detail. There is no reason that this should be different in the research on the origin of life.'[131]

But that doesn't seem to have affected the materialistic faith that chemical evolution happened. One example of this dogmatism is Robert Shapiro, cited before. In his interesting popular-level book *Origins: A Skeptic's Guide to the Creation of Life in the Universe*, he effectively critiques many origin-of-life scenarios (indeed, some of the most effective criticisms of any chemical evolutionary theory come from fellow chemical evolutionists with faith in a rival theory). But he says, in a striking admission, that no amount of evidence would upset his faith:

> 'some future day may yet arrive when all reasonable chemical experiments run to discover a probable origin of life have failed unequivocally. Further, new geological evidence may yet indicate a sudden appearance of life on the earth. Finally, we may have explored the universe and found no trace of life, or processes leading to life, elsewhere. Some scientists might choose to turn to religion for an answer. Others, however, myself included, would attempt to sort out the surviving less probable scientific explanations in the hope of selecting one that was still more likely than the remainder.'[132]

George Wald, who won the 1967 Nobel Prize in Physiology or Medicine for his work on the chemistry of vision,[133] also admitted his faith in chemical evolution:

> 'One only has to contemplate the magnitude of the task to conclude that spontaneous generation of a living organism is impossible. ... Yet we are here—as a result, I believe, of spontaneous generation.'[134]

Why is a leading scientist so irrational? Because he admits:

131. Yockey, H.P., *Information Theory and Molecular Biology*, p. 336, Cambridge University Press, UK, p. 336, 1992.
132. Shapiro, R., *Origins: A Skeptic's Guide to the Creation of Life in the Universe*, Penguin, London, p. 130, 1986,1988. Shapiro then wishfully continues: 'We are far from that state now.'
133. <http://nobelprize.org/nobel_prizes/medicine/laureates/1967/wald-bio.html>.
134. Wald, G., The Origin of Life, *Scientific Amer.* **191**:46, August 1954.

> 'the only alternative to some form of spontaneous generation is a belief in supernatural creation.'[135]

Wald much later reaffirmed his belief that chemical evolution must be a fact if supernatural creation is rejected:

> 'We tell this story [of Pasteur's experiments disproving spontaneous generation] to beginning students of biology as though it represents a triumph of reason over mysticism. In fact it is very nearly the opposite. The reasonable view was to believe in spontaneous generation; the only alternative, to believe in a single, primary act of supernatural creation. There is no third position.'[136]

This merely reaffirms Yockey's point that chemical evolution is taken for granted, regardless of the overwhelming evidence against it. It is 'blind faith' for sure.

---

135. Wald, G., Innovation and Biology, *Scientific Amer.* **199:**100, 1958.
136. Wald, G., The Origin of Life; in *Life: Origin and Evolution*, p. 24, W.H. Freeman, San Francisco, 1979.

CHAPTER 12

WHAT ABOUT 'POORLY DESIGNED' THINGS?

Critics of design often claim that Nature is filled with evidence of bad design—obvious evidence of jury rigging that shows our evolutionary past, such as 'junk DNA', vestigial organs, and eye imperfections. From the time of Darwin, evolutionists have claimed that alleged poor design is something no designer would produce, so evolution *must* have done it. However, there are a number of problems with this approach:

- In using this argument, evolutionists are tacitly supporting the *two-model* approach—that an argument against creation is an argument for evolution. This form of argument is known as a *disjunctive syllogism*, and works only if these are the only two possibilities. Yet evolutionists often rail against creationists for using an identical form of argument, i.e. using arguments against evolution to support creation!

- An assertion about what a designer would do is actually a *pseudo-theological* argument, *not* a scientific argument that mutations and natural selection could produce this unique developmental pattern.

- Similarly, a claim that a designer might have designed something badly at best proves that the designer is less than perfect, not that there is no designer. This is not my belief, as will be shown, but it still demonstrates a hole in the critics' logic.

- And a complaint about all the nasty things in nature can at best prove that the designer is mean, not that there is none. (Again, this is not my own belief—chapter 13 elaborates on a cogent explanation, and points out that the 'Intelligent Design' (ID) movement doesn't offer one.)

- A single *feature* may not be optimal, but the *combination* of features may be. E.g. a thicker shell, considered only for its protective properties, works better against predators and environmental damage. But if it is too thick, its manufacture wastes resources, and even worse, could weigh down the creature, so *as a whole*, the creature is worse off.

- It's important to remember that multi-cellular life forms begin from a single cell, and there is a continuous development into the adult form. Yet for the adult even to exist, these younger stages must be viable. Thus there are some features in the adult that are genuine vestigial organs, but they are *vestiges of ontogeny not phylogeny*. I.e. the adult could not exist if the embryo didn't have the features that have since degenerated in the adult. For example, the adult mammal has vestiges of the circulatory system that connected with its mother's placenta, and the shunt that re-routed the blood to the lungs at birth.

- Similarly, the design must work from the materials available.
- Some accusations of poor design reflect ignorance, the evolutionist's own version of 'the argument from personal incredulity' ('I can't see why it was designed that way, so it must be badly designed'). In many cases, when more information comes to hand, the 'poor design' turns out to be excellent.
- An organ may not be *necessary*, but it may still be *nice* to have. Such organs can be removed, but this doesn't prove they are functionless. Many designed systems have back-up features that make the system as a whole less likely to break down. This would explain the two kidneys and two lungs we have, although we can get by on one of each. Indeed, such redundancy is a problem for evolution because the selective advantage (increased fitness) for an individual having the redundancy freshly evolved (assuming this could even happen) would be so small under normal circumstances as to be not selectable by natural selection. It would be lost by what is known as genetic drift.
- It is impossible to prove that an organ is useless, and thus a 'vestige' of evolution. The function may simply be unknown and its use may be discovered in future. This has happened with more than 100 formerly alleged useless vestigial organs in humans that we now know are essential.
- Under the biblical framework, a particular biological system that appears poorly designed may not have been originally designed that way, but has gone downhill since the Fall. Thus many organs that are claimed to be vestiges of evolution would really prove 'devolution' not evolution. However, the particles-to-people evolution model needs to find examples of *nascent* organs, i.e. those which are *increasing* in complexity.

WWII TANK DESIGNS AS AN ANALOGY

Properly coordinated tank warfare was a great innovation in WWII, so not surprisingly, many new tanks were invented. Of course, no one doubts that they were *designed*, but they illustrate the logical flaws of some of the anti-design arguments:

- The thicker the armour, the more resistant to shelling damage a tank would be. However, there is a limit. One of the biggest German tanks was the Elefant (actually a *Panzerjäger* (tank hunter)). This had 200-mm-thick armour, which protected it very well from Soviet anti-tank weapons. But its immense mass of 70 tonnes meant that it used up massive amounts of fuel (1100 L/100km or ¼ mpg), it broke down frequently, and

TECHNICAL DETAILS

couldn't use most of the roads and bridges in Italy. This is a case of over-optimization in one feature at the expense of overall functionality.

- A tank without a revolving turret would seem to be a huge design flaw, because the whole tank must turn to hit the target. But the Germans made huge numbers of such a turretless tank, called the *Sturmgeschütz* ('assault gun'). These were quite successful, because the lack of a turret had compensating advantages, such as the lower profile (so harder to hit), and more space for a crew and the ability to mount a more powerful gun. This illustrates that an apparent design flaw considered in isolation may be an advantage when the machine as a whole is considered.

  Also, this was an easier, cheaper and quicker tank to make, since it didn't need the complex machinery of the turret, as well as needing far fewer ball bearings, which were in short supply in Germany. Similarly, many living creatures lack some complex features, but are successful because they can develop quickly and in large numbers.

- The Soviet T-34 tank is sometimes called the best tank of the war. When the Germans first met them, their own tanks were no match for them, because of its superior design features. It had a wide track, good suspension and large engine giving it unparalleled cross-country performance. Even more importantly, it had *sloped armour*. This means that the tank has a greater chance of deflecting a projectile, because of the more glancing blow. And even if it penetrated, the projectile had to pass through a greater distance of the armour, thus losing more momentum. Eventually the Germans made very expensive and complex tanks that could outmatch the T-34, but this greatly slowed production, so the Soviets heavily outnumbered them.[1]

- Thus the vertical armour of the early German tanks could be considered a design flaw. But this doesn't mean that the tanks were not designed!

- Of course, tanks were weapons of destruction and to some extent defenders against enemy weapons. But it would be folly to argue that designed-to-kill entails no design at all!

CASE STUDIES IN BIOLOGY

Kenneth Miller claims that the eye has 'profound optical imperfections', so is proof of 'tinkering' and 'blind' natural selection. Richard Dawkins has made similar claims. But neither of them has

---

1. The total figures for all Panther types was 6,557, and all Tiger types 2,027; but there were 22,559 of the T-34-85 alone.

presented an argument *for* evolution *per se* at all—because they present no step-by-step way for the retina (for example) to have evolved. This is an example of the evolutionary two-model approach discussed on p. 191—this is no argument *for* evolution but merely *against* a designer. This is of course also an attack on Miller's own Darwinian version of 'god', one who has chosen to create indirectly (via evolution), since under this view this 'god' is still ultimately responsible for the creature.

THE INVERTED EYE—EXAMPLE OF BAD DESIGN?

Many evolutionists have raised the old canard of the backwardly wired vertebrate retina. Some even claim that the eye's 'nerves interfere with images', and that the so-called 'blind spot' is a serious problem. But these arguments have been refuted, as shown below.

It would be nice if anti-creationists actually learnt something about the eye before making such claims—invariably the critics are unqualified in either physical optics or eye anatomy. Some names include the atheists Richard Dawkins, Massimo Pigliucci, Daniel Dennett, and Jared Diamond; and Kenneth Miller, the Roman Catholic mentioned earlier in this chapter, whose views on origins are practically indistinguishable from the atheists'. It would also help their case if they showed that the eye didn't function properly as a result. In fact, any engineer who designed something remotely as good as the eye would probably win a design award! If these people disagree, then I challenge them to design a better eye with all the versatility of the vertebrate eye (colour perception, resolution, coping with range of light intensity, night vision as well as day vision, etc.)! And they must do this under the constraints of embryonic development.

Regenerating photoreceptors

Someone who *does* know about eye design is the ophthalmologist Dr George Marshall, who said:

> 'The idea that the eye is wired backward comes from a lack of knowledge of eye function and anatomy.'[2]

---

2. Marshall, G. (interviewee), An eye for creation. *Creation* **18**(4):20–21, 1996; <creationontheweb.com/

He explained that the nerves could not go behind the eye, because the choroid occupies that space. This provides the rich blood supply needed for the very metabolically active retinal pigment epithelium (RPE). This is necessary to regenerate the photoreceptors, and to absorb excess heat. So it is necessary for the nerves to go in front rather than behind. But as will be shown on p. 195, the eye's design overcomes even this slight drawback.

In fact, what limits the eye's resolution is the *diffraction* of light waves at the pupil (proportional to the wavelength and inversely proportional to the pupil's size); so alleged improvements of the retina would make no difference to the eye's performance.

It's important to note that the 'superior' design of Miller/Dawkins with the (virtually transparent) nerves behind the photoreceptors would require either:

- The choroid in front of the retina—but the choroid is opaque because of all the red blood cells, so this design would be as useless as an eye with a hemorrhage!
- Photoreceptors not in contact with the RPE and choroid at all—but if our eyes lost this ability to absorb heat, then it would probably take months before we could see properly after we were photographed with a flashbulb or we glanced at some bright object.

Are squid eyes 'properly' wired?

Some evolutionists claim that the cephalopod (e.g. squid and octopus) eye is somehow 'right', i.e. with nerves behind the receptor. They use this as a counter-argument to the points in the previous section about the need for the 'backward' wiring. But no-one who has actually bothered to study cephalopod eyes could make such claims with integrity. In fact, cephalopods don't see as well as humans, e.g. no colour vision, and the octopus eye structure is totally different and much simpler. It's more like 'a compound eye with a single lens'. And it is no accident that we say 'eyes like a hawk/ eagle' rather than 'eyes like a squid', because the former really are sharper despite their alleged 'backward' wiring.

Fibre optic plate

The above section explains why the vertebrate retina must be wired the way it is. But scientists at Leipzig University have recently shown that the vertebrate eye has an ingenious feature that overcomes even the slight disadvantage of nerves in front of the light receptors.[3]

The light is collected and funnelled through the nerve net to the receptors by the *Müller cells*, which act as *optical fibres*. Each cone

---

marshall>.

3. Franze *et al.*, Müller cells are living optical fibers in the vertebrate retina, *Proc. Nat. Acad. Sci. USA*, 10.1073/pnas.0611180104, published online before print 7 May 2007; <www.pnas.org/cgi/content/abstract/0611180104v1>.

cell has one Müller cell guiding the light to it, while several rods can share the same Müller cell.

The Müller cells work almost exactly like a *fibre optic plate* that optical engineers can use to transmit an image with low distortion without using a lens. The cells even have the right variation in refractive index for 'image transfer through the vertebrate retina with minimal distortion and low loss.'[3]

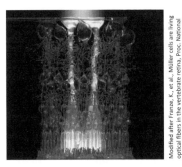

Müller cells working as optical fibres

Modified after Franze, K., et al., Müller cells are living optical fibers in the vertebrate retina, Proc. National Academy of Sciences USA 104(20):8287–8292, 15 May 2007.

Indeed, Müller cells are even better than optical fibres, because they are funnel-shaped, which collects more light for the receptors. The wide entrances to Müller cells cover the entire surface of the retina, so collect the maximum amount of light.

One of the research team, Andreas Reichenbach, commented:

'Nature is so clever. This means there is enough room in the eye for all the neurons and synapses and so on, but still the Müller cells can capture and transmit as much light as possible.'[4]

Blind spot

Ophthalmologist Peter Gurney gives a detailed response to the question, 'Is the inverted retina really "bad design"?'[5] He addresses the claim that the blind spot is bad design, by pointing out that the blind spot occupies only 0.25% of the visual field, and is far (15°) from the visual axis so that the normal visual acuity of the region is only about 15% of the foveola, the most sensitive area of the retina right on the visual axis. And having two eyes effectively means there is no blind spot. So the alleged defect is only theoretical, not practical. The blind spot is not considered handicap enough to stop a one-eyed person from driving a private motor vehicle. The main problem with only one eye is the lack of stereoscopic vision.

Retinal detachment

Materialists have also alleged that the retina is badly designed because it can detach and cause blindness. But few people experience this, indicating that the design is pretty good. In fact, retinal detachment is more due to the vitreous ('glassy') humour liquefying from its normally fairly rigid gel state with advancing age. The remaining gel pulls away from the retina, leaving tiny holes, so the liquefied humour can lift off the retina. A recently-developed

4.   Sheriff, L., Living optical fibres found in the eye: Moving light past all those synapses, *The Register*, 20007; <www.theregister.co.uk/2007/05/01/eye_eye/>.

5.   Gurney, P., Is our 'inverted' retina really 'bad design'? *J. Creation* 13(1):37–44, 1999.

treatment entails draining the liquid and injecting magnetized silicone gel, which can be moved into place with a magnetic field, to push the retina back and block the holes.[6] The occasional failures in the eye with increasing age reflect the fact that we live in a fallen world—so what we observe today has deteriorated from the original physically perfect state, where for example deterioration with age didn't occur.

Eye's 'poor focus'

As stated above, the eye focuses sharply mainly at the fovea, while it is less focused for peripheral vision, so the blind spot is mainly a theoretical disadvantage. But the German physicist Hermann von Helmholtz, Darwin's contemporary, angrily claimed:

> 'If an optician sold me an instrument having the errors exhibited by the eye, it would be in order for me to express my dissatisfaction with the quality of his work in the strongest terms, and return his instrument forthwith.'[7]

He didn't actually find an optician who had sold a better instrument, of course, considering all the eye's features. And his main error was treating the eye as a *static* instrument, like a camera, which needs to focus all areas finely to generate a picture. But he ignored the key feature of the eye—that it is a *dynamic* instrument that would be useless without *processing its information in the brain.*

If he had understood the *fovea/saccade* system (see ch. 1, pp. 28–29), he might have realized that the system has at least two advantages over a hypothetical eye that focused perfectly in the periphery:

- The lack of focus in the periphery has a certain advantage, in that we can concentrate more easily on the objects finely focused in our central vision.
- A perfect focus in the periphery would be wasted unless our brains could process this information, and that would require heads too big to fit through a doorway, as explained on p. 28. [8]

COMPOUND EYES

Some evolutionists have claimed that the compound eye is a bad design that no good designer would use, so it must have evolved. However, it is actually an excellent design for small creatures, enabling bees to navigate by the highly efficient *optic flow* method (see chapter 5, pp. 83–85).

---

6. Sample, I, Visual attraction: Push detached retinas back into place with the help of a little magnetism, *New Scientist* 174(2338):18, 2002.
7. Helmholtz, H. von, 1863; cited in Gitt, W., *The Wonder of Man*, CLV, Beilefeld, Germany, p. 17, 1999. Helmholtz lived 1821–1894, cf. Darwin 1809–1882.
8. Catania, K.C., The nose takes a starring role, *Scientific American* 287(1):40, 2002.

And when analyzed closely as evidence for evolution rather than alleged evidence against a Designer, there are huge problems. Recent molecular evidence counts strongly against the idea that compound eyes all evolved from a common ancestor, and instead points to multiple independent origins. The researchers claimed:

> 'These results illustrate exactly why arthropod compound eye evolution has remained controversial, because one of two seemingly very unlikely evolutionary histories must be true. Either compound eyes with detailed similarities evolved multiple times in different arthropod groups or compound eyes have been lost in a seemingly inordinate number of arthropod lineages.'[9]

This is consistent with separate creations by a single designer.

THE HUMAN SPINE[10]

Problems with bad backs have often been blamed on a design flaw in our spines, supposedly because we imperfectly evolved from four-legged creatures. However, experts on the spine disagree. For example, Prof. Richard Porter (1935–2005) was Director of Education and Training for the Royal College of Surgeons of Edinburgh from 1995 to 97, published over 60 papers in peer-reviewed journals on spinal disorders alone, and was awarded the first Volvo Award in 1979 for work on spinal stenosis.[11]

Lordosis: essential curvature for upright creatures

Prof. Porter explains the common evolutionary claim:

> 'For example, the inward curve of the lumbar spine—the lordosis—was thought by evolutionists to be a problem, the result of man standing upright. Therefore some researchers may look at a patient with back pain and say it's because mankind has recently stood upright, and the spine has not yet evolved satisfactorily. If therapists have the wrong starting assumption, then it's not surprising that they have advocated treatments to reduce the lordosis, which made the problem worse.'[12]

However, he explains how the design perspective has been much more helpful to his research than evolutionary assumptions:

---

9. Oakley, T.H., and Cunningham, C.W., Molecular phylogenetic evidence for the independent evolutionary origin of an arthropod compound eye, *Proc. Nat. Acad. Sci. USA* **99**(3):1426–1430, 2002.

10. After: Standing upright for creation: Jonathan Sarfati chats with human spine expert Richard Porter about his science and faith, *Creation* **25**(1):25–27, 2002; <creationontheweb.com/porter>.

11. His obituary in the *British Medical Journal* noted his scientific achievements, as well his strong Christian faith and generosity to overseas doctors and refugees <www.bmj.com/cgi/content/full/332/7534/182-e/DC1>.

12. See also Bergman, J., Back problems: how Darwinism misled researchers, *J. Creation* **15**(3):79–84, 2001; <creationontheweb.com/backproblem>.

'I start from quite a different position and say—from my understanding of human anatomy and physiology and my understanding of God, the form of God's creation always matches its function. So you can be sure that the form of the spine is perfectly designed for its function. God has made a wonderful spine. It you start with that premise, it gives you a head start when trying to understand the mechanism of the spine.

'When you start to examine the biomechanics of the curved spine asking why it's that shape, and what's good about it, you find that the arch of the spine has a beautiful purpose, it's like the arch of a bridge, it adds strength. Because of that arch in the lumbar spine, a man with a lumbar lordosis can lift proportionally more weight than a Gorilla with its kyphotic (outwardly curving) spine!

'Thus it's not surprising that treating back pain with postures and exercises that *restore* the lordosis work exceedingly well.'[13]

Spine design

Furthermore, according to Prof. Porter, the human spine exhibits very good design features:

'My inaugural lecture in Aberdeen [as Professor of Orthopaedic Surgery at the University of Aberdeen, Scotland] was "Upright man" and I tried to explain how the wonderful human spine is a perfect match between form and function. Things go wrong with the spine when we abuse it (if we fail to keep ourselves fit, or overload it, or have an accident). We are learning to use 'foam filling' in building, (a sandwich of honeycomb material between two plates) to make something that is both light and strong, but the bones of the spine have been 'foam filled' with cancellous bone (with an open, latticed, or porous structure) surrounded by harder cortical bone since creation.

'The vertebral bodies increase in cross sectional area as you go further down the spine, because in the upright position the lower ones have to take more load. The bones are not denser, they are just bigger. By contrast, animals that walk on all fours have a roughly horizontal spine that has a roughly equal load all the

---

13. Smail, R., Oh my aching back! *Creation* 12(4):20–21, September 1990; <creationontheweb.com/backache>. The therapist Robin McKenzie, from New Zealand, discovered this lordosis-restoring treatment by chance in 1956. While not a Design advocate, McKenzie's work lends considerable support to the Design model.

way. So they have vertebrae of similar cross sectional area all down the spine. Form matches function. We would have expected our vertebral bodies to be like quadrupeds if we had only recently stood upright, but that is not the case.'

'We designed radial-ply tyres for motor cars, and then find God had constructed the rim of the intervertebral disc with radial-ply fibres from the beginning. That construction makes a healthy disc stronger than the bones. When you examine the way the human body is formed and how it works, you are constantly amazed. It's like looking at a piece of beautiful bone china and seeing the maker's mark beneath.'[14]

THYMUS GLAND

This is a gland behind the breast bone in the upper chest. It is quite large and active in babies and children, but shrinks with age. Thus it was considered to be an evolutionary vestige and sometimes removed. However, when the immunological system was studied in detail in the 1950s and 60s, the thymus was found to program certain blood cells (called T lymphocytes) to attack foreign tissue. And despite having a limited role in adults, it is essential to babies. Children born without this gland are very vulnerable to infection and die very quickly without treatment.[15]

THE PANDA'S 'THUMB'

Evolutionists have long cited the panda's clumsy-looking 'thumb' as evidence of evolution, rather than intelligent design. Gould even wrote a book which says that the panda's thumb 'wins no prize in an engineer's derby'.[16]

On closer inspection, however, there is nothing clumsy at all about the panda's design.[17] Instead, the 'thumb' is part of an elaborate and efficient grasping structure that enables the panda to strip leaves from bamboo shoots.[18]

Claims that the panda's thumb is some kind of non-designed 'contraption' is a smokescreen to distract from the real question— that evolution simply does not explain how life could start in a pond and finish with a panda.[19]

14. See also Wieland, C., *Adam's Rib: Creation & the Human Body*, Answers in Genesis, 2001.
15. Performing surgery upon evolutionary thinking: Jonathan Sarfati interviews pediatric surgeon Ross Pettigrew, *Creation* **29**(3):46–48, 2007.
16. Gould, S.J., *The Panda's Thumb: More Reflections in Natural History*, W.W. Norton & Co., New York, p. 24, 1980.
17. See Woodmorappe, J., The Panda thumbs its nose at the dysteleological arguments of the atheist Stephen Jay Gould, *J. Creation* 13(1):45–48, 1999.
18. Endo, H. *et al.*, Role of the giant panda's 'pseudo-thumb', *Nature* **397**(6717):309–310, 1999.
19. See Catchpoole, D., The bamboozling panda, *Creation* **23**(2):28–32, 2001; <creationontheweb.com/panda>.

HUMAN KNEE JOINT

Sometimes, the human knee can break down, which happens from time to time with joggers and people who lift heavy weights. Some ID critics have thus invoked the knee joint as an example of poor design.

However, the knee problems are usually due to *overuse*, such as repeated jolting on hard surfaces. Similarly, a small car is fine for getting for A to B, but will severely strain the engine if it tows a heavy trailer all the time. And the critics don't explain how the knee joint could have evolved.

Indeed, biomimeticist Prof. Stuart Burgess argues cogently that the knee joint is an example of irreducible complexity. 'The knee joint is a particularly sophisticated kind of four-bar hinge' entailing 'at least 16 critical characteristics, each requiring thousands of precise units of information to exist simultaneously in the genetic code.'[20]

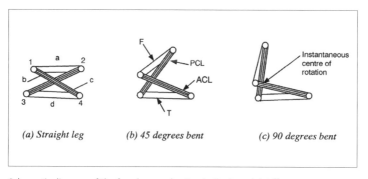

(a) Straight leg   *(b) 45 degrees bent*   *(c) 90 degrees bent*

Schematic diagram of the four-bar mechanism in the knee joint.[20]

The knee is a very distinct type of joint, called a *condylar joint*,[21] connecting the two longest bones in the human body, the femur (thigh-bone) and tibia (shin-bone). The joint is so called because the femur has two bumps on the knee end called *condyles*. These roll against two matching concave grooves in the tibia.

The knee is held in place by two cruciate ligaments that cross each other (Latin *crux crucis* = cross). This enables the knee to have a variable axis of rotation, unlike a simple pivot joint. This is because the axis approximately coincides with the cross-over point, which moves as the joint opens and closes.

There is no known, or conceivable, evolutionary intermediate between the condylar joint and other two main types, the ball and socket joint (e.g. hip and shoulder) and the pivot joint (e.g. elbow).

---

20.   Burgess, S., Critical characteristics and the irreducible knee joint, *J. Creation* **13**(2):112–117, 1999.
21.   Guyot, J., *Atlas of Human Limb Joints*, Springer-Verlag, New York, p. 20, 1981.

POWERFUL-TOOTHED GIANT RAT-KANGAROO

The extinct Australian marsupial, the powerful-toothed giant rat-kangaroo (*Ekaltadeta ima*) had a tooth that has been touted as proof of evolution.[22] That is, one of its 'baby teeth', the second premolar (P2), instead of being lost, was withdrawn and turned so it buttressed a large adult tooth, the third premolar (P3). The author of the article claimed that it would be 'far cleaner and more aesthetically pleasing' to eject the baby tooth and use extra bone to support P3. Supposedly, like the panda's 'thumb', this is proof that no designer was involved, so evolution *must* have done it. Note again the two-model approach.

Of course, it matters not what the *author* thinks is 'cleaner' or 'more aesthetically pleasing', but what is good for this *rat-kangaroo*. The author himself admits: 'the P3 of *Ekaldateta* had the potential to bite through just about anything'—this hardly sounds like bad design![23]

PLANTARIS MUSCLE

This is a very short and slender muscle in the calf that has a very long tendon. While it has a role in plantarflexing the foot ('pointing the toes') and flexing the knee, this role is overshadowed by the large soleus and gastrocnemius muscles. Indeed, this is sometimes called 'freshman's nerve' because beginning medical students mistake the long tendon for a nerve. Evolutionists have often claimed that this is a vestigial muscle, and surgeons have used the tendon as a disposable source to repair tendons in the hand.

However, muscles are not only used for movement, but for sensation. The particular sense is not one of the five senses most people think about, but another sense called *proprioception* or *kinesthesia*. This is how you know where your limbs are even without sight. Without this sense, you could not drive or type without looking where your feet or fingers are, catch a ball or be able to walk in the dark. Drunkenness impairs proprioception, which is why some police test suspected drivers by asking them to touch their nose—it is this sense that enables you to find your nose even in the dark (and why blind people have no trouble putting food in their mouths).

The plantaris happens to be ideal for proprioception, because its shortness means that its *relative* length changes much more than if it were longer. It also has an unusually high density of proprioceptive nerve receptors.[24]

---

22.   Wroe, S., The Killer Rat-Kangaroo's Tooth, *Nature Australia* 27(1):28–31, 2001.
23.   Sarfati, J., Rats! A toothless argument for evolution, *Creation* 24(1):45 2001.
24.   Menton, D., The plantaris and the question of vestigial muscles in man, *J. Creation* 14(2):50–53, 2000.

Indeed, the idea that a muscle is vestigial is absurd on the face of it, because unused muscles quickly degenerate or atrophy. This is a danger for patients confined to bed for long periods and for weightless astronauts. So the fact that the plantaris has not atrophied should have signalled that it was doing *something*.[24]

PROSTATE[25]

This is a walnut-sized gland in male mammals that secretes a clear, slightly alkaline liquid that comprises about 10–30% of the volume of semen. Thus it is a vital musculoglandular organ for reproduction. Some ID critics complain that it is badly designed because the urethra passes through it, so if the prostate enlarges, it restricts urine flow.

However, the positioning makes a great deal of sense. Rather than the urethra going through the prostate, it is more accurate to consider the prostate as a thickening of the urethral wall. It produces a major component of semen (other than the sperm, which come from the testicles; the testicles have to be outside the body for cooling purposes; much of the liquid is produced by the seminal vesicles). The prostate's secretions have to be injected into the urethra at the right time to join up with the spermatozoa from the testicles. The prostate arrangement means that its 30–50 glands secrete into 16–32 ducts that open independently into the urethra. The whole prostate contracts during ejaculation, and its smooth muscle quickly empties its contents and forces the semen along. The prostate also contains nerve plexuses, and is responsible for much of the pleasure of male sexual activity.

So why did the designer not simply place the prostate alongside the urethra? Presumably because it would require a new duct system, and extra systems to propel its secretions and propel the semen along.

The prostate also acts as a spacer between the bladder and the urogenital diaphragm. This provides a support for the bladder, and prevents the urethra kinking when the bladder is full. Otherwise extra ligaments and attachment structures would be required. This positioning could also be necessary to shut off urine flow during ejaculation. Indeed, one potential problem with prostate removal is incontinence.

As for the problems with enlargement, they are not normal features but *pathological* ones, so in a biblical framework they would be regarded as *post-Fall*. In any case, even by age 80, only about half of men actually have significant enlargement of the gland, and only a quarter have any urinary symptoms. In many men, the

---

25. Thanks to Dr Don Batten for much of the information in this section, as well as Dr Jerry Bergman, Was the prostate poorly designed? *Creation Research Society Quarterly* 44(3):230–235, 2008.

prostate actually shrinks as they get older.[26] If this was a design problem, all men would suffer from it. Factors involved in prostate problems include hormone imbalance, obesity, infections, medicinal side effects, and mutations.

Japanese men living in Japan have much less problem, whereas Japanese men living in America develop the same level of problems as Americans from other ethnic backgrounds. The reason for this is thought to be differences in diet. The Japanese diet comprises a lot of fish, which is rich in omega-3 fatty acids, which are anti-inflammatory, and zinc, which inhibits an enzyme involved in conversion of testosterone (male hormone) to dihydrotestosterone, which stimulates hypertrophy (enlargement) of the gland. The traditional Japanese diet also includes regular portions of tofu, which has mild oestrogenic effects that counter the deleterious effects of sometimes excessive dihydrotestosterone on prostate hypertrophy. Inadequate vegetable consumption quadrupled the risk of prostate problems in one study. Clearly, a defective diet could be a large factor in the men who suffer from prostate enlargement.[27]

Overall then, the prostate normally functions extremely well throughout a man's life. Other mammals have a similar design; if it were as bad as evolutionary critics say, then surely natural selection would have eliminated this design.

WISDOM TEETH

This is the popular term for our third molars, which often don't develop properly. Instead, they can be impacted against their adjoining teeth, or partially erupt so the gum doesn't form a bacterially-tight seal, leaving the tooth vulnerable to infection, or erupt crookedly and then cut the cheek frequently. Thus they are often removed. A typical evolutionary explanation is:

> ' ... our ancestors had larger jaws, so there was room in the human mouth for 32 permanent teeth, including third molars—wisdom teeth. But now our jaws are smaller. The result: There's no longer room in most of our mouths to house 32 teeth. So the last teeth we develop—our wisdom teeth—often become impacted, or blocked from erupting.'[28]

However, modern dental research recognizes *diet* as a factor in smaller jaws. In non-technological cultures, impacted wisdom teeth are almost unknown. Their tougher diet exercises their jaw muscles properly in chewing, and this helps the jaw itself develop properly. The grittier diet also results in tooth wear, and the normal compensation for this loss of tooth surfaces is *mesial migration* (tooth

---

26.   Isaacs J.T., Etiology of benign prostatic hyperplasia. *Eur. Urology.* **25**(suppl 1):6–9, 1994.
27.   Araki, H., *et al.*, High-risk group for benign prostatic hypertrophy, *Prostate* **4**:253–64, 1983.
28.   Ebbert, S. and Sangiorgio, M., Facing the dreaded third molar, *Prevention* **43**(7):108–110, 1991.

movement towards the front of the mouth), making more room for the back molars. The modern diet fails *both* to provide the same jaw exercise, so the jaw doesn't develop to full size, *and* to provide the tooth wear that would enable them to avoid crowding.[29]

USELESS SHORT MUSCLE FIBRES IN THE HORSE?

Fast-running animals such as horses and camels are very energy-efficient. This is due to elastic tendons that stretch and recoil, enabling the animals to 'bounce' along the ground, a bit like a pogo stick. These long (60 cm, two ft) tendons spanning several joints are 93% efficient at returning the energy stored in their stretching.

They are connected to very short muscle fibres (less than 6 mm, ¼ inch). The muscles were assumed to be useless remnants of evolution. But recent research has shown that these muscles help to damp the strong vibrations generated every time a foot hits the ground.[30] This is essential, because the vibrations would otherwise cause fatigue damage in these tendons, which must be thin enough to stretch effectively.

The muscle and tendon combination is an optimal biomechanical system. If the tendons themselves had to be dampers as well, they would be less effective as springs. Also, the 7% of energy that's not returned as motion is dissipated as heat, so less-springy tendons would release more heat. With the huge amounts of energy involved in a galloping horse, this extra heat could damage the tendons.

Well-known expert in biomechanics, McNeill Alexander, commented that this research 'makes us wonder whether other vestiges (such as the human appendix) are as useless as they seem.'[31]

WINGS ON BIRDS THAT DO NOT FLY[32]

There are at least two possibilities as to why flightless birds such as ostriches and emus have wings:

1.   The wings are indeed 'useless' and derived from birds that once could fly. This is possible in the creationist model. Loss of features is relatively easy by natural processes, whereas acquisition of new complex characters, requiring specific new DNA information, is impossible. Loss of wings most probably occurred in a beetle species that colonized a windy island. Again, this is *loss* of genetic

29.   Bergman, J., Are wisdom teeth (third molars) vestiges of human evolution? *J. Creation* **12**(3):297–304, 1998; <creationontheweb.com/wisdom-teeth>.

30.   Wilson, A.M. *et al.*, Horses damp the spring in their step, *Nature* **414**(6866):895–899, 2001.

31.   Alexander, R.McN., Damper for bad vibrations, [Comment on Ref. 30], *Nature* **414**(6866):855–857, 2001.

32.   The remaining examples are adapted with permission from chapter 7 of Batten, D. (Ed.), Catchpoole, D., Sarfati, J. and Wieland, C., *The Creation Answers Book*, Creation Book Publishers, 2007.

information, so it is not evidence for microbe-to-man evolution, which requires masses of new genetic information.[33]

2. The wings have a function. Some possible functions, depending on the species of flightless bird, are: balance while running, cooling in hot weather, warmth in cold weather, protection of the rib-cage in falls, mating rituals, scaring predators (emus will run at perceived enemies of their chicks, mouth open and wings flapping), sheltering of chicks, etc. If the wings are useless, why are the muscles functional, allowing these birds to move their wings?

PIGS WITH TWO TOES THAT DO NOT REACH THE GROUND

Does this mean that the shorter toes have no function? Not at all. Pigs spend a lot of time in water and muddy conditions for cooling purposes. The extra toes probably make it easier to walk in mud (a bit like the rider wheels on some long trucks that only touch the road when the truck is heavily loaded). Perhaps the muscles attached to the extra toes also give strength to the 'ankle' of the pig.

WHY DO MALES HAVE NIPPLES?

Males have nipples because of the common plan followed during early embryo development. Embryos start out producing features common to male and female—again an example of 'design economy'. Nipples are a part of this design economy. However, as Bergman and Howe[34] point out, the claim that they are useless is debatable.

What is the evolutionist's explanation for male nipples? Did males evolve (devolve) from females? Or did ancestral males suckle the young? No evolutionist would propose either of these. Male nipples are neither evidence for evolution nor evidence against creation.

WHY DO RABBITS HAVE DIGESTIVE SYSTEMS THAT FUNCTION 'SO POORLY THAT THEY MUST EAT THEIR OWN FECES'?

This is an incredible proposition. One of the most successful species on Earth would have to be the rabbit! The rabbit's mode of existence is obviously very efficient (what about the saying 'to breed like rabbits'?) Just because eating feces may be abhorrent to humans, it does not mean it is inefficient for the rabbit! Rabbits have a special pouch called the *caecum*, containing bacteria, at the

---

33. Wieland, C., Beetle bloopers: even a defect can be an advantage sometimes. *Creation* **19**(3):30, 1997.
34. Bergman J. and Howe, G., *'Vestigial Organs' are Fully Functional, Creation Research Society Monograph* **4**, Creation Research Society Books, Terre Haute, Indiana, 1990.

beginning of the large intestine. These bacteria aid digestion, just as bacteria in the rumen of cattle and sheep aid digestion. Indeed, rabbits 'chew the cud' in a manner that parallels sheep and cattle.

The rabbit produces two types of fecal pellet, a hard one and a special soft one coming from the caecum. It is only the latter that the rabbit eats to enrich its diet with the nutrients produced by the bacteria in the caecum. In other words, this ability of rabbits is a design feature; it is not something they have learned to do because they have 'digestive systems that function so poorly'. It is part of the variety of design, which speaks of creation, not evolution.

Skeptics have claimed the Bible is in error in saying that the rabbit 'chews the cud' (Lev. 11:6). The Hebrew literally reads, 'raises up what has been swallowed'. The rabbit does re-eat what has been swallowed—its partly digested fecal pellets. The skeptics are wrong.

LEGLESS LIZARDS

It is quite likely that legless lizards could have arisen through loss of genetic information from an original created kind, and the structures are consistent with this. 'Loss' of a structure is of no comfort to evolutionists, as they have to find a mechanism for creating new structures, not losing them. Loss of information cannot explain how evolution 'from ameba to man' could occur. Genesis 3:14 suggests that snakes may have once had legs.[35]

Adaptation and natural selection are biological facts; ameba-to-man evolution is not. Natural selection can only work on the genetic information present in a population of organisms—it cannot create new information. For example, since no known reptiles have genes for feathers, no amount of selection will produce a feathered reptile. Mutations in genes can only modify or eliminate existing structures, not create new ones. If in a certain environment a lizard survives better with smaller legs, or no legs, then varieties with this trait will be selected for. This might more accurately be called **devolution**, not **evolution**.

Rapid minor changes in limb length can occur in lizards, as demonstrated on Bahamian islands by Losos et al.[36,37] The changes occurred much faster than evolutionists thought they could. Such changes do not involve new genetic information and so give no support to microbe-to-man evolution.[38] They do illustrate how

35. Brown, C., The origin of the snake (letter), *Creation Research Society Quarterly* **26**:54, 1989. Brown suggests that monitor lizards may have been the precursors of snakes.

36. Losos, J.B., Warheit, K.I. and Schoener, T.W., 1997. Adaptive differentiation following experimental island colonization in anolis lizards. *Nature* **387**:70–73. See comment by Case, T.J., *Nature* **387**:15–16, and *Creation* **19**(4):9.

37. Losos, J., *et al.*, Rapid temporal reversal in predator-driven natural selection, *Science* **314**(5802):1111, 2006.

38. See Catchpoole, D., Lizard losers (and winners), *Creation* **30**(1):35–37, 2007; <creationontheweb.com/lizard>.

quickly animals could have adapted to different environments after the Flood.

THE HUMAN APPENDIX

It is now known that the human appendix contains lymphatic tissue and helps control bacteria entering the intestines. It functions in a similar way to the tonsils at the upper end of the alimentary canal, which are known to fight throat infections. Tonsils also were once thought to be useless organs.[39,40]

Researchers at Duke University recently discovered an important role for the appendix as a safe house for 'good' bacteria, so that the intestine can be repopulated after flushing out a pathogen.[41] One report of this research stated:

> 'The function of the appendix seems related to the massive amount of bacteria populating the human digestive system, according to the study in the *Journal of Theoretical Biology*. There are more bacteria than human cells in the typical body. Most are good and help digest food.

> 'But sometimes the flora of bacteria in the intestines die or are purged. Diseases such as cholera or amoebic dysentery would clear the gut of useful bacteria. The appendix's job is to reboot the digestive system in that case.

> 'The appendix "acts as a good safe house for bacteria", said Duke surgery professor Bill Parker, a study co-author. Its location—just below the normal one-way flow of food and germs in the large intestine in a sort of gut cul-de-sac—helps support the theory, he said.

> 'Also, the worm-shaped organ outgrowth acts like a bacteria factory, cultivating the good germs, Parker said.

> 'That use is not needed in a modern industrialized society, Parker said.

> 'If a person's gut flora dies, it can usually be repopulated easily with germs they pick up from other people, he said. But before dense populations in modern times and during epidemics of cholera that

39. Ham, K. and Wieland, C., 1997. Your appendix ... it's there for a reason, *Creation* **20**(1):41–43; <creationontheweb.com/appendix>.
40. Glover, J.W., 1988. The human vermiform appendix—a general surgeon's reflections, *J. Creation* **3**:31–38; <creationontheweb.com/appendix2>.
41. Bollinger, *et al.*, Biofilms in the large bowel suggest an apparent function of the human vermiform appendix, *J. Theoret. Biol.* **249**(4):826–831, 2007 | doi:10.1016/j.jtbi.2007.08.032.

affected a whole region, it wasn't as easy to grow back those bacteria, so the appendix came in handy.

'In less developed countries, where the appendix may be still useful, the rate of appendicitis is lower than in the U.S., other studies have shown, Parker said.

'He said the appendix may be another case of an overly hygienic society triggering an overreaction by the body's immune system.'[42,43]

And to show how absurd the vestigial organ explanation is, man's alleged primate ancestors show no evidence of a more developed structure of which the appendix could be a vestige. The Duke University researchers stated:

'The human vermiform ("worm-like") appendix is a 5–10 cm long and 0.5–1 cm wide pouch that extends from the cecum of the large bowel. The architecture of the human appendix is unique among mammals, and few mammals other than humans have an appendix at all. The function of the human appendix has long been a matter of debate, with the structure often considered to be a vestige of evolutionary development despite evidence to the contrary based on comparative primate anatomy. The appendix is thought to have some immune function based on its association with substantial lymphatic tissue, although the specific nature of that putative function is unknown. Based (a) on a recently acquired understanding of immune-mediated biofilm formation by commensal bacteria in the mammalian gut, (b) on biofilm distribution in the large bowel, (c) the association of lymphoid tissue with the appendix, (d) the potential for biofilms to protect and support colonization by commensal bacteria, and (e) on the architecture of the human bowel, we propose that the human appendix is well suited as a "safe house" for commensal bacteria, providing support for bacterial growth and potentially facilitating re-inoculation of the colon in the event that the contents of the intestinal tract are purged following exposure to a pathogen.'[41]

HIP BONES IN WHALES

Some evolutionists claim that these bones show that whales evolved from land animals. However, Bergman and Howe point

---

42. Purpose of appendix believed found, CNN.com, 5 October 2007.
43. See also Doyle, S., Appendix: a bacterial 'safe house': New research suggests function for appendix in maintaining good digestive bacteria populations, <creationontheweb.com/appendix3>, 2007.

out that they are different in male and female whales. They are not useless at all, but help with reproduction (copulation).[44]

TEETH IN EMBRYONIC BALEEN WHALES

Evolutionists claim that these teeth show that baleen whales evolved from toothed whales. However they have not provided an adequate mechanism for scrapping one perfectly good system (teeth) and replacing it with a very different system (baleen or whalebone). Also, the teeth in the embryo function as guides for the correct formation of the massive jaws.

As Scadding, an evolutionist, said, '... vestigial organs provide no evidence for evolutionary theory.'[45]

'JUNK' DNA

Overview of Junk DNA points
1. 'Junk DNA' (or, rather, DNA that doesn't directly code for proteins) is not evidence for evolution. Rather, its alleged junkiness is a deduction from the false *assumption* of evolution.
2. Just because no function is known, it doesn't mean there is no function.
3. Research is revealing many uses for this 'non-coding' DNA.
4. There is good evidence that it has an essential role as part of an elaborate genetic network, and also helps in the formatting of the genetic information. This could have a crucial role in the growth and development of many-celled creatures from a single fertilized egg, and also in the post-Flood diversification (e.g. a canine kind giving rise to dingoes, wolves, coyotes etc.).
5. A shattering new discovery shows that rather than only 2% of the genome being transcribed, a startling (for evolutionists) 93% is, and possibly even more.
6. Indeed, the 'junk' is about *50 times more active* than the genes, as shown by the amount of RNA transcripts.

This is basically the vestigial organs argument applied to DNA, and is probably now the most popular one. Each time that evolutionists discover new strands of DNA that have no known function, they like to describe it as 'junk' DNA that is a leftover of evolution.

Introns and the spliceosome

The DNA of organisms more complex than bacteria contains regions called *exons* that code for proteins, and non-coding interspersed regions called *introns*. Cellular machinery removes the introns and splices the exons together to form the mRNA (messenger RNA) that is finally decoded to form the protein (see diagram). Richard Roberts and Phillip Sharp won the 1993 Nobel Prize in

---

44. See Wieland, C., 1998. The strange tale of the leg on a whale, *Creation* **20**(3):10–13.
45. Scadding, S.R., Do vestigial organs provide evidence for evolution? *Evolutionary Theory* **5**:173–176, 1981.

Physiology or Medicine for discovering introns in 1977. It turns out that 97–98% of the genome may be introns and other non-coding sequences, but this raises the question of why introns exist at all. Thus it became part of the prevailing wisdom that only 2% of the genome was functional.

The splicing requires elaborate machinery called a *spliceosome*. This assembles on the intron, chops it out at exactly the right place and joins the exons together. This must be in the right direction and place, because it makes a huge difference if the exon is joined even one 'letter' off.[46]

But it's absurd that more complex organisms should evolve such elaborate machinery to splice the introns if they were really useless. Rather, natural selection would favour organisms that did *not* waste resources processing a genome filled with 98% of junk.

Demonstrated functions for 'junk DNA'

There have been many functions for junk DNA discovered, such as in overall chromosome structure and regulation of genes. It might also have enabled rapid post-Flood diversification.[47] Damage to introns can be disastrous—one example involved deleting four 'letters' in the centre of an intron, preventing the spliceosome from binding to it. This resulted in the intron being included.[48]

Mutations in introns interfere with imprinting, the process by which only certain maternal or paternal genes are expressed, not both. Expression of both genes results in a variety of diseases and cancers.[49]

The exon/intron arrangement of genes allows for rearrangement of the exons to produce different proteins. For example, the

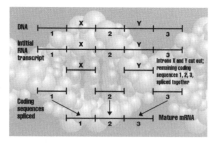

Introns are edited from DNA transcripts to form protein-coding mRNA.

cSlo gene produces at least 576 different proteins in the hair cells of the inner ear of chickens.[50] These variant proteins tune different hair cells to resonate at different frequencies, so they are sensitive to different sound pitches. Such high levels of 'alternative splicing' are apparently common in nerve cells.[51] This system probably explains

46. Cf. Staley, J.P. and Guthrie, C., Mechanical devices of the spliceosome: motors, clocks, springs, and things, *Cell* **92**(3):315–26, 1998.
47. For an overview, see Walkup, L., Junk DNA: evolutionary discards or God's tools? *J. Creation* **14**(2):18–30, 2000.
48. Cohen, P., New genetic spanner in the works, *New Scientist* **173**(2334):17, 2002.
49. Batten, D., 'Junk' DNA (again), *J. Creation* **12**(1):5, 1998; <creationontheweb.com/junkdna>.
50. Black, D.L., Minireview: splicing in the inner ear: a familiar tune, but what are the instruments? *Neuron* **20**:165–168, 1999.
51. Durandy, A., Activation-induced cytidine deaminase: a dual role in class-switch recombination and somatic

how humans, with some 25,000 'genes', can produce over 100,000 different proteins. Researchers do not know yet how cells regulate such mRNA editing to generate different proteins, but the control systems almost certainly reside in the so-called 'junk DNA'. The complexity of this system surely should make those who research it question the adequacy of the evolutionary story.[52]

Andrew Fire and Craig Mello won the 2006 Nobel Prize for Physiology or Medicine for their 1998 discovery of *RNA interference*, where double-stranded RNA can silence the gene, i.e. block protein synthesis. Many of our genes encode small RNA molecules called microRNAs that contain pieces of the code of other genes. These can form a double-stranded structure with mRNA, stopping its translation into proteins, thus instigating 'RNA interference'.[53]

Some non-coding RNAs called microRNAs (miRNAs) seem to regulate the production of proteins coded in other genes, and seem to be almost identical in humans, mice and zebrafish. The recent sequencing of the mouse genome[54] surprised researchers and led to headlines such as '"Junk DNA" Contains Essential Information.'[55] They found that 5% of the genomes were basically identical but only 2% of that was actual genes. So they reasoned that the other 3% must also be identical for a *reason*. The researchers believe the 3% probably has a crucial role in determining the behaviour of the actual genes, e.g. the order in which they are switched on.[56]

Introns needed for electrical function

Scientists at the University of Pennsylvania School of Medicine found that introns were essential for guiding the construction of electrical channels of neurons. Although the intron doesn't code for the channel proteins themselves, it controls the number of mRNAs that are to be translated into these proteins. When this intron is removed, the electric properties are distorted.[57] One report on this research states:

'Researchers at the University of Pennsylvania School of Medicine have discovered that introns, or junk DNA to some, associated with RNA are an

hypermutation, *Eur. J. Immunol.* **33**(8):2069–73, 2003.

52. Batten, D., Yet another way of getting more from less, *Journal of Creation*, **18**(2):7, 2004; <creationontheweb. com/moreless>.

53. <nobelprize.org/nobel_prizes/medicine/laureates/2006/press.html>.

54. Waterston, R.H., *et.al.*, Initial sequencing and comparative anallsis of the mouse genome, *Nature* **420**(6915):509–590, 2002.

55. Gillis, J., 'Junk DNA' contains essential information—DNA has instructions needed for growth, survival, *Washington Post*, 4 December 2002.

56. Evolutionists call the almost identical sequences 'highly conserved,' because they *interpret* the similarities as arising from a common ancestor, but with natural selection eliminating any deviations in this 5% because precision is essential for it to function properly. However, it is reasonable to interpret the same evidence as evidence of a designer creating the sequences in a precise way, because that's necessary for it to function.

57. Bell, T.J. *et al.*, Cytoplasmic BKCa channel intron-containing mRNAs contribute to the intrinsic excitability of hippocampal neurons, *Proc Natl Acad Sci USA.* **105**(6):1901–6 12 February 2008; <www.pnas.org/cgi/content/short/105/6/1901>.

important molecular guide to making nerve-cell electrical channels. …

'[T]he group has found that an RNA encoding for a nerve-cell electrical channel, called the BK channel, contains an intron that is present outside the nucleus. This intron plays an important role in ensuring that functional BK channels are made in the appropriate place in the cell.

'When this intron-containing RNA was knocked out, leaving the maturely spliced RNA in the cell, the electrical properties of the cell became abnormal. "We think the intron-containing mRNA is targeted to the dendrite where it is spliced into the channel protein and inserted locally into the region of the dendrite called the dendritic spine. The dendritic spine is where a majority of axons from other cells touch a particular neuron to facilitate neuronal communication" says Eberwine. "This is the first evidence that an intron-containing RNA outside of the nucleus serves a critical cellular function."

'"The intron acts like a guide or gatekeeper," says Eberwine. "It keys the messenger RNA to the dendrite for local control of gene expression and final removal of the intron before the channel protein is made. Just because the intron is not in the final channel protein doesn't mean that it doesn't have an important purpose."

'The group surmises that the intron may control how many mRNAs are brought to the dendrite and translated into functional channel proteins. The correct number of channels is just as important for electrical impulses as having a properly formed channel.

The investigators believe that this is a general mechanism for the regulation of cytoplasmic RNAs in neurons.'[58]

Functioning 'pseudogenes'

A major class of 'junk DNA' is 'pseudogenes'—some 20,000 have been identified in the human genome.[59] They are supposed to be crippled copies of real genes (the corresponding gene is called *paralogous*). However, with the new research in genes coding for

---

58. RNA-associated introns guide nerve-cell channel production, *Physorg.com*, 2008, <www.physorg.com/news121436419.html>.

59. Pondrom, S., Researchers in Japan and UCSD discover novel role for pseudogenes, University of California, San Diego News, <http://ucsdnews.ucsd.edu/newsrel/health/Pseudogenes.htm>, 30 April 2003.

regulatory RNA, it is rash to conclude that lack of coding for proteins means that the gene has no function.

For example, one pseudogene in a snail was found to code for a short RNA strand. This RNA complexes with the mRNA produced from the paralogous gene for neuronal nitric oxide synthase (nNOS), thus regulating the amount of the enzyme (protein) produced.[60,61]

The *Makorin1-p1* pseudogene in mice seemed at first to be a corrupted and crippled version of the Makorin1 gene. But researchers discovered serendipitously that the pseudogene actually helps the expression of the gene. Mice with a defective pseudogene have 80% mortality.[62] Normally, there are repressor molecules that hinder the expression of the gene, or possibly they act on the mRNA coded by the gene. However, the similar sequence of the pseudogene means that it, or its mRNA, can attract the repressor molecules, thus leaving the gene free to be expressed.[63]

Advanced operating system?

John Mattick of the University of Queensland in Brisbane, Australia, has published a number of papers arguing that the non-coding DNA regions, or rather their non-coding RNA 'negatives', are important for a complicated genetic network.[64,65,66] These interact with each other, the DNA, mRNA and the proteins. Mattick proposes that the introns function as *nodes*, linking points in a network. The introns provide many extra connections, and so enable what in computer terminology would be called multi-tasking and parallel processing.

Recent discoveries about 'jumping genes' support this. Researchers found that this type of transposable element (TE) controls embryonic development.[67] A report on this discovery said:

'The research, published in the October issue of *Developmental Cell*, suggests that retrotransposons may not be just the 'junk DNA' once thought, but rather appear to be a large repository of start sites for initiating gene expression. Therefore, more than one third of the mouse and human genomes, previously thought to be non-functional, may play some role in

60. Korneev, S.A., Park, J.-H. and O'Shea, M., Neuronal expression of neural nitric oxide synthase (nNOS) protein is suppressed by an antisense RNA transcribed from a NOS pseudogene, *Journal of Neuroscience* **19**:7711–7720, 1999.
61. Woodmorappe, J., Pseudogene function: regulation of gene expression, *J. Creation* **17**(1):47–52, 2003; p. 49.
62. Hirotsune, S., Yoshida, N., *et al.*, An expressed pseudogene regulates the messenger-RNA stability of its homologous coding gene, *Nature* **423**:91–96, 2003; perspective by Lee, J.T., Complicity of gene and pseudogene, *same issue* pp. 26–28.
63. Woodmorappe, J., Pseudogene function: more evidence, *J. Creation* **17**(2):15–18, 2003; p. 49.
64. Mattick, J.S. Non-coding RNAs: The architects of eukaryotic complexity, *EMBO Reports* **2**:986–991, November 2001; <embo-reports.oupjournals.org/cgi/content/abstract/2/11/986>.
65. Cooper, M., Life 2.0, *New Scientist* **174**(2346):30–33, 2002.
66. Dennis, C., The brave new world of RNA, *Nature* **418**(6894):122–124, 2002.
67. Peaston, A.E., Evsikov, A.V. *et al.*, Retrotransposons regulate host genes in mouse oocytes and preimplantation embryos, *Developmental Cell* **7**(4):597–606.

the regulation of gene expression and promotion of genetic diversity.'[68]

So fully one third of the alleged junk now has a vital function. However, this 'non-coding' DNA only seems to function during egg and embryo development, so its functions would have been missed in studies of cells of mature organisms.[69]

In the case of life, this could control the order in which genes are switched on and off. This means that a tremendous variety of multicellular life could be produced by 'rewiring' the network. In contrast, 'early computers were like simple organisms, very cleverly designed, but programmed for one task at a time.'[70] The older computers were very inflexible, requiring a complete redesign of the network to change anything.

Evolutionary interpretation

Mattick suggests that this new system somehow evolved (despite the irreducible complexity) and in turn enabled the evolution of many complex living things from simple organisms. The same evidence is better interpreted from a biblical framework—indeed this system does enable multicellular organisms to develop from a 'simple' cell—but this is the fertilized egg. This makes more sense, since the fertilized egg has all the programming in place for all the information for a complex life form to develop from an embryo. It is also an example of good design economy pointing to a *single* designer as opposed to many. In contrast, the first 'simple' cell to evolve the complex splicing machinery would have no information to splice.

But Mattick may be partly right about diversification of life. According to the Bible's account of history, we can deduce that life indeed diversified—after the Flood. However, this diversification involved no *new* suites of genetic information. Some creationists have proposed that certain parts of currently non-coding DNA could have enabled faster diversification,[71] and Mattick's theory could provide still another mechanism.

Evolutionary notions hindering science

A severe critic of Mattick's theory, Jean-Michel Claverie of CNRS, the national research institute in Marseilles, France, said something very revealing:

'I don't think much of this work. In general, all these global ideas don't travel very far because they fail to take into account the most basic principle of biology: things arose by the additive addition of

68.   James, R., Junk DNA guides embryo formation, <www.Sciscoop.com/story/2004/10/13/33731/304>.
69.   Batten, D., No joy for junkies, *J. Creation* **19**(1):3, 2005; <creationontheweb.com/junkies>.
70.   Cooper, Ref. 65, p. 32.
71.   E.g. Wood, T.C., Altruistic Genetic Elements (AGEs), cited in Walkup, Ref. 47.

evolution of tiny subsystems, not by global design. It is perfectly possible that one intron in one given gene might have evolved—by chance—some regulatory property. It is utterly improbable that all genes might have acquired introns for the future property of regulating expression.'[72]

Two points to note:

1. He agrees that if the intron system really is an advanced operating system, it really would be irreducibly complex and evolution could not build it stepwise.
2. It illustrates the role of materialistic assumptions behind evolution and how evolutionary thinking actually impedes scientific investigation.

Information formatting

James Shapiro of Chicago University also argues along the lines of a computer operating system:

'Despite its abundance, the repetitive component of the genome is often called "junk", "selfish", or "parasitic" DNA. … We feel it is time to present an alternative "functionalist" point of view. The discovery of repetitive DNA represents a conceptual problem for traditional gene-based notions of hereditary information. … We argue here that a more fruitful interpretation of sequence data may result from thinking about genomes as information storage systems with parallels to electronic information storage systems. From this informatics perspective, repetitive DNA is an essential component of genomes; it is required for formatting coding information so that it can be accurately expressed and for formatting DNA molecules for transmission to new generations of cells.'[73]

MOST OF THE GENOME IS TRANSCRIBED AFTER ALL![74]

The ENCODE (Encyclopedia of DNA Elements) project then reported on a detailed study of the RNA transcripts from only 1% of the human genome. This overturned much of the prevailing 'junk thinking' about DNA. In particular, rather than only 2% of the genome being coding, they inferred that about **93%** of the genome

---

72. Cited in Cooper, Ref. 65.
73. Shapiro, J.A. and Sternberg, R.V., Why repetitive DNA is essential to genome function, *Biological Reviews* **80:**227–250, 2005.
74. After Williams, A., Astonishing DNA complexity uncovered, <creationontheweb.com/dnacomplex>, 2007.

is transcribed (that is, copied to RNA).[75,76] Further study may even raise this to 100%.

Also, in likely support of Mattick's theory, ENCODE found that exons are not gene-specific but are modules that can be joined to many different RNA transcripts. One exon can be used in combination with up to 33 different genes located on 14 different chromosomes. This means that one exon can specify one part shared in common by many different proteins.

ENCODE also discovered that DNA is even more efficient as an information storage medium. Not just one strand, but *both* strands (sense and anti-sense) of the DNA are fully transcribed. And transcription proceeds not just one way but both backwards and forwards.

<wikipedia.org>

Furthermore, Williams summarized:

> 'The untranslated regions (now called UTRs, rather than 'junk') are far *more* important than the translated regions (the genes), as measured by the number of DNA bases appearing in RNA transcripts. Genic regions are transcribed on average in **five** different overlapping and interleaved ways, while UTRs are transcribed on average in **seven** different overlapping and interleaved ways. Since there are about 33 times as many bases in UTRs than in genic regions, that makes the 'junk' about *50 times more active* than the genes.'[77]

CHAPTER SUMMARY

The argument against design from allegedly badly designed features suffers from many flaws.

- It is really a *theological* argument, not a scientific one. This is because it doesn't really dispute design *per se*, but makes assumptions about what a designer should have done.
- In many cases it is an *argument from personal incredulity*, in that the critic can't see a reason for the particular design. But more information demonstrates the advantages of the allegedly inferior design. This is demonstrated in the 'backwardly wired' vertebrate retina, and new uses are constantly being found

75. Birney, E. *et al.*, Identification and analysis of functional elements in 1% of the human genome by the ENCODE pilot project, *Nature* **447**: 799–816, 2007.
76. Philipp Kapranov, P., Willingham, A.T. and Gingeras, T.R., Genome-wide transcription and the implications for genomic organization, *Nature Reviews Genetics* **8**: 413–423, 2007.
77. Williams, A., Astonishing DNA complexity update, <creationontheweb.com/DNAupdate>, 2007.

for 'junk DNA', as well as for many other organs previously assumed to be useless vestiges.

- A feature may not seem optimal considered *in isolation*, but for the creature as a whole what matters is the optimization of many features combined. This requires trade-offs between different characteristics, e.g. thickness of armour vs. weight. While 'mere design' (ID) theory may be unable to explain real cases of poor functionality, the biblical model includes the Fall and subsequent deterioration and thus recognizes degeneration as a cause of less-than-optimum functionality.

CHAPTER 13

WHY ARE THERE 'BAD THINGS' IN NATURE?

There are certainly many features of the living world that all agree are beautiful. But what about the creatures that seem well designed to inflict harm on others? And if things are so well designed, why did so many go extinct? To illustrate this sort of argument, Sir David Attenborough receives many letters from creationists who ask him why he doesn't give credit to a Creator for the wonderful design features he demonstrates on his shows. He answers:

> 'When Creationists talk about God creating every individual species as a separate act, they always instance hummingbirds, or orchids, sunflowers and beautiful things.

> 'But I tend to think instead of a parasitic worm that is boring through the eye of a boy sitting on the bank of a river in West Africa, [a worm] that's going to make him blind.

> 'And [I ask them], "Are you telling me that the God you believe in, who you also say is an all- merciful God, who cares for each one of us individually, are you saying that God created this worm that can live in no other way than in an innocent child's eyeball? Because that doesn't seem to me to coincide with a God who's full of mercy."'[1]

It is important to note that this is a *theological* argument rather than a scientific argument—it is about what God supposedly would or would not do rather than about the scientific evidence. It's ironic that Attenborough claims that creation is about theology while evolution is about science, yet his main anti-creation argument is theological rather than scientific!

All the same, the ID movement has problems answering this type of argument because they lack a *history* of the acts of a designer, since its proponents commonly refuse to acknowledge the Bible with its teaching of the Fall (and Flood).

The Bible doesn't specifically explain how carnivory originated, but since creation was finished after Day 6 (Genesis 2:1–3), there

---

1.   Buchanan, M, Wild, Wild Life, *Sydney Morning Herald*, The Guide, p. 6, 24 March 2003.

is no possibility that God later created new carnivorous animals. Instead, biblical creationists have three explanations in general, although the specific explanation depends on the particular case.[2]

1. *The Bible appears not to regard insects and other invertebrates as 'living', in the same sense as humans and vertebrate animals*

The Hebrew never refers to an invertebrate as *nephesh chayyāh* (נפש היה 'living soul/creature'), unlike humans and even fish (Genesis 1:20, 2:7). This is consistent with the Bible saying that 'the life of the flesh is in the blood' (Leviticus 17:11) and the fact that insects don't have the same sort of 'blood' that vertebrates do. Therefore, the pre-Fall diet of animals did not necessarily exclude invertebrates. Interestingly, insects do not appear to have a complex enough brain to register a stimulus as 'pain':

> 'Some insects normally show no signs of painful experience at all. A dragonfly, for example, may eat much of its own abdomen if its tail end is brought into the mouthparts. Removal of part of the abdomen of a honeybee does not stop the animal's feeding. If the head of a blow-fly (*Phormia*) is cut off, it nevertheless stretches its tubular feeding organ (proboscis) and begins to suck if its chemoreceptors (labellae) are brought in touch with a sugar solution; the ingested solution simply flows out at the severed neck.'[3]

2. *Before the Fall, many attack/defence structures could have been used in a vegetarian lifestyle.*

For example, spiders normally now use their webs for trapping insects and other prey. But some baby spiders catch pollen for food,[4] providing a possible clue to a pre-Fall function for the spider web.[5]

There are modern examples of lions that didn't eat meat,[6,7] and the converse of 'herbivores' (cow, sheep) eating chickens.[8,9] And a 'seed-eating' bird (finch) has turned to blood-sucking,[10] So some of the behaviour can be learned. That there can be very similar species, clearly derived from the one original created kind, with one a vegetarian and the other a carnivore, shows how animals can adapt to carnivory from vegetarianism. Examples include vegetarian and

2. Batten, D., Catchpoole, D., Sarfati, J. and Wieland, C., *The Creation Answers Book*, ch. 6., Creation Book Publishers, 2007.
3. 'Sensory Reception: Mechanoreception', *Encyclopædia Britannica* (Electronic edition on CD).
4. White, T., Pollen-eating spiders, *Nature Australia* **26**(7):5, Summer 1999–2000.
5. Pollen-eating spiders, *Creation* **22**(3):5, 2000.
6. Catchpoole, D., The lion that wouldn't eat meat, *Creation* **22**(2):22–23, 2000; <creationontheweb.com/lion>.
7. Catchpoole, D., Lea, the spaghetti lioness, *Creation* **29**(4):44–45, 2007.
8. Carnivorous cow, *Creation* **29**(4):7, 2007.
9. Wild and woolly, *Creation* **21**(4):9, 1999.
10. Catchpoole, D., Vampire finches of the Galápagos, *Creation* **29**(3):52–53, 2007.

carnivorous piranhas[11] and the palm-nut vulture,[12] which is largely vegetarian, while a 'bird of prey' (oilbird) is totally vegetarian.[13]

The Fall could have resulted in benign features becoming used for attacking. The *need* to attack may have arisen for several reasons. For some animals, the curse upon them (Genesis 3:14) may have resulted in their losing the ability to synthesise certain essential protein components (amino acids) from ingested plant material, hence their need to eat other animals containing those nutrients. Similarly, with the curse on the ground (Genesis 3:17–18), plants might have lost nutritional value such that some animals, which could no longer survive on the available plants, turned to eating the animals that could. Thus animals with the right conveniently-predesigned features (e.g., claws, venom) could turn to predation to gain their required nutrients.

With regard to poisons, the concept of 'poison' depends on amounts—'the dose *makes* the toxin'. Many poisons have benefits in small amounts, e.g. the potent digitalis toxin in foxglove plants in tiny amounts eases the symptoms of congestive heart failure. Conversely, even 'good' things like oxygen and water can act as poisons in large amounts.[14] Before the Fall, the levels of toxins would have been low enough for them not to be toxic. Following the Fall, plants could, through mutational loss of information, lose control of the synthesis of substances that then accumulate to toxic levels, or lose enzymes in metabolic pathways such that the substrates for those enzymes accumulate to toxic levels.

3. *God foreknew the Fall, so He programmed creatures with the information for attack and defence features, which they would need in a cursed world. This information was 'switched on' at the Fall.*

It's notable that the development of every individual multi-celled creature involves a programmed switching off of genetic information. Each individual begins as a single cell—a *zygote* or an ovum fertilized by a spermatozoon. This fertilized ovum has all the instructions coded in the DNA to make us what we are physically (given the right environmental conditions).

But as the embryo grows, different cells in different places have to specialize, so that only certain instructions are executed—the cells become *differentiated*. The instructions are there, but turned off somehow. There are complicated genetic switches involved, and also a process called *methylation*—attaching methyl groups to the

11. Catchpoole, D., Piranha, *Creation* 22(4):20–23, 2000; <creationontheweb.com/piranha>.
12. Catchpoole, D., The 'bird of prey' that's not, *Creation* 23(1):24–25, 2000; <creationontheweb.com/vulture>.
13. Bell, B., The super-senses of oilbirds: Bizarre birds elude an evolutionary explanation, *Creation* 28(1):38–41, 2005; <creationontheweb.com/oilbird>.
14. Bergman, J., Understanding Poisons from a Creationist Perspective, *J. Creation* 11(3):353–360, 1997; <creationontheweb.com/poison>.

chemical 'letters' of DNA that code for instructions that need to be 'turned off'.

All the on/off switching must occur in the right sequence; the information for this sequencing is partly encoded in the DNA, but there are also controls outside the genes, hence the term *epigenetic* (see p. 169). This is why it would be impossible to clone dinosaurs and mammoths even if we found intact DNA—we would need the ovum (mother's egg) too.

The result of these elaborately designed switching sequences is that bone cells execute only instructions pertaining to bone—the instructions for blood, nerves, skin, etc. are still in the cells' DNA, but turned off. Similarly for blood, skin and other types of cells.

Thus if one can believe that this switching-off information was programmed by a Master Genetic Programmer, it is plausible that this Programmer could also have switched on information at the Fall.

This seems to be the best explanation for the clearly designed features such as the jellyfish sting, another type of catapult mechanism (see ch. 6). Evolutionary notions of its origin are contradicted by the evolutionary time frame. One evolutionist admitted:

> 'It is inconceivable that large predatory organisms like jellyfish could have existed at a time when there was nothing else around for them to feed on!'[15]

This applies to stinging for defence, because large predators had not evolved yet. But the evidence is consistent with the Fall affecting all creatures at the same time.[16]

Pathogens and creation

Some people wonder where disease germs fit into the biblical framework, if God created everything 'very good'. Under this framework, obviously the Fall was responsible for disease, but how, if God had finished creating at the end of Creation Week?

However, even something usually known as a deadly germ can have a mild variant that causes no illness. Presumably, something like this was created during Creation Week—even today, *Vibrio cholerae*, the germ that causes cholera, has a non-virulent form. This also has a role in the ecosystems of brackish waters and estuaries, and the original may have had a role living symbiotically with some people. Even its toxin may have a beneficial function in small amounts, like most poisons. The virulence arose after the Fall, by natural selection of varieties producing more and more toxin as contaminated water became more plentiful. This process would need no new genetic information. Also, recent evidence shows that

15. Phylum Cnidaria, <www.palaeos.com/Invertebrates/Coelenterates/Cnidaria.htm>, 2003.
16. Catchpoole, D., Skeptics challenge: a 'God of love' created a killer jellyfish? Crush, kill, destroy— why do creatures have equipment to attack, kill and eat other animals? *Creation* 25(4):34–35, 2003; <creationontheweb.com/jellyfish>.

the *loss* of *chemotaxis*—the ability to move in response to changes in chemical concentrations—will 'markedly increase infectivity in an infant mouse model of cholera.'[17]

The leprosy germ is another good example. The form that causes disease, *Mycobacterium leprae,* has lost more than 2000 genes, about a quarter of its total genome.[18]

Another likely example of virulence arising by information loss involves the *mycoplasmas,* the smallest known self-reproducing organisms (parasitic bacteria with no cell walls and fewer than 1,000 genes, which are found in the respiratory system and urogenital tracts of humans). Loss of genetic information, e.g. for amino acid synthesis, could have resulted in the mycoplasmas' becoming increasingly dependent on their hosts for survival.[19,20]

Similarly, too, with viruses: the most harmful viruses seem to have *de*volved, e.g. the most pathogenic HIV strains are also the least fit (they don't survive as well as less virulent strains).[21]

Some clues to possible benign pre-Fall roles for viruses can be gleaned from functions they have even today. Viruses are non-living entities, because they can't reproduce on their own, but need the copying machinery of more complex cells. But they have a number of useful functions even now, including transporting genes among plants and animals, keeping soil fertile, keeping water clean and regulating gases in the atmosphere.[22] So, once again, some alleged evidence for evolution actually provides support for the Creation/ Fall model.

We should also note that microbes 'help prime the immune system' and many allergies might be due to a living environment that's too clean. Note that the immune system would be important even before the Fall to distinguish between 'self' and 'non-self'.

EXTINCTIONS

Some object to a Designer on the grounds that allegedly 95–99 percent of species have become extinct. However, the *known* record of extinct and extant species does not support this. The number of fossil species *actually found* is estimated to be about 250,000, while there are about three million living 'species,' or even more, depending on who's telling the story. But if this >95% claim were

17. Merrell, D.S. et al., Host-induced epidemic spread of the cholera bacterium, *Nature* **417**(6889):642–644, 2002.
18. Eiglmeier, K. The decaying genome of *Mycobacterium leprae*, *Lepr. Rev.*, 72:387–398, 2001.
19. Wood, T.C., Genome decay in the Mycoplasmas, *Impact* **340**, October 2001; <www.icr.org/pubs/imp/imp-340.htm>.
20. Wieland, C., Diseases on the Ark (Answering the critics), *J. Creation* **8**(1):16–18, 1994, explains important related concepts.
21. Wodarz, D. and Levy, D.N., Human immunodeficiency virus evolution towards reduced replicative fitness *in vivo* and the development of AIDS, *Proc. Royal Soc. B*, 31 July 2007 | DOI:10.1098/rspb.2007.0413.
22. See also Bergman, J., Did God make pathogenic viruses? *J. Creation* **13**(1):115–125, 1999; Kim, M., Biological view of viruses: creation vs evolution, *J. Creation* **20**(3):12–13, 2006.

correct, we would expect there to be many more fossil species than living ones.

The only plausible explanation is evolutionary bias. For evolution to be true, there would have been innumerable transitional forms between different types of creatures. Therefore, for every known fossil species, many more must have existed to connect it to its ancestors and descendents. This is yet another example of evolutionary conclusions coming before the evidence. Really, the claim is an implicit admission that large numbers of transitional forms are predicted, which heightens the difficulty for evolutionists, given how few there are that even they could begin to claim were candidates.

As for extinctions in general, while 'mere design' would have some problems, the biblical model explains them. This is because it includes the Fall and the Flood, and the likely aftermath of the Flood, the Ice Age.

CHAPTER 14

OBJECTIONS TO DESIGN

The theory of design undermines dogmatic materialism, so it is not surprising that materialists (and some of their allies in the Church) have fought back hard. This chapter deals with a number of objections not covered in the previous two chapters on alleged poor and malevolent design.

GOD OF THE GAPS, PERSONAL INCREDULITY

This argument asserts that design is just an appeal to gaps in our knowledge, and as science advances, these gaps will keep disappearing. Compromising theologians likewise tut-tut about this, claiming such arguments result in God getting smaller and smaller.

The fallacy of this objection is that it presumes that the design argument is an appeal to ignorance. But it is rather an argument from *analogy* with what we *do* know. Leading ID theorist Bill Dembski explains:

William Albert Dembski lecturing at University of California, Berkeley (2006).

> 'Certain biological systems have a feature, call it IC (irreducible complexity). Darwinians don't have a clue how biological systems with that feature originated. ... We know that intelligent agency has the causal power to produce systems that exhibit IC (e.g., many human artifacts exhibit IC). Therefore, biological systems that exhibit IC are likely to be designed. Design theorists, in attributing design to systems that exhibit IC, are simply doing what scientists do generally, which is to attempt to formulate a causally adequate explanation of the phenomenon in question.'[1]

Also, if we do *not* know, why are evolutionists so dogmatic that they *do* know that evolution is responsible for the origin and development of life? And they are very keen on *natural-selection-of-the-gaps*–type arguments, giving 'natural selection' creator-like miraculous qualities to explain the seemingly inexplicable.[2]

---

1. Dembski, W.A., Still spinning just fine: a response to Ken Miller, <www.designinference.com/documents/2003.02.Miller_Response.htm>, 2003.
2. See also Weinberger, L., Whose god? The theological response to the god-of-the-gaps, *Journal of Creation* **22**(1):120–127, 2008.

CHEATING WITH CHANCE

Since design arguments can often come down to probability, evolutionists often bluff by arguing that improbable things happen every day, so what is the problem? For example, they say the odds of winning the lottery are pretty remote, but someone wins it every week. Or Kenneth Milller, on an anti-ID program:[3]

> One of the mathematical tricks employed by ID involves taking the present-day situation and calculating probabilities that the present would have appeared randomly from events in the past. And the best example I can give is to sit down with four friends, shuffle a deck of 52 cards and deal them out, and keep an exact record of the order in which the cards were dealt. We could then look back and say, my goodness, how improbable this is … . Nonetheless, you dealt them out and you got the hand which you did.
>
> *Narrator*: The chances of life evolving, just like the chance of getting a particular hand of cards, could not be calculated backwards. By doing so, the odds were unfairly stacked. Played that way, cards and life would always appear impossible.

Or the exact combination and arrangement of people walking across a busy city street is highly improbable, but such improbable arrangements happen all the time. Or the chances of someone winning the lottery are very remote, but people are winning lotteries all the time. So they argue from these analogies to try to dilute the force of this powerful argument for creation.

However, there is a glaring fallacy in this 'cheating with chance'.[4]

In all the analogies cited above, there has to be an outcome. There is a 100% probability of getting **some** hand. There **will** be people walking across the busy street. Someone **has** to win the lottery. But what is the probability that the same hand will be dealt in the next game, that the same people will be walking in the street at the same time tomorrow, and that the same number will win the lottery?

Conversely, there are vastly more ways of being dead than alive, so there is by no means 100% probability of ANY old arrangement of amino acids forming the proteins required for life (see ch. 11, p. 158). So there need not be any living outcome *at all*, and the probabilities are strongly against it. That is the whole point of the argument.

3.   'A War on Science', *Horizon* program, BBC, 2006. See critique, Grigg, R. and Sarfati, J., Intelligent Design—'A War on Science' says the BBC, <creationontheweb.com/waronscience>, 2006.

4.   Batten, D., Cheating with chance, *Creation* **17**(2):14–15, 1995; <creationontheweb.com/chance>

Some evolutionists have then replied that it *did* happen because we are here! This is circular reasoning at its worst.

Furthermore, if Miller and his hero-worshipping narrator were right, one would *never* be able to tell that someone is stacking the deck of cards. That is, if a dealer always gets an ace at the right time, it doesn't mean that he had one up his sleeve, because all hands are equally improbable ... Poker players in the Wild West might not have swallowed this as easily as Miller does. In reality, it is not just the low probability, but the low probability of *duplicating a specific hand* that would give cheats away. It is not any old order, but certain *specific arrangements*, which have a very low probability of just happening, that indicate intelligent input rather than chance.

CRYSTALS PROVE THAT DESIGN-LIKE STRUCTURES CAN OCCUR NATURALLY?

But this ignores a fundamental difference between crystals and living creatures, as Orgel explained (pp. 16–17). To elaborate, a *crystal* is a repetitive arrangement of atoms, so is *ordered*. Such ordered structures usually have the *lowest energy*, so will form *spontaneously* at low enough temperatures. And the information of the crystals is *already present* in their building blocks, for example, directional forces between atoms. But proteins and DNA, the most important large molecules of life, are *not* ordered (in the sense of repetitive), but have high *specified complexity*. Without specification external to the system, i.e. the programmed machinery of living things or the intelligent direction of an organic chemist, there is no natural tendency to form such complex specified arrangements at all. When their building blocks are combined (and even this requires special conditions), a *random* sequence results. The difference between a crystal and DNA is like the difference between a book containing nothing but ABCD repeated and a book of Shakespeare. However, this doesn't stop many evolutionists (ignorant of Orgel's distinction) claiming that crystals prove that specified complexity can arise naturally—they merely prove that *order* can arise naturally, which no creationist contests.[5]

Crystals *vs* biomolecule information content

To show that *crystals have low information content*, consider what happens if you break up a large crystal of salt into smaller crystals—you still have salt. Another way of putting it is that the information needed to have Na^+ and Cl^- spontaneously form into a salt crystal *is already inherent in the ingredients*—nothing has to be imposed from the outside.

---

5.   An extensive discussion on information and thermodynamics, order and complexity, is found in Thaxton, C.B., Bradley, W.L. and Olsen, R.L., *The Mystery of Life's Origin*, Philosophical Library Inc., New York, 1984, chapter 8.

But in biomolecules, *the sequences are not caused by the properties of the constituent amino acids and nucleotides themselves.* This is a *huge contrast* to crystal structures, which **are** caused purely by the properties of their constituents. Experiments have shown that there is poor correlation between the chemical bonding energies and sequences in DNA and proteins. If there really was some chemical determinism involved in protein formation, we should see a strong correlation, and also we would not expect such a huge variety of proteins. That's why we never find insulin or cytochrome if we just throw amino acids in a flask with a condensing agent; rather, we merely get random polypeptides.

Crystals and unit cells

The smallest unit of a crystal is often considered to be its *unit cell*, and the crystal is built up simply by repetitions of this by specific multiples of translation vectors. My own Ph.D. thesis included published papers on $CuBrSe_3$ and $CuISe_3$, and the latter has a very complex structure by normal inorganic chemical standards, with 18 formula units in each hexagonal unit cell, or six per rhombohedral unit cell (see diagram, right). But the information content of this is *tiny* compared with that of DNA or most proteins.

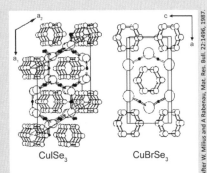

CuISe3   CuBrSe3

Crystal structures of CuISe3 and CuBrSe3; black circles = Cu, small open circles = Se, large open circles = Br or I. From J.D. Sarfati and G.R. Burns: 'The pressure, temperature and excitation frequency dependent Raman spectra; and infrared spectra of CuBrSe3 and CuISe3', *Spectrochimica Acta* **50A**: 2125–2136, 1994.

After W. Milius and A Rabenau, Mat. Res. Bull. 22:1496, 1987.

CURIE DISSYMMETRY PRINCIPLE

This is one of the 'laws' to explain regularity, named after the French physicist Pièrre Curie (1859–1906). This states that a *dissymmetry in a physical effect is always present in its physical cause.* This explains several types of order that evolutionists have used as supposed counterarguments to the design filter:

Convection patterns

The evaporation and redistribution of ocean water on the planet could be considered an ordered system. An even better example is the hexagonal Rayleigh–Bénard Convection Cell pattern that can sometimes be seen in shallow liquids in frying pans.

For any convection system, there are certain important boundary conditions, e.g. a *definite order of heat source—intermediate systems—sink.* Such boundary conditions do introduce information

TECHNICAL DETAILS

content—in this case, specifying a *lowering of symmetry* by *introducing a preferred direction* compared with an isotropic system with no dissymmetry.

Gravitational sorting

Consider a mixture of sand grains that becomes naturally sorted by size. A random mixture in zero gravity has no dissymmetry (it is isotropic). Introduce a gravitational field, then there is a dissymmetry because of the direction of the field. Then the sand grains can 'self-sort' with the density increasing with depth. But this new arrangement, with the directional arrangement of sand grains, *actually reflects the dissymmetry of the direction of the gravitational field that causes the separation.*

In other words, these trivial examples of ordered arrangements are fully explained by the physics of each situation. And the order does not convey any information; any specifications for anything.

WHO DESIGNED THE DESIGNER?

A number of sceptics ask this question. But God *by definition* is the *uncreated* creator of the universe, so the question 'Who created God?' is illogical, just like 'To whom is the bachelor married?'

So a more sophisticated questioner might ask: 'If the universe needs a cause, then why doesn't God need a cause? And if God doesn't need a cause, why should the universe need a cause?' In reply, Christians should use the following reasoning:

1. Everything **which has a beginning** has a cause.
2. The universe has a beginning.
3. Therefore the universe has a cause.

It's important to stress the words in **bold type**. The universe requires a cause because it had a **beginning,** as will be shown below. God, unlike the universe, had **no beginning**, so doesn't need a cause. In addition, Einstein's general relativity, which has much experimental support, shows that time is linked to matter and space. So *time itself* would have begun along with matter and space. Since God, by definition, is the creator of the whole universe, he is the creator of time. Therefore He is not limited by the time dimension He created, so has *no beginning* in time—God is 'the high and lofty One that inhabits eternity' (Isaiah 57:15).[6]

This reasoning is sometimes called the *Kalām* Cosmological Argument. Its most prominent modern defender is the philosopher and apologist Dr William Lane Craig.[7]

In his book *The God Delusion*, Dawkins trots out a variant of the above tired old sceptical argument:

6. See Sarfati, J., If God created the universe, then who created God? *Journal of Creation* 12(1):20–22, 1998, <creationontheweb.com/whomadeGod>; Refuting Compromise pp. 179–183, 2004.
7. Craig, W.L., *The Kalām Cosmological Argument*, Barnes & Noble, New York, 1979; God, Creation and Mr Davies, *Brit. J. Phil. Sci.* 37:163–175, 1986.

'However statistically improbable the entity you seek to explain by invoking a designer, the designer himself has got to be at least as improbable. God is the Ultimate Boeing 747.'

He claims that a designer intelligent enough to explain the complexity of the living world must be at least as complex. So if biology demands an intelligent designer, then so must the Designer demand a Meta-Designer, and so on. Several further problems exist with this argument, to add to the point above that a created god really is a delusion.

1. This argument would be regarded as spurious when applied to arrowheads, SETI signals, Mt Rushmore etc. E.g. if an archaeologist argues that stone implements in a burial site were designed, it would be crass to ask, 'who designed the designer of these implements?' then argue that this refutes the design claim. Whether something has been designed can be decided on its own merits.

2. Classical theology states that God is not complex, but simple. This is true of Roman Catholic teaching from Aquinas,[8] as well as Protestant teaching, e.g. the Belgic Confession: God is 'a single and simple spiritual being.'[9] And Dawkins has forgotten that he contradicts his own definition of complexity: having parts that are 'arranged in a way that is unlikely to have arisen by chance alone.'[16] But since the God of the Bible is a spirit, not material, He has no parts, let alone any arranged in a certain way.[10]

3. There cannot be an infinite series of material causes, because material life has not existed forever. Even the idea of alien life preceding ours (see pp. 150–151) cannot be taken back indefinitely, because the universe has not existed indefinitely. A hypothetical big bang, preceded by an even more conjectural big crunch, would have destroyed any life. So as there was no material intelligent designer for the first life, it is legitimate to invoke a non-material designer for life.

IT'S NOT SCIENCE

The real reason for rejecting the creation explanation is the commitment to naturalism. As shown by a number of admissions, evolutionists have turned science into a materialistic 'game', and creation/design is excluded by their self-serving rules that exclude

8. Duggan, G.H., Review of *The Blind Watchmaker* by Richard Dawkins. *Apologia,* 6(1):121–122, 1997.
9. The Trinity doctrine does not claim that the three persons are parts of God, but that the one God exists in three Persons or centres of consciousness. See Sarfati, J., Jesus Christ our Creator: A biblical defence of the Trinity, *Apologia* 5(2):37–39, 1992; <creationontheweb.com/trinity>.
10. Plantinga, A., The Dawkins Confusion: *Naturalism ad absurdum, Christianity Today* (Books and Culture), March/April 2007; <www.christianitytoday.com/bc/2007/002/1.21.html>.

supernatural creation *a priori*.[11] See for example this proclamation by the evolutionary biochemist Richard Dickerson:

'Science is fundamentally a game. It is a game with one overriding and defining rule:

'Rule No. 1: Let us see how far and to what extent we can explain the behavior of the physical and material universe in terms of purely physical and material causes, without invoking the supernatural.'[12]

In practice, the 'game' is extended to trying to explain not just the behaviour, but the *origin* of everything without the supernatural.

Professor Richard Lewontin, a geneticist (and self-proclaimed Marxist), is a renowned champion of neo-Darwinism, and certainly one of the world's leaders in promoting evolutionary biology. He recently wrote this very revealing comment that illustrates the implicit philosophical bias against Genesis creation—regardless of whether or not the facts support it (emphases in original):

'We take the side of science *in spite* of the patent absurdity of some of its constructs, *in spite* of its failure to fulfil many of its extravagant promises of health and life, *in spite* of the tolerance of the scientific community for unsubstantiated just-so stories, because we have a prior commitment, a commitment to materialism.

'It is not that the methods and institutions of science somehow compel us to accept a material explanation of the phenomenal world, but, on the contrary, that we are forced by our *a priori* adherence to material causes to create an apparatus of investigation and a set of concepts that produce material explanations, no matter how counter-intuitive, no matter how mystifying to the uninitiated. Moreover, that materialism is an absolute, for we cannot allow a Divine Foot in the door.

'The eminent Kant scholar Lewis Beck used to say that anyone who could believe in God could believe in anything. To appeal to an omnipotent deity is to allow that at any moment the regularities of nature may be ruptured, that Miracles may happen.'[13]

Scott Todd, an immunologist at Kansas State University said much the same:

'Even if all the data point to an intelligent designer, such an hypothesis is excluded from science because it is not naturalistic'.[14]

11. Wieland, C., Science: The rules of the game, *Creation* **11**(1):47–50, 1988.
12. Dickerson, R.E., *J. Molecular Evolution* **34**:277, 1992; *Perspectives on Science and the Christian Faith* **44**:137–138, 1992.
13. Lewontin, R., 'Billions and billions of demons', *The New York Review*, 9 January 1997, p. 31.
14. Todd, S.C., correspondence to *Nature* **401**(6752):423, 1999.

Therefore, *although many denounce design as 'unscientific'*, this appears to be derived more from the rules of the game than from any evidence. A glaring example is Dawkins, who said:

> 'Even if there were no actual evidence in favor of the Darwinian theory, we should still be justified in preferring it over all rival theories.'[15]

Even some anti-creationist philosophers of science have strongly criticized the evolutionary scientific and legal establishment over these word games. They rightly point out that we should be more interested in whether creation is *true* or *false* than whether it meets some self-serving criteria for 'science'.[16]

Many of these word games are self-contradictory, so one must wonder whether their main purpose is to exclude creation at any cost rather than for logical reasons. For example, a much publicized teachers' guidebook, produced by the National Academy of Science, *Teaching about Evolution* ... claims on p. 55:

> 'The ideas of "creation science" derive from the conviction that God created the universe—including humans and other living things—all at once in the relatively recent past. However, scientists from many fields have examined these ideas and have found them to be scientifically insupportable. For example, evidence for a very young earth is incompatible with many different methods of establishing the age of rocks. Furthermore, because the basic proposals of creation science are not subject to test and verification, these ideas do not meet the criteria for science.'[17]

The *Teaching about Evolution* definition of creation science is almost right, although creationists following biblical assumptions would claim that different things were created on different days. However, *Teaching about Evolution* claims that the ideas of creation science have been examined and found unsupportable, then they claim that the 'basic proposals of creation science are not subject to test and verification'. So how could its proposals have been examined (tested!) if they are not subject to test?[18]

The historian and philosopher of science Stephen Meyer concluded:

15. Dawkins, R., *The Blind Watchmaker: Why the evidence of evolution reveals a universe without design*, p. 6, W W Norton & Company, New York, 1986.

16. Laudan, L., Science at the Bar—Causes for Concern; Quinn, P.L., The Philosopher of Science as Expert Witness; both in Ruse, M. (Ed.), *But is it Science?* Prometheus Books, Buffalo, NY, 1988, pp. 351–355, 367–385. Ruse was the philosopher of science who most influenced American judges that creation is 'unscientific', and Laudan and Quinn refute his fallacious arguments. Ruse later admitted that evolution was a religion, How evolution became a religion: creationists correct? *National Post*, pp. B1,B3,B7 13 May 2000.

17. *Teaching about Evolution and the Nature of Science*, p. 55, National Academy of Sciences, USA, 1998; see refutation, Sarfati, J., *Refuting Evolution*, Creation Book Publishers], Australia 1999, 2008; <creationontheweb.com/refuting>.

18. The NAS sequel, *Science, Evolution and Creationism (2008), makes the same objections. For refutation, see Sarfati, J., Science, Creation and Evolutionism, <creationontheweb.com/nas>, 8 February 2008.

'... we have not yet encountered any good in principle reason to exclude design from science. Design seems just as scientific (or unscientific) as its evolutionary competitors ...

'An openness to empirical arguments for design is therefore a necessary condition of a fully rational historical biology. A rational historical biology must not only address the question "Which materialistic or naturalistic evolutionary scenario provides the most adequate explanation of biological complexity?" but also the question "Does a strictly materialistic evolutionary scenario or one involving intelligent agency or some other theory best explain the origin of biological complexity, given all relevant evidence?" To insist otherwise is to insist that materialism holds a metaphysically privileged position. Since there seems no reason to concede that assumption, I see no reason to concede that origins theories must be strictly naturalistic.'[19]

IT IS NOT PEER-REVIEWED[20]

This is merely an excuse to reject design arguments. In the first place, there are several creationist peer-reviewed journals, including *Journal of Creation* and *Creation Research Quarterly*, and there is plenty of mainstream literature with design argument, although the authors have to hide the implication to get published.[21]

Second, there is much evidence that overt advocacy of design will result in automatic rejection of the paper. One "intelligent design" paper that slipped through the "paper curtain" was Stephen Meyer's one on the origin of basic types in the Cambrian explosion, published in the peer-reviewed journal, *Proceedings of the Biological Society of Washington.* However, evolutionist groups wrote to the journal railing that the article was substandard—before they'd even read it! Then the Biological Society's governing council capitulated, claiming that had they known about it beforehand, they 'would have deemed this paper inappropriate for the pages of the *Proceedings,*' and promised that 'Intelligent Design ... will not be addressed in future issues of the [journal].' The editor, Dr Richard Sternberg, actually lost his job at the Smithsonian—so much for open-minded academic freedom and peer review.

So it's ironic for evolutionists to pontificate that a scientific movement must publish a peer-reviewed article in order to be

19. Meyer, S.C., The Methodological Equivalence of Design and Descent: Can there be a 'Scientific Theory of Creation'? in: J.P. Moreland, ed., *The Creation Hypothesis*, InterVarsity Press, Downers Grove, IL, 1994, pp. 98, 102.

20. For an excellent overview, see Kulikovsky, A., Creationism, Science and Peer Review, *J. Creation* 22(1):44–49, 2008; <creationontheweb.com/peer>.

21. See documentation in Buckna, D., Do creationists publish in notable refereed journals? <creationontheweb.com/publish>

considered legitimate, and then turn around and complain that it wasn't legitimate for a journal to publish any peer-reviewed article from that movement! It really boils down to a stipulative definition with all that entails about circularity:

1. Creation isn't real science because it isn't peer-reviewed.
2. Creation isn't peer-reviewed because it isn't real science.

And even apart from the design issue, peer review has come under fire. Alison McCook wrote in *The Scientist:*

'Everyone, it seems, has a problem with peer review at top-tier journals. The recent discrediting of stem cell work by Woo-Suk Hwang at Seoul National University sparked media debates about the system's failure to detect fraud. Authors, meanwhile, are lodging a range of complaints: Reviewers sabotage papers that compete with their own, strong papers are sent to sister journals to boost their profiles, and editors at commercial journals are too young and invariably make mistakes about which papers to reject or accept. Still, even senior scientists are reluctant to give specific examples of being shortchanged by peer review, worrying that the move could jeopardize their future publications.

'Despite a lack of evidence that peer review works, most scientists (by nature a skeptical lot) appear to believe in peer review. It's something that's held "absolutely sacred" in a field where people rarely accept anything with "blind faith", says Richard Smith, former editor of the *BMJ* and now CEO of UnitedHealth Europe and board member of *PLoS*. "It's very unscientific, really."

'Indeed, an abundance of data from a range of journals suggests peer review does little to improve papers. In one 1998 experiment designed to test what peer review uncovers, researchers intentionally introduced eight errors into a research paper. More than 200 reviewers identified an average of only two errors. That same year, a paper in the *Annals of Emergency Medicine* showed that reviewers couldn't spot two-thirds of the major errors in a fake manuscript. In July 2005, an article in *JAMA* showed that among recent clinical research articles published in major journals, 16% of the reports showing an intervention was effective were contradicted by later findings, suggesting reviewers may have missed major flaws.'[22]

Robert Higgs, a scientist with many years experience as a researcher, university professor and peer reviewer, had this to say:

'Peer review, on which lay people place great weight, varies from important, where the editors and the referees are competent and responsible, to a complete farce, where they are not. As a rule, not surprisingly, the process operates somewhere in the middle, being more than a joke but less than the nearly flawless system of Olympian scrutiny that outsiders imagine it to be. *Any journal editor who desires, for whatever reason, to knock down a submission can easily do so by choosing referees he knows full well will knock it down*; likewise, he can easily obtain favorable referee reports. As I have always counseled young people whose work was rejected, seemingly on improper or insufficient grounds, *the system is a crap shoot.*

'*Personal vendettas, ideological conflicts, professional jealousies, methodological disagreements, sheer self-promotion and a great deal of plain incompetence and irresponsibility are no strangers to the scientific world*; indeed, that world is rife with these all-too-human attributes. In no event can peer review ensure that research is correct in its procedures or its conclusions. The history of every science is a chronicle of one mistake after another. In some sciences these mistakes are largely weeded out in the course of time; in others they persist for extended periods; and in some sciences, such as economics, actual scientific retrogression may continue for generations under the misguided belief that it is really progress.

'At any given time, consensus may exist about all sorts of matters in a particular science. In retrospect, however, that consensus is often seen to have been mistaken. ...

'Researchers who employ unorthodox methods or theoretical frameworks have great difficulty under modern conditions in getting their findings published in the "best" journals or, at times, in any scientific journal. Scientific innovators or creative eccentrics always strike the great mass of practitioners as nut cases—until it becomes impossible to deny their

---

22. McCook, A., Is peer review broken? *The Scientist* **20**(2):26, February 2006.

findings, a time that often comes only after one generation's professional ring-masters have died off. Science is an odd undertaking: everybody strives to make the next breakthrough, yet when someone does, he is often greeted as if he were carrying the ebola virus. Too many people have too much invested in the reigning ideas; for those people an acknowledgment of their own idea's bankruptcy is tantamount to an admission that they have wasted their lives. Often, perhaps to avoid cognitive dissonance, they never admit that their ideas were wrong. Most important, as a rule, in science as elsewhere, to get along, you must go along.

'Research worlds, in their upper reaches, are pretty small. Leading researchers know all the major players and what everybody else is doing. They attend the same conferences, belong to the same societies, send their grad students to be postdocs in the other people's labs, review one another's work for the NSF, NIH, or other government funding organizations, and so forth. If you do not belong to this tight fraternity, it will prove very, very difficult for you to gain a hearing for your work, to publish in a "top" journal, to acquire a government grant, to receive an invitation to participate in a scientific-conference panel discussion, or to place your grad students in decent positions. The whole setup is tremendously incestuous; the interconnections are numerous, tight, and close.

'In this context, a bright young person needs to display cleverness in applying the prevailing orthodoxy, but it behooves him not to rock the boat by challenging anything fundamental or dear to the hearts of those who constitute the review committees for the NSF, NIH, and other funding organizations.'[23]

Finally, peer review has not prevented fraud, but has blocked plenty of science now known to be good. E.g. the leading journal *Nature* also admitted in a *mea culpa* editorial:

'(T)here are unarguable *faux pas* in our history. These include the rejection of Cerenkov radiation, Hideki Yukawa's meson, work on photosynthesis by Johann Deisenhofer, Robert Huber and Hartmut Michel, and the initial rejection (but eventual acceptance) of Stephen Hawking's black-hole radiation.'[24]

---

23. Higgs, R., Peer review, publication in top journals, scientific consensus, and so forth, *George Mason University's History News Network*, <hnn.us/blogs/entries/38532.html>, 7 May 2007. (Emphasis added).
24. Coping with peer rejection, *Nature* **425**:645, 2003.

CHAPTER 15

COSMIC DESIGN

A SINGLE DESIGNER

It is notable that throughout the living world, there is much uniformity. This is consistent with a particular subset of ID: the *biotic message theory*, as proposed by Walter ReMine.[1] That is, the evidence from nature points to a *single* designer, but with a pattern which thwarts evolutionary explanations. Also, in most cultures around the world, such a *pattern of commonality would bring honour to a Designer*, and would also indicate the Designer's authority over and mastery of His designs.[2]

Uniformity of the universe

This uniformity is even more notable with subatomic particles, e.g. all electrons in the universe have exactly the same mass and charge, and exactly the opposite charge to all protons. The universe as a whole also has a uniformity of temperature throughout, as shown by the cosmic microwave background (CMB) radiation, to within 1 part in 100,000)[3]. This is a problem for evolutionists, because for the temperature to be so even after the extreme unevenness of the alleged big bang, energy must have been transferred from hot parts to cold parts. The fastest this can occur naturally is the speed of light, but even given the evolutionary age of the universe, light could only have traversed about a tenth of the distance needed to equilibrate the temperature. Incidentally, this is a light-travel–time problem for believers in the big bang.[4]

Cosmologists call this the *horizon problem*, and they have invented a number of mathematical fudges like 'inflation' and claims that light travelled faster in the past to solve it. But the observations of uniformity in the entire cosmos are consistent with a *single* Creator of space and time who holds the universe together (Colossians 1:17).

Also, the physical laws and constants appear to be exquisitely and uniquely fine-tuned to permit not only stars, planets and galaxies to exist, but ourselves, too.[5] Someone dubbed it the 'Goldilocks factor', because it is all astonishingly 'just right'. Similarly with features of the earth and solar system—these, too, are consistent

---

1. ReMine, W.J., *The Biotic Message: Evolution Versus Message Theory*, Saint Paul Science, Saint Paul, Minnesota, USA, 1993; see review: Batten, D., *J. Creation* 11(3):292–298, 1997; <creationontheweb.com/biotic>.
2. Holding, J.P., 'Not to Be Used Again': Homologous Structures and the Presumption of Originality as a Critical Value, *J. Creation* 21(1):13 –14, 2007; <creationontheweb.com/original>.
3. Peebles, P.J.E., *Principles of Physical Cosmology*, Princeton University Press, 1993; p. 404.
4. Lisle, J., Light travel-time: a problem for the big bang, *Creation* 25(4):48–49, 2003; <creationontheweb.com/lighttravel>.
5. A comprehensive study of the fine-tuning of universe is the book by J. Barrow and F. Tipler, *The Anthropic Cosmological Principle*, 1986.

with a single designer. Former atheist Sir Fred Hoyle (1915–2001) stated:

> 'Would you not say to yourself, "Some super-calculating intellect must have designed the properties of the carbon atom, otherwise the chance of my finding such an atom through the blind forces of nature would be utterly minuscule." Of course you would ... A common sense interpretation of the facts suggests that a superintellect has monkeyed with physics, as well as with chemistry and biology, and that there are no blind forces worth speaking about in nature. The numbers one calculates from the facts seem to me so overwhelming as to put this conclusion almost beyond question.'[6]

For the universe as a whole:

- The electromagnetic coupling constant binds electrons to protons in atoms. If it was smaller, fewer electrons could be held. If it was larger, electrons would be held too tightly to bond with other atoms, so molecules like water would not form.
- Ratio of electron to proton mass (1:1836). Again, if this was larger or smaller, molecules could not form.
- Carbon and oxygen nuclei have finely tuned energy levels.
- Electromagnetic and gravitational forces are finely tuned, so the right kind of star can be stable.
- Our sun is an 'exceptional' star for many reasons:[7,8]
  - Right mass. If it were larger, its brightness would change too quickly and there would be too much high energy radiation. If it were smaller, the planetary distance would be so close to the star that tidal forces would disrupt the planet's rotational period.
  - Right orbit. The sun is in a special location in the galaxy: the co-rotation radius. Only here does a star's orbital speed match that of the spiral arms—otherwise the sun would cross the arms too often and be exposed to supernovae. Its orbit is fairly circular, meaning that it won't go too near the inner galaxy where supernovae, extremely energetic star explosions, are more common. It also orbits almost parallel to the galactic plane—otherwise, crossing this plane would be very disruptive.
- The earth has a number of special features:
  - The earth's distance from the sun is crucial for a stable water cycle. Too far away, and most water would freeze;

---

6. Hoyle, F., The Universe: Past and Present Reflections, *Engineering and Science*, pp. 8–12, November 1981.
7. Chown, M., What a star! *New Scientist* **162**(2192):17, 1999.
8. Sarfati, J., The sun: our special star, *Creation* **22**(1):27–31, 1999; <creationontheweb.com/sun>.

too close and most water would boil.
- The earth's gravity, axial tilt, rotation period, magnetic field, crust thickness, oxygen/nitrogen ratio, carbon dioxide, water vapour and ozone levels are just right to create a habitable environment.
- The formation of the earth in evolutionary scenarios required such 'freak' conditions that Astronomer Thomas Clarke of the University of Central Florida in Orlando recently made an astonishing admission: 'It's a bit depressing to think that Earth-like planets are too special.'[9]

Objection 1: Anthropic principle

A common response to the apparent design of the universe is the so-called 'anthropic principle' (from Greek *anthrōpos* ἄνθρωπος = man). This basically states that the reason the universe appears to be designed for us is that otherwise we wouldn't be here to draw that conclusion!

This sounds profound but it's actually no explanation at all. As Christian philosopher and apologist William Lane Craig pointed out:

If you were dragged before a trained firing squad, and they fired and missed:
- it is true that you should not be surprised to observe that you are not dead, but
- it is equally true that you *should* be surprised to observe that you are alive.

If you were asked, 'How did you survive?', it would be inadequate to answer, 'If I didn't, I would not be here to answer you.'[10]

Objection 2: Multiverses

If antitheists actually try to offer an explanation, it is often on the lines of, 'Yes, it is highly unlikely for one universe to have these properties. But if there are, or were, lots of other universes, with the laws of physics a little bit different in each one, then it would become probable that at least one would happen to have the properties required for intelligent observers to exist. In this 'grand lottery of universes', only those where the laws were hospitable to life would

---

9.   Earth was a freak, *New Scientist* **177**(2388):24, 2003. The standard evolutionary model has the earth formed by accretion of small fragments that collided and melted together. But in reality, they would bounce off each other rather than melt. So Clarke proposes the 'speculative' idea of the 'remote' possibility of a supernova explosion within 50 light years from Earth that supplied the nebula with radioactive aluminium-26, which would decay and provide the necessary heat. See Sarfati, J., Earth is 'too special'? *Creation* **28**(3):42–44, 2006; <creationontheweb.com/earthspecial>.

10. Barrow and Tipler, Ref. 5, use this objection to evade the implications of a Designer. However, Christian philosopher and apologist William Lane Craig points out the fallacy in 'Barrow and Tipler on the Anthropic Principle *vs.* Divine Design', *Brit. J. Phil. Sci.* **38**:389–95, 1988. Once this fallacy is removed, the book becomes a compendium of data of modern science which point to design in nature inexplicable in natural terms and therefore pointing to a Divine Designer. However, some of the alleged design features presuppose a big bang, so are not considered here.

produce observers, so the theory goes, in a sort of 'natural selection competition among universes'.

This is really special pleading, i.e. an explanation these atheists accept for the universe but would not tolerate for a second to explain anything else. Consider if we found a pattern of markings on a beach which spelled your name. Naturally you would conclude that an intelligence had written it. This is more plausible than thinking that wind and wave erosion somehow produced that pattern by chance, *even though there is an extremely tiny, but real, probability of this happening.*

But under multiverse reasoning, there are an infinite number of parallel universes containing every possible quantum state, 'In infinite space, even the most unlikely events must take place somewhere.'[11]

So if a person had an *a priori* bias that no one could have written your name, he could argue that we just happen to be in one of the tiny fraction of universes where this improbable erosion pattern arose naturally. If this sounds totally unreasonable, then by the same logic, so is the atheistic preference for an infinite number of universes over a Creator.[12]

In fact, there are even more troubling possibilities that must occur in an infinite multiverse scenario. Since there is an infinitesimally small possibility that matter might spontaneously arrange itself into *anything*, this must logically include a bizarre universe with a brain in a vat that contains the *true* thought, 'I am a spontaneously generated brain in an otherwise dead universe.' Another universe might have a spontaneously generated brain that has the *false* thought, 'I am a real human with memories and history', when *in that universe's reality* it is a lone brain with *false* memories and *illusions* of reading history.

But one who proposes such an infinite multiverse scenario has no way of ruling out the possibility that *he* is such a lone brain with illusions.

This means that the infinite multiverse scenario entails that *we can't be sure of our own reality*. While it pretends to be a scientific theory, it entails that *science itself might be a big illusion*. This is a *reductio ad absurdum* of this theory.[13]

11. Tegmark, M., *Parallel* universes: Not just a staple of science fiction, other universes are a direct implication of cosmological observations, *Scientific American* **288**:30–41, May 2003. Of course, there is *no actual observation* of these other universes, just observation of fine-tuning in ours that is explained *away* by multiverses.
12. Sarfati, J, *Refuting Compromise*, ch. 5, Master Books, Green Forest, AR, 2004.
13. Behe, M., *The Edge of Evolution: The search for the limits of Darwinism*, pp. 224–227, Free Press, NY, 2007.

CHAPTER 16

WHO IS THE DESIGNER?

Nature does not reveal the identity of the Intelligent Designer. This was a point made by atheistic philosopher Raymond Bradley in a debate on Christianity with the Christian classical scholar E.M. Blaiklock (1903–1983) at Auckland University in New Zealand, around 1965. The atheist began with a Parable of the Gardener, often used by the then atheist Antony Flew:

Isabelle Grosjean, <wikipedia.org>

'Once upon a time two explorers came upon a clearing in the jungle. In the clearing were growing many flowers and many weeds. One explorer says, "Some gardener must tend this plot." The other disagrees, "There is no gardener." So they pitch their tents and set a watch. No gardener is ever seen. "But perhaps he is an invisible gardener." So they set up a barbed-wire fence. They electrify it. They patrol with bloodhounds. (For they remember how H.G. Well's *The Invisible Man* could be both smelt and touched though he could not be seen.) But no shrieks ever suggest that some intruder has received a shock. No movements of the wire ever betray an invisible climber. The bloodhounds never give cry. Yet still the Believer is not convinced. "But there is a gardener, invisible, intangible, insensible, to electric shocks, a gardener who has no scent and makes no sound, a gardener who comes secretly to look after the garden which he loves." At last the Sceptic despairs, "But what remains of your original assertion? Just how does what you call an invisible, intangible, eternally elusive gardener differ from an imaginary gardener or even from no gardener at all?"'[1]

Blaiklock first pointed out that while the gardener might not be seen, his *effects* certainly are, where the skeptic sees only the weeds. Indeed, as shown in chapter 11, Flew himself now recognizes the need for a 'gardener' to start life in the first place.

But then Blaiklock extended the parable. Another man appeared, and spoke to the two explorers:

---

1.   Flew, A., Theology and Falsification, *University*, 1950–51.

'I understand that you were wondering about whether this garden has a gardener. Indeed there is, because I am the gardener's son. And if you want to know what the gardener is like, look at me, for I am his spitting image.'

Indeed, looking at the garden can tell us only so much. For us to really understand the gardener, he would have to tell us himself, or send a reliable emissary to do so.

Blaiklock was an expert in the language and culture of the New Testament period. His research convinced him that the man Jesus of Nazareth was indeed the emissary from the Designer, and the Designer's Son who is the exact representation of the Designer.[2] The Son proved his credentials impeccably by his words and deeds.

Later, in 1985, Flew himself debated philosopher and theologian Gary Habermas on the most important reported deed of all, the proposition that Jesus Christ, conquered death itself.[3] This debate was held in Dallas in front of a crowd of three thousand people. It was judged by two panels of experts from leading American universities: one panel comprised five philosophers who were asked to judge the content of the debate, and the other comprised five professional debate judges who were asked to judge the quality of the arguments.

Four of the five on the philosophers panel voted that Habermas had won, i.e. the case he made for the Resurrection was stronger than Flew's attempts to refute it, and one scored it a draw. The panel of professional debate judges voted three to two to Habermas. The following comments from two of the judges follow:

'I am of the position that the affirmative speaker [Habermas] has a very significant burden of proof in order to establish his claims. The various historical sources convinced me to adopt the arguments of the affirmative speaker. Dr Flew, on the other hand, failed, particularly in the rebuttal period and the head-to-head session, to introduce significant supporters of his position. Dr Habermas placed a heavy burden on Dr Flew to refute very specific issues. As the rebuttals progressed, I felt that Dr Flew tried to skirt the charges.'

'I conclude that the historical evidence, though flawed, is strong enough to lead reasonable minds to conclude that Christ did indeed rise from the dead.

2.	Hebrews 1:1–3 '… God … has spoken to us by his Son, whom he appointed the heir of all things, through whom also he created the world. He is the radiance of the glory of God and the exact representation of his being, and he upholds the universe by the word of his power.'

3.	Habermas, G.R. and Flew, A.G.N., *Did Jesus Rise from the Dead? The Resurrection Debate*, ed. Terry L. Miethe, T.L., Harper & Row, San Francisco, 1987.

> Habermas has already won the debate. … By defeating the Hume-inspired skeptical critique on miracles in general offered by Flew and by demonstrating the strength of some of the historical evidence, Habermas does end up providing "highly probably evidence" for the historicity of the resurrection "with no plausible naturalistic evidence against it." Habermas, therefore, in my opinion, wins the debate.'

The two debaters became friends after this, so when Flew renounced atheism 20 years later, he was happy to be interviewed by Habermas, as cited in chapter 11.[4]

More recently, James Patrick Holding has shown that there are at least 17 factors that meant Christianity could not have succeeded in the ancient world, unless it were backed up with irrefutable proof of Jesus' Resurrection.[5]

WHAT THE DESIGNER EXPECTS FROM US

Furthermore, the historical evidence shows that Jesus believed that a collection of books we call the Bible was the authoritative revelation of the Designer's message to His creatures.[6,7] This includes telling us *that* He created, *when* He created, and the *sequence* of creative acts.[8] And that book defeats all other explanations decisively as an explanation of the world as we find it, with both exquisite design and the present ugliness.[9] This also explains geology (the Flood), languages (evolutionists have no Babel), population distribution, origin of agriculture, all things that 'mere design' can't explain.

In this book, the Designer has also told us what He expects from those whom He made, and how their disobedience resulted in death and cutting off from Himself.[10] But the same book reveals His rescue plan. His Son Jesus Christ came into the world to take upon Himself the penalty for our sins, and endure death and shame in our place. He rose from the dead, proving that He had paid the price and conquered death.[11]

---

4. My Pilgrimage from Atheism to Theism: an exclusive interview with former British atheist Professor Antony Flew by Gary Habermas, *Philosophia Christi*, Winter 2005; <www.illustramedia.com/IDArticles/flew-interview.pdf>.

5. Holding, J.P., *The Impossible Faith*, Xulon Press, Florida, USA, 2007; < www.tektonics.org/lp/nowayjose.html>.

6. Sarfati, J., The Authority of Scripture, *Apologia* 3(2):12–16 1994; <creationontheweb.com/authority>. While Jesus walked the Earth, the only Bible at the time was what is now called the Old Testament, but He also gave authority to his Apostles to write the Scriptures we now call the New Testament.

7. Livingston, D., Jesus Christ on the infallibility of Scripture, in: 'A Critique of Dewey Beegle's book titled: *Inspiration of Scripture'*, M.A. Thesis, 2003; <creationontheweb.com/jesus_bible>.

8. See also Sarfati, J., Genesis: Bible authors believed it to be history, *Creation* 28(2):21–23, 2006, <creationontheweb.com/gen_hist>.

9. See also Catchpoole. D., Holy books? Which one are you going to trust? *Creation* 26(1):1, 2003; <creationontheweb.com/holybooks>.

10. For more information, see Sarfati, J., The Fall: a cosmic catastrophe—Hugh Ross's blunders on plant death in the Bible, *J. Creation* 19(3):60–64, 2005; <creationontheweb.com/plant_death>.

11. See also Good news! <creationontheweb.com/goodnews>.

SUMMARY

The evidence of exquisite machinery in life and the fine-tuning of the universe both point not only to intelligent design, but to a *single* intelligent *Designer*. And while we can't work out the identity of the Designer solely from His handiwork, He has sent His Son to humanity to reveal exactly what He is like. Furthermore, the Son affirmed a series of books as true history of the Designer's creative acts and interactions with His creatures, and what He expects of us.

INDEX BY ORDER IN THIS BOOK

INDEX

A

B

C

M

N

O

P

V

W

Y

Z